A TEXT-BOOK OF HEAT

Books by G. R. Noakes

A TEXT-BOOK OF LIGHT

A TEXT-BOOK OF ELECTRICITY AND MAGNETISM

A
TEXT-BOOK OF HEAT

BY

G. R. NOAKES, M.A. (Oxon.), F.Inst.P.

CHELTENHAM COLLEGE

FORMERLY SENIOR SCIENCE MASTER AT GIGGLESWICK SCHOOL

MACMILLAN AND CO., LIMITED
ST. MARTIN'S STREET, LONDON
1947

PRINTED IN GREAT BRITAIN

PREFACE

THIS book provides a logical course in Heat which will meet the needs of sixth-form students specialising in Science. Thus the range and standard are roughly those at present expected of candidates for Higher School Certificate and University Scholarship examinations, and the subject is treated with the thoroughness which may justly be required at this stage.

The chief difficulties experienced in the study of Heat by such students are not mathematical, but lie in the great care demanded to ensure that the principles are properly grasped, and that simple experiments are carried out reasonably well with due regard to the limitations imposed by the apparatus. The necessity for such care has been kept before the reader continually. Most of the commoner pitfalls have therefore been pointed out and carefully explained, and I have tried to be precise on matters such as Newton's Law of Cooling and Kirchhoff's Law, which are often expounded somewhat uncritically. Stress has also been laid on the importance of considering the accuracy of experimental work, and this is dealt with mathematically in Appendix II. Throughout the book the abbreviation " ln " has been used to signify natural logarithms, as this seems to be in accordance with modern mathematical practice.

It will be realised that a book of this nature is largely an accumulation of ideas and methods that have been found good and assimilated during years of teaching, and can only be acknowledged in a general way. The works on which I have relied during the actual preparation of the book are acknowledged separately in the hope that the list may serve the student as a guide for further reading.

I must thank the firms who have kindly supplied me with facts and illustrations, particularly the Cambridge Instrument Company, the British Oxygen Company, the Foster Instrument Company, and Messrs. Radiation, Ltd. ; also the many authors and publishers who have generously allowed the use of diagrams from their books ; and Prof. W. E. S. Turner, of the University of Sheffield, who helped me with information about the fracture of glassware. I am also grateful to the Controller of H.M. Stationery Office for permission to use material from the *Meteorological Glossary*, the Science Museum "Handbooks on Very Low Temperatures," and from Dr. R. C. Sutcliffe's *Meteorology for Aviators* which forms the basis of Chapter X. The source from which each illustration is derived is acknowledged beneath it.

The questions at the ends of the chapters are taken from recent Higher School Certificate and Scholarship papers, by kind permission of the various Examining Bodies. These also are acknowledged individually, and a key to the letters used is given below :

C :   Cambridge Higher School Certificate.
C.S. :   Cambridge Scholarship Examinations.
B. :   Bristol University Higher School Certificate.
N. :   Northern Universities' Joint Matriculation Board H.S.C.
O. :   Oxford Higher School Certificate.
L. :   London University, Higher Schools Examination.
C.W.B. : Central Welsh Board Higher School Certificate.
O. & C. : Oxford and Cambridge Joint Board Higher Certificate.
O.S. :   Oxford Scholarship Examination.

I am greatly indebted to Mr. J. R. Clarke, of the University of Sheffield, for undertaking the immense labour of working through the examples and reading the proofs, and making many suggestions for improvements ; and to Mr. A. J. V. Gale, who has given me great assistance and encouragement at all stages of the work, and has done so much to bring it to its present state.

G. R. NOAKES

CONTENTS

CHAPTER   PAGE

I. TEMPERATURE - - - - - - - - - - 1

II. THE MEASUREMENT OF HEAT - - - - - - 29

III. EXPANSION OF SOLIDS AND LIQUIDS - - - 81

IV. THE EXPANSION OF GASES AND THE GAS LAWS - 122

V. VAPOURS AND VAPOUR PRESSURE - - - - 178

VI. HEAT AND WORK - - - - - - - - 228

VII. HEAT ENGINES : THE SECOND LAW OF THERMO-
DYNAMICS - - - - - - - - - - 277

VIII. LIQUEFACTION OF GASES AND PRODUCTION AND
MEASUREMENT OF LOW TEMPERATURES - - 307

IX. TRANSFERENCE OF HEAT - - - - - - 327

X. HEAT PHENOMENA IN THE ATMOSPHERE - - - 416

APPENDIX I - - - - - - - - - 446

APPENDIX II - - - - - - - - - 452

INDEX - - - - - - - - - - 462

ANSWERS TO EXAMPLES - - - - - - 467

BIBLIOGRAPHY

The Theory of Heat, by Thomas Preston. Third Edition (Macmillan and Co. Ltd.).

Heat and Thermodynamics, by J. K. Roberts (Blackie and Co. Ltd.).

A Treatise on Heat, by M. N. Saha and B. N. Srivastava (Allahabad).

A Textbook of Physics, by J. Duncan and S. G. Starling (Macmillan and Co. Ltd.).

A Textbook of Practical Physics, by H. S. Allen and H. Moore (Macmillan and Co. Ltd.).

Experimental Physics, by G. F. C. Searle (Cambridge University Press).

Principles of Thermodynamics, by G. Birtwistle (Cambridge University Press).

Low Temperature Physics, by M. and B. Ruhemann (Cambridge University Press).

The Separation of Gases, by M. Ruhemann (Oxford University Press).

An Introduction to Physical Chemistry, by James Walker (Macmillan and Co. Ltd.).

British Scientists of the Nineteenth Century, by J. G. Crowther (Penguin Books, Ltd.).

General and Inorganic Chemistry, by P. J. Durrant (Longmans, Green and Co. Ltd.).

An Introduction to Heat Transfer, by Brown and Marco (McGraw Hill Book Co., Inc.).

Dimensional Analysis, by P. W. Bridgman (Oxford University Press).

A Short Course of Elementary Meteorology, by W. H. Pick.

The Meteorological Glossary.

Meteorology for Aviators, by R. C. Sutcliffe.

Hygrometric Tables (1940 Edition).

The Science Museum Handbooks to the Exhibition on Very Low Temperatures.

⎫ His Majesty's Stationery Office.

Weather Study, by D. Brunt (Thomas Nelson and Co. Ltd.).

A Discussion on Hygrometry (Physical Society).

Reports on Progress in Physics, Vol. VII, 1940 (Physical Society).

A Dictionary of Applied Physics (Macmillan and Co. Ltd.).

Physical and Chemical Constants, by G. W. C. Kaye and T. H. Laby (Longmans, Green and Co. Ltd.).

The Accurate Measurement of Temperature (Cambridge Instrument Co. Ltd.).

CHAPTER I

TEMPERATURE

THE words " hot " and " cold " describe certain bodily sensations, which cannot be defined in other words. " Hotness " and " coldness " are *qualities* which we ascribe to the things which produce these sensations on contact with our bodies. The scientific name for hotness is temperature ; later we shall try to examine the nature of temperature, but at this stage any further attempt at explanation would be profitless and confusing. **Temperature means hotness.** In everyday life people speak of " the heat of an oven ", " red heat ", " sweltering heat ", and so on, when they mean " hotness " in each case. It is pedantic to quarrel with phrases which convey a perfectly definite meaning from the speaker to the hearer, as these do. But this use of the word " heat " must be carefully avoided in scientific work, for the word has been reserved as a name for the form of energy whose transference from body to body, and whose change to or from other forms of energy, is the subject of this book.

We cannot, in the strict sense of the word, *measure* temperature, but we can tell which of two bodies is the hotter (or at the higher temperature) and which the cooler (or at the lower temperature) ; that is, temperatures can be *compared*. A qualification is needed here, for ordinary observations will not justify us in saying that, for example, a coal fire is ten times as hot as a cup of tea ; we usually observe *differences* in hotness, not ratios between hotnesses, and the practical measurement of temperature is thus really the *comparison of temperature differences*. In later chapters, when dealing with the behaviour of gases, we shall employ ratios between temperatures ; but this does not affect the truth of the above statement in connection with the present problem of practical temperature measurement.

There are two parts to the problem : (1) the selection of a standard temperature difference, or *fundamental interval*; and (2) the arrangement of a suitable instrument to compare other temperature differences with this ; such an instrument is called a **thermometer.**

1

PRINCIPLES OF THERMOMETRY

The fundamental interval. It has been established that, for pure substances, the change of state from solid to liquid and the change of state from liquid to vapour, take place at temperatures which at the same pressure are always reproducible. These temperatures at which solid and liquid can exist together in equilibrium, and at which liquid and vapour can exist together in equilibrium, are called the **melting point** and **boiling point** respectively.

The fixed temperatures chosen to define the fundamental interval are the **ice point**, which is the equilibrium temperature between ice and air-saturated water at standard atmospheric pressure ; and the **steam point**, which is the temperature of equilibrium between liquid water and its vapour at a pressure of one standard atmosphere. *Pure* ice and *pure* water and " ordinary " water-substance are of course understood ; dissolved impurities cause very considerable alterations in the equilibrium temperatures. The effect of change of pressure, small in the case of the ice point, but considerable for the steam point, is discussed later.

Standard atmospheric pressure is defined as the pressure due to a column of mercury 760 mm. high, of density 13·5951 gm./c.c., subject to gravitational acceleration 980·665 cm./sec.², and equals 1,013,250 dynes per square centimetre.

The fundamental interval is the difference in temperature between the ice point and the steam point. On the **centigrade** (C.) notation this interval is subdivided into a hundred equal degrees, the ice point being quite arbitrarily named 0° C. and the steam point 100° C. *One centigrade degree* is thus a temperature interval which is one hundredth of the fundamental interval. The statement that " the temperature of the room is 15° C." means that the difference between the temperature of the room and the ice point is 15/100 of the temperature difference between the steam point and the ice point.

In the **Fahrenheit** (F.) notation the fundamental interval is divided into 180 equal degrees, the ice point and steam point being called quite arbitrarily 32° F. and 212° F. One Fahrenheit degree is a temperature interval which is 1/180 the fundamental interval, and is 5/9 of a centigrade degree. The statement " I have a temperature of 101° F." means that the difference between the temperature of my body and the ice point is 69 Fahrenheit degrees, or 69/180 the temperature difference between the steam point and the ice point.

The student may feel that this is carrying precision of statement to excess, for every time a metre stick is used we are ultimately comparing an interval of space with a fundamental space interval engraved on the standard metre, and similar considerations apply to the use of a balance and a clock; but little stress is laid on these points in elementary work. Surely we just " read a thermometer ". But suppose that all dividing engines were subject to large systematic errors, and that only a sundial was available to measure time intervals; we should then have to think very carefully about each measurement of length and time. Thermometry has difficulties of this kind. A thermometer must not be regarded as giving absolute readings of temperature : it is a means of relating observed temperature differences, more or less satisfactorily, to the fundamental interval.

Scale of temperature. Any property of any suitable substance which varies as the temperature is changed can be used to compare temperature differences with the fundamental interval. For example, the volume of a liquid enclosed in a vessel, the volume of a fixed mass of gas maintained at constant pressure, the pressure of a fixed mass of gas maintained at constant volume, the electrical resistance of a piece of metal, the saturated vapour pressure of a liquid, are among the many measurable physical properties which alter as the temperature changes. Any one of these can be made the basis of a scale of temperature (the word *scale* here meaning *system of dividing the scale*, rather than the notation employed) in the following way.

Consider any one quantity the magnitude of which changes as the temperature changes, and denote this quantity by X. Let X_0 be the value of X at the ice point, and X_{100} its value at the steam point. Let X_t be the value at some unknown temperature $t°$ C., which is to be determined. Let equal changes in the value of X denote equal changes in temperature, so that changes in X are proportional to changes in temperature.

A rise in temperature of 100 centigrade degrees (from 0° C. to 100° C.) causes a change of $(X_{100} - X_0)$ *; a rise in temperature

---

* The name " fundamental interval " is often given to $(X_{100} - X_0)$; we are using the term to mean " fundamental *temperature* interval ".

of t centigrade degrees (from $0°$ C. to $t°$ C.) causes a change of $X_t - X_0$:

so $\qquad t = k (X_t - X_0)$, where k is some constant,

and $\qquad 100 = k (X_{100} - X_0)$,

whence $\qquad \dfrac{t}{100} = \dfrac{(X_t - X_0)}{(X_{100} - X_0)}$;

and the temperature " $t°$ C. on the scale employing the property X " is given by the equation :

$$t = 100 \, \frac{(X_t - X_0)}{(X_{100} - X_0)} \; °C.$$

Now, there is a theoretical absolute scale of temperature called the **Kelvin Absolute Thermodynamic Scale**, which is quite independent of the properties of any individual substance, and is identical with the **Ideal Gas Scale** (p. 142), in which X is the product *pressure × volume* for a fixed mass of an ideal gas. This is the standard scale of temperature. A number of " fixed points " (melting points of different substances, etc.) have been determined accurately on this scale, and the gas thermometer described later gives a scale which fits the standard scale fairly closely. This is discussed later ; all that is needed at present is the knowledge that such a standard scale exists. Now, according to this standard scale, not one of the properties listed on p. 3 increases uniformly as the temperature increases. This means that, except at the ice point and the steam point, at which all scales must agree, no actual scale of temperature can agree with the standard scale. The same difficulty is made evident, without the background of the absolute scale, if a mercury thermometer is used to measure the change of resistance of a piece of metal with temperature, or the variation of the saturated vapour pressure of a liquid with temperature ; it is found that, when temperatures are measured on the scale of the mercury thermometer, equal changes in temperature do not lead to equal changes in resistance or of saturated vapour pressure. Similarly, a resistance thermometer, or a vapour-pressure thermometer, used to examine the expansion of mercury, would show that when the temperature is measured on the resistance (or vapour-pressure) scale, equal rises in temperature do not cause equal increases in the volume of mercury contained in a glass vessel. Thus, equal ranges of temperature on the mercury thermometer scale are not represented by equal ranges of temperature on the resistance or vapour-pressure scales, and the scales cannot agree except at the fixed points. There is no question of one of these *arbitrarily selected* scales being " right " and the others " wrong ", for each scale is quite consistent in itself. All scales of temperature must necessarily agree at the ice point and the steam point.

THERMOMETERS

Mercury-in-glass thermometer. The choice of a suitable glass is just as important as the choice of a suitable liquid for a liquid-in-glass thermometer. Mercury is easily visible, expands considerably, expands fairly regularly according to the standard scale, and enables a wide range of temperatures to be measured, as its melting point is about −39° C. and its normal boiling point about 357° C. The glasses used for mercury thermometers for accurate work are specially made for the purpose, named types for which data appear in Kaye and Laby's " Tables " being the French *verre dur*, Jena 16′′′, Jena 59′′′ ; most of them carry one or more coloured stripes so that they may be identified. The part played by the glass can be seen from the fact that at 300° C. the readings of a Jena 16′′′ and a Jena 59′′′ thermometer differ by more than 2° C. It should be added that mercury thermometers are not nowadays used when high accuracy is required.

The mercury is contained in a thin-walled glass bulb of suitable size attached to a uniform capillary tube, which is sealed at the other end. The space above the liquid is usually (not always) evacuated.

The quantity X which is observed is the length of the mercury column above the bulb. Equal changes in length denote equal changes in temperature on the mercury-in-glass scale. Let l_0 be the length at the ice point, l_{100} the length at the steam point, and l_t the length at $t°$ C. Then, as on p. 4,

$$\frac{t}{100} = \frac{l_t - l_0}{l_{100} - l_0},$$

and the temperature $t°$ C. on the mercury -in-glass thermometer scale is

$$t = 100 \, \frac{l_t - l_0}{l_{100} - l_0} \, °C.$$

Each type of glass gives its own scale differing slightly from all the others, while as the behaviour of a given specimen of glass at any

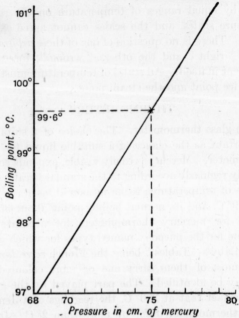

Fig. 1.—Graph of boiling point of water against pressure.

time depends to some extent on its previous treatment, it is probably correct to say that each instrument has an individual scale of its own.

A thermometer is graduated by marking on the stem the positions of the mercury levels at the ice point and the steam point, and dividing the portion of the stem between these marks into a hundred equal divisions. The following experiment with an ungraduated thermometer adds a little interest to the routine operation of determining the fixed points, and illustrates simply the basic principle underlying the use of the instrument.

To find the temperature of the room using an ungraduated mercury thermometer. (a) *The ice point reading.* A large funnel is filled with chips of pure ice moistened with distilled water. The thermometer is held upright with the bulb immersed in the mixture, so that the steady level of the mercury is just visible. After about ten minutes the level of the top of the mercury column is marked by means of a piece of adhesive paper. The thermometer is removed, and the distance of the paper from the bottom of the bulb (a more convenient reference point than the bottom of the stem—since the lengths are subtracted the actual choice of reference point does not matter) is measured ; this is l_0. Small changes in the barometric pressure cause no appreciable change in the ice point, and pure ice is readily obtained.

(b) *The steam point reading.* The three important points are (1) the bulb of the thermometer must be immersed in steam, not boiling water ; the reason for this is that, whether the original water is pure or not, a thermometer in the vapour, on which some pure liquid has in any case condensed, registers the equilibrium temperature between pure water and its vapour ; (2) the whole thermometer stem is immersed in the steam, so that the mercury thread is just visible ; (3) the barometer must be read carefully, since a pressure change of 1 cm. of mercury causes about 0·4 centigrade degrees change in the boiling point at 100° C. (Fig. 1).

The thermometer is placed in a hypsometer (Fig. 2), in which the bulb and stem are surrounded with a double jacket of steam when the water in A is boiled. The pressure gauge at the side shows whether the pressure inside the apparatus is that of the atmosphere. The thermometer is left for about ten minutes in the steam, and the position of the top of the mercury column marked as before. The length of the mercury column is then measured. The barometer is read, and the true value of the boiling point for this pressure obtained from the graph of Fig. 1. Suppose the barometric pressure to be 750 mm. of mercury. The corresponding boiling point is 99·6° C. If the thermometer were being permanently graduated, the correct position of the 100° C. mark would be found by proportion, since $l_{100} - l_0 : l_{99·6} - l_0 = 100 : 99·6$; as this is not actually needed, we can in the final calculation simply say that $l_{99·6} - l_0$ corresponds to a temperature interval of 99·6 centigrade degrees.

(c) *The air temperature reading.* It is not as easy as it would seem to take the temperature of the air, for it is essential that

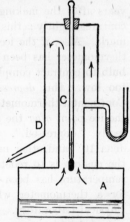

Fig. 2.—Hypsometer.

the thermometer should reach the temperature of the air, and it is not possible to tell with certainty when this has happened. Some long time should be allowed, and it is usually recommended that the thermometer be waved about, or that a current of air should be drawn past it, during this time. When the level of the mercury is steady, the position of the top of the column is noted, and the length l_t of the thread is measured.

For the calculation, using the figure for the boiling point actually found,

$$\frac{t}{99\cdot6} = \frac{l_t - l_0}{l_{99\cdot6} - l_0} \quad \text{and} \quad t = 99\cdot6 \frac{l_t - l_0}{l_{99\cdot6} - l_0} \text{ °C}.$$

on the scale of this particular mercury thermometer.

Errors of the mercury thermometer. The following is a summary of the chief sources of error which have to be corrected for in accurate work. For further details, see a standard treatise, such as Preston's " Theory of Heat ", 3rd Edn., pp. 113-125.

1. *Lack of uniformity of the bore of the capillary.* The thermometer (if of the solid stem type) may be calibrated by detaching a thread of mercury and measuring the number of degree divisions it occupies at different parts of the tube.

2. *Error in marking the fixed points.* This of course affects readings at all points on the scale, and once the error of the fixed point markings has been found it is simple to construct a correction graph.

3. *Change of zero.* Glass contracts slowly after heating, and for years after the making of the thermometer the bulb continues to contract slightly ; this causes a gradual creep upwards of the zero mark. Also, if the ice point is determined immediately after the thermometer has been used at a high temperature, failure of the bulb to contract completely at once causes the zero reading to be too low. This *depression of the zero* is an important error in Continental thermometers, since the practice abroad is to determine the ice point *after* the steam point, so that the 0° C. graduation is really " depressed ". The depression under this treatment for Jena 16‴ and other modern glasses is as much as 0·04°. In use, the custom is to redetermine the zero afresh immediately after a temperature has been observed. But this trouble is unnecessary for a thermometer which has been calibrated at the National Physical Laboratory.

4. *Internal pressure.* A vertical column of mercury 25 cm. long

exerts a pressure of about one third of an atmosphere, approximately 5 lb./sq. in. This is about the length of the thread of a thermometer reading a high temperature. Hence, when the thermometer is vertical there may be a very considerable pressure distending the bulb slightly ; when it is horizontal, this pressure is absent, so the reading will be higher.

5. *External pressure.* When the bulb is immersed below the surface of a liquid there is a hydrostatic pressure tending to make the bulb contract, and the reading too high. Changes in the atmospheric pressure are also sufficient to cause an appreciable error of the same kind.

6. *Emergent column error.* The fixed points are determined with the mercury-filled portion of the stem at the same temperature as the bulb, and the thermometer should really be used in this way, but this is not always possible. If the bulb only is heated, the mercury in the stem is at air temperature, and the reading (if above air temperature) is therefore too low. The correction to be added is then $0{\cdot}00016n\,(t-t_s)$ centigrade degrees, where n is the length of the exposed column in degrees, t the indicated temperature of the bulb, and t_s the mean temperature of the exposed column, which usually cannot be ascertained very accurately.

Range of liquid-in-glass thermometers. Mercury freezes at about $-39°$ C. and boils at $357°$ C. under normal pressure, so that the range of an ordinary mercury thermometer is between its freezing point and about $300°$ C. If the space above the mercury is filled with nitrogen, or some other inactive gas, the pressure of the gas, when both compressed by the rising mercury thread and heated, raises the boiling point, and such a thermometer can be used for temperatures considerably above the normal boiling point of mercury, in fact up to $500°$ C. Kohlrausch gives $800°$ C. as an upper limit for mercury in quartz. Alcohol (b.p. $78°$ C.) may be used in thermometers between $60°$ C. and $-130°$ C., liquid pentane down to $-200°$ C. Alcohol thermometers and others, the range of which does not embrace both the ice point and the steam point, must be graduated by comparison with a mercury, or other, thermometer.

Clinical thermometer. This instrument (Fig. 3) used for determining the temperature of the human body, has a short, very fine, capillary tube, constricted with a slight kink close to the junction of stem and bulb. When the bulb is put in the mouth or armpit,

FIG. 3.—Clinical thermometer.

the expanding mercury forces its way past the constriction, but when the bulb is removed the contracting mercury does not pull the thread back, so it is left in the stem recording the highest temperature reached ; it is reset by shaking the thread down. The normal temperature of the human body is said to be 98·4° F. ; actually it varies from 97·5° to 98·5°. The scale is graduated from 95° F. to 110° F. The front is usually shaped to act as a lens, so that the fine thread is observed as a wide ribbon when the eye is in the right position. The thermometer must be left in position for some time, half a minute to two minutes according to the make of instrument, in order to reach the temperature of the body.

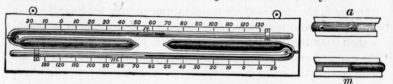

FIG. 4.—Rutherford's maximum and minimum thermometers.

Maximum and minimum thermometers. (1) **Rutherford's.** Two separate thermometers are used, mounted on the same stand (Fig. 4). A mercury thermometer records the maximum temperature reached in the interval since the previous setting. A small iron index m is pushed forward by the mercury surface when the mercury expands, and is left in position when the thread recedes. It is reset by a magnet. The minimum thermometer contains alcohol ; inside the thread is a small glass index a. When the alcohol expands, it flows past the index ; when the temperature falls and the thread moves back, the alcohol surface on meeting the index pulls it back by surface tension. The index is reset by tilting the thermometer slightly, when it slides along to the surface. In both thermometers, it is the end of the index directed towards the surface of the liquid which marks the required temperature.

(2) **Six's self-registering thermometer** (Fig. 5). The thermometer bulb proper, A, contains alcohol or some other suitable liquid ; BC is a thread of mercury ; above C there is more alcohol, which also partly

fills the bulb D. Above the surface of
the mercury at both B and C is a light
steel index (shown enlarged at the
side) with a spring to prevent slipping.
When the alcohol in A expands, the
thread BC is pushed round, sending
the index above C upwards, and leaving
that above B in position ; when the
alcohol in A contracts, the thread BC is
drawn back, leaving the C index recording the maximum temperature reached.
The B index similarly records the minimum temperature. To reset, each index
is drawn down by a magnet.

Constant Volume Gas Thermometer.
Consider a fixed mass of gas maintained
at constant volume, in a vessel fitted
with means of measuring the pressure.
Let p_0 and p_{100} be the pressures at the
ice point and steam point respectively,
and p_t the pressure at some unknown
temperature t °C. Let us state that
equal changes in pressure denote equal
changes in temperature. Then

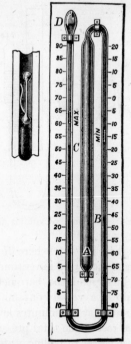

$$\frac{t}{100}=\frac{p_t-p_0}{p_{100}-p_0} \quad \text{and} \quad t=100\,\frac{p_t-p_0}{p_{100}-p_0}\ \text{°C}.$$

on the constant volume gas thermometer scale of the particular
gas used.

It is not necessary here to discuss the behaviour of individual
gases or of an ideal gas. It does happen that the so-called permanent gases behave in such a way that equal changes of temperature
measured on the absolute thermodynamic scale cause very nearly
equal increases in pressure, and this was a reason for choosing the
constant volume gas thermometer as a practical standard. But it
is best to put these ideas aside for the moment, as they may tend
to confuse the main point, which is that *the constant volume gas scale
is based on the statement that equal changes of pressure shall denote
equal changes of temperature.*

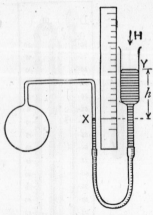

FIG. 6.—Constant volume air thermometer.

Jolly's Constant Volume Air Thermometer. Determination of the boiling point of brine on the constant volume air thermometer scale. Jolly's constant volume air thermometer (Fig. 6) consists of a glass bulb of about 100 c.c. capacity, containing dry air, connected by a fine glass capillary tube and rubber pressure tubing to a movable manometer reservoir. A fixed mark X on the capillary is the "constant volume" mark. The vertical height of the level Y in the open limb above X is called the "head", h. The total pressure of the gas in the bulb is then $(H + h)$, where H is the atmospheric pressure, all pressures being measured in centimetres of mercury.

First read the barometer to determine H. Then immerse the bulb in a vessel containing ice and distilled water; after leaving for at least ten minutes level the mercury at X, measure the head h_0, and record the total pressure $p_0 = (H + h_0)$. Next, immerse the bulb in a vessel of boiling water. Strictly, the bulb should be immersed in steam, and the true temperature of the steam obtained as on p. 7; but in this exercise the temperature of the boiling water is taken as the steam point. After at least ten minutes, level the mercury at X, measure the head h_{100}, check the barometer reading, and record the total pressure $p_{100} = (H + h_{100})$. Before removing the bulb from the boiling water, lower the reservoir as far as possible, to prevent mercury being sucked into the bulb as it cools. Finally, place the bulb in a vessel of boiling brine. After at least ten minutes, measure the head h_t, check the barometer reading, and record the total pressure $p_t = (H + h_t)$. The boiling point of brine is given by the equation

$$t = 100 \frac{p_t - p_0}{p_{100} - p_0} \text{ °C.}$$

on the constant volume air thermometer scale.

Apart from the rough-and-ready steam point, there are several defects in this experiment. First, the air is not maintained at constant volume, for the glass bulb expands appreciably. Also, the air in the capillary tube is practically at room temperature. It is possible to allow for the expansion of the glass if we know exactly (a) how much the glass expands, and (b) what effect this has on the pressure ; the " emergent column " error of the capillary is harder to allow for, but could be reduced by making the capillary very narrow and the bulb much larger. It is a nuisance to have to read the barometer every time an observation is made.

Constant Volume Gas Thermometer as a standard. The Kelvin Absolute Thermodynamic Scale has been adopted by international agreement as the standard scale. Unfortunately no instrument can be made to realise this exactly. In 1887, the International Committee of Weights and Measures decided to adopt as a practical standard the centigrade scale of a constant volume hydrogen thermometer, the fixed points being the ice point and the steam point, and the pressure of the hydrogen at 0° C. being equal to one metre of mercury. In principle, any gas the behaviour of which has been determined would do as well as hydrogen ; helium is employed at low temperatures and nitrogen at high temperatures.

A constant volume gas thermometer is most inconvenient to use, and mercury thermometers, resistance thermometers, thermocouples, etc., are the actual instruments employed. But we do not express the readings of each instrument in terms of its own natural scale. The instrument is compared with the gas thermometer, and either it is calibrated to read constant volume hydrogen scale temperatures directly, or else conversion formulæ to enable these temperatures to be deduced from readings on its own scale are calculated. Further corrections obtained from a knowledge of the behaviour of the gas are needed to convert constant volume gas temperatures to absolute thermodynamic temperatures.

This seems a lengthy chain of operations, and recent progress has enabled a number of " fixed points " to be determined as accurately on the thermodynamic scale as present knowledge permits. These fixed points constitute the **International Temperature Scale** (p. 23). The real object of this step, taken in 1927, is to save tedious repetition of readings of the constant volume gas thermometer.

One important consideration in the original choice of the constant volume hydrogen thermometer as a standard is the ease with which it can be reproduced. Pure materials are easily obtainable, and the instrument is made to standard specifications. The second consideration is the small disagreement between the constant volume hydrogen scale and the absolute thermodynamic scale. Thirdly, the scale can be realised over a wide range of temperature, from – 200° C. to 500° C. with hydrogen itself.

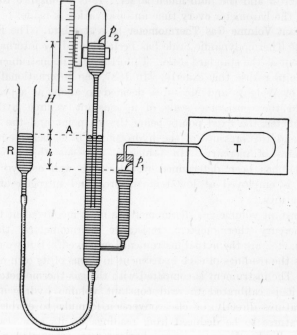

Fig. 7.—Scheme of standard constant volume hydrogen thermometer.

In the original standard hydrogen thermometer of Chappuis (Fig. 7), the bulb T is a cylinder of platinum-iridium, of length 110 cm., and volume one litre, communicating by a narrow tube to the manometer. The expansion of T is calculated and allowed for, and the fraction of the total gas in the communicating tube is small, so that two of the chief defects of the simple gas thermometer are overcome. The constant volume mark is a small pointer p_1 inside the manometer tube. The manometer incorporates a barometer, the glass tube of which is free to move vertically, carrying a vernier

which moves over a scale.   There is a small pointer p_2 inside the
" Torricellian vacuum " space of the barometer, and the level of
the mercury is brought to coincide with this.   To measure the
pressure, the reservoir R is first moved to adjust the mercury to p_1,
then the barometer is raised or lowered until p_2 just touches its
mercury surface (this upsets the first adjustment slightly, and there
is a " fine adjustment ", not shown, to allow for it).   The vertical
distance between p_2 and p_1 gives the total pressure $(H + h)$ of the
gas, as is easily seen from the figure, for the pressure at the level A
is atmospheric.

Above 500° C. hydrogen diffuses through platinum and attacks
glass or porcelain ; for higher temperatures, up to 1500° C., nitrogen
(the constant volume *nitrogen* scale) is used instead.   This substitution means that slightly different corrections are applied to
obtain the absolute thermodynamic temperatures from the readings.
The accuracy at 1500° C. is to within 2°, while between the fixed
points the readings are accurate to 0·005°.

Platinum resistance thermometer.   The resistance of pure metals
increases as the temperature rises.   Callendar showed that the
resistance of a piece of pure platinum varies with the gas thermo-
meter temperature θ according to the formula $R = R_0(1 + \alpha\theta + \beta\theta^2)$,
where R_0 and R are the resistances at 0° C. and θ° C., and α and β
are constants for the particular specimen used.

Now, on the platinum resistance scale of temperature, we say that
equal changes in resistance denote equal changes in temperature.
If R_0 and R_{100} be the resistances at the ice point and the steam point
respectively, and R_t the resistance at t_p° C., then

$$\frac{t_p}{100} = \frac{R_t - R_0}{R_{100} - R_0}, \quad \text{and} \quad t_p = 100\,\frac{R_t - R_0}{R_{100} - R_0}\,°\text{C}.$$

on the platinum resistance scale.   This differs appreciably from
the gas thermometer reading for the same temperature.   Callendar
showed that the difference between the gas thermometer temperature θ and the platinum resistance temperature t_p is represented
over a wide range by the formula

$$\theta - t_p = \delta\left\{\left(\frac{\theta}{100}\right)^2 - \frac{\theta}{100}\right\},$$

where δ is a constant for the particular specimen of wire, which

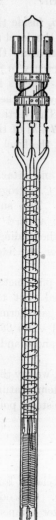

FIG. 8.—Platinum resistance thermometer.

may be obtained from a single observation at the boiling point of sulphur, for which θ is accurately known.

Fig. 8 shows the platinum resistance thermometer. The wire is wound doubled on itself (non-inductively) on a flat strip of mica which is enclosed in a tube of hard glass or glazed porcelain. The tube is either evacuated or filled with dry air. The leads are of copper (for use up to 700° C.), or platinum (for higher temperatures).

A modified Wheatstone's Bridge, called **Callendar and Griffiths' Bridge**, is used for measuring the resistance. In this, the ratio arms (Fig. 9) R_1 and R_2 are equal. The thermometer of resistance T with leads of resistance l is connected in the third arm, and the fourth arm contains a known resistance R, in series with a pair of dummy leads exactly similar to those going to the thermometer itself, but connected together at the far end, which run alongside the actual leads so that they undergo the same change in temperature and therefore the same change in resistance. Between these arms is a uniform resistance wire, of resistance ρ ohms per centimetre ; a sliding contact of the usual kind is moved along this wire (EF in the figure), until there is no deflection in the galvanometer. Then, as $R_1 = R_2$, calling $ED = x$ and $DF = y$,

$$R + l + x\rho = T + l + y\rho$$
$$T = R + (x - y)\rho.$$

The platinum thermometer has a wide range, from $-200°$ C. to 1000° C. It is extremely accurate over the whole of this range. Its chief disadvantage is the long time needed for it to take up the temperature of the surroundings, and time required for making an observation, so that it cannot follow rapidly changing temperatures. The time lag is reduced in some low-temperature types by using a silver case filled with dry air.

A high precision Wheatstone Bridge was designed by F. E. Smith for the accurate measurement of temperatures with platinum resistance thermometers. The connections are so arranged that leads resistance may be eliminated during tests. Instead of the bridge-wire, a series of 30 shunted coils is employed. This arrangement ensures permanency of calibration and gives greater precision and facility than the slide-wire method. The bridge coils are immersed in oil, which is circulated by means of a stirrer. If a suitable thermometer is used and the necessary precautions are taken, readings may be made with this bridge to within $\pm 0.002°$ C. over a range of $-200°$ to $+600°$ C.

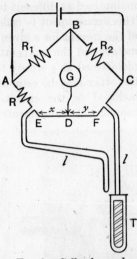

FIG. 9.—Callendar and Griffiths' Bridge.

It is possible to construct recording instruments, in which any deflection of the galvanometer pointer causes automatic adjustment of the slide-wire of a Callendar and Griffiths' bridge, and a simultaneous movement of the recording pen across a chart.

Thermoelectric thermometers. When a closed circuit made of two dissimilar metals or alloys has the two junctions (Fig. 10 a)

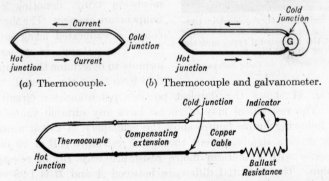

(a) Thermocouple.   (b) Thermocouple and galvanometer.

(c) Practical thermoelectric thermometer for high temperatures.

FIG. 10.

maintained at different temperatures, a current flows in the circuit. This arrangement is called a **thermocouple**. The size and direction of the current for a given pair of wires depends on the nature of the metals and the temperatures of the junctions. If one junction is maintained at a steady temperature, say 0° C., the temperature of the other may be estimated from the reading of a galvanometer G included in the circuit (Fig. 10 b). This is the basis of many commercial instruments, particularly those designed to give continuous records of temperature.

An industrial thermoelectric pyrometer in use. The thermocouple is of the base-metal type, and the circuit that of Fig. 10 (c).

By courtesy of the Foster Instrument Co., Ltd.

In theory, it is more satisfactory to measure the electromotive force (E.M.F.) developed, instead of the current this causes, because the E.M.F. depends only on the temperatures for two given materials, while the current depends on the total resistance of the circuit, which alters considerably as the temperature changes. In the laboratory, the E.M.F. would be measured by a *potentiometer* ; in industrial instruments, a high-resistance millivoltmeter is used. It is not usual to employ a " thermocouple scale ", with equal increments in E.M.F. denoting equal temperature changes. The thermocouple is calibrated using several fixed temperatures, or an agreed formula to determine the temperature from the E.M.F. is used.

Fig. 11 shows the simplest possible potentiometer circuit set up. The resistances may of course have any suitable values, but the following simple figures show the principle. A 2-volt accumulator gives a steady current through a resistance AB of 99 ohms, in series with a uniform metre resistance wire BC of resistance 1 ohm. The potential difference between A and B is 1·98 volts, and that between B and C is 0·02 volt, so that the potential drop down each centimetre of BC is 0·0002 volt. One connection of the thermocouple goes to *B*, and the other is joined to the sensitive galvanometer *G*, and the circuit is completed by a sliding contact *D* which can move along *BC*. When *D* is in such a position that no current flows through *G*, the potential difference between *B* and *D* down the wire must just balance the E.M.F. of the thermocouple. The

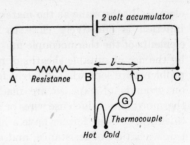

Fig. 11.—Simple potentiometer circuit.

distance *BD* is then measured. If this is *l* cm., the E.M.F. of the thermocouple is $l \times 0.0002$ volt. A circuit of this type suffices for rough work only ; for accurate work a more complicated circuit incorporating a standard cell is needed.

The combinations chiefly used in practice, the E.M.F. when one junction is at 0° C. and the other at 100° C., and the maximum temperature at which the hot junction may be kept (much above the maximum temperature for continuous use) are given below :

Platinum with platinum-rhodium (an alloy usually containing 13 per cent. of rhodium), 0·65 millivolts (thousandths of a volt), 1600° C.

" Chromel " with " alumel " (two alloys known by these trade names), 4·1 millivolts, 1260° C.

Iron with " constantan " (a copper-nickel alloy used for making resistances), 5·3 millivolts, 1090° C.

Copper with constantan and antimony with bismuth couples are used in the laboratory for limited ranges of temperature ; the E.M.F. of the first is a little less, and of the second two or three times greater, than that of the iron-constantan couple.

Platinum with platinum-iridium (90 per cent. Pt, 10 per cent. Ir) is used up to about 1000° C., above which the iridium tends to volatilise.

In constructing a high-temperature thermometer (or **pyrometer**) using thermocouples, three considerations are important. First, the total resistance of the circuit must be made so high that chance temperature variations of resistance cannot affect the millivoltmeter reading appreciably ; secondly, some means of keeping the cold junction at a steady temperature must be found—this may be done by using " extensions " made of materials which are thermoelectrically the same as the materials of the couple, so that the cold junction is effectively close to the galvanometer; thirdly, the elements of the thermocouple must be protected from contamination by the use of suitable sheaths of metal or refractory material. The problems are somewhat different for *rare metal* thermocouples, which on grounds of expense are made of thin wires, and *base metal* thermocouples, which use wires or concentric tubes of any convenient thickness. The former have a higher resistance, a larger temperature variation of resistance, and a smaller E.M.F.

Fig. 10 (c) shows the scheme adopted in the thermoelectric pyrometers made by the Foster Instrument Co., Ltd.; the "ballast" resistance is included to make the total resistance of the circuit high enough.

Figures, kindly supplied by this firm, are contrasted below for a typical example of a rare metal thermocouple pyrometer of platinum with platinum-rhodium and a base metal outfit of chromel with alumel:

	Rare Metal.	*Base Metal.*
Resistance of thermocouple stem when cold	2 ohms.	0·1 ohm.
Probable variation of thermocouple resistance due to insertion to different depths and into furnaces at different temperatures	1 ohm.	0·01 ohm.
Resistance of copper cable	1 ohm.	0·25 ohm.
Resistance of copper coil in indicating millivoltmeter	24 ohms.	2 ohms.
Probable change in resistance of cable and coil due to change in atmospheric temperature	1 ohm.	0·09 ohm.
Therefore probable total change in circuit resistance	2 ohms.	0·1 ohm.
Minimum total resistance by addition of ballast in order that above change in resistance does not exceed 1% of the total resistance	200 ohms.	10 ohms.
E.M.F. of thermocouple at 1000° C.	10 millivolts.	40 millivolts.
Current flowing in moving coil of indicating millivoltmeter, generating the operating force, in milliamperes (thousandths of an ampere) at 1000 °C.	$\frac{10}{200} = 0·05$ m.a.	$\frac{40}{10} = 4$ m.a.

The rare-metal couple clearly needs a millivoltmeter eight times as sensitive, and therefore less robust, than the other, for corresponding accuracy in temperature indications.

Sheathing is also a difficulty with the platinum alloy couples, since the sheath must not only prevent contamination by furnace gases, but must also be at the same time stout enough to afford mechanical support and thin enough to prevent undue lag in following changing temperatures. 1400° C. is the highest temperature such pyrometers can be used for, since although the *couple* is effective up to 1600° C., no sheathing material which is satisfactory above 1400° C. has been found.

The electrical instrument is, in every case, graduated to read the temperature directly in degrees ; by causing the pointer to mark a rotating drum, continuous records are obtainable.

OTHER METHODS OF MEASURING TEMPERATURE

(a) **Mercury-in-steel thermometers.** The expansion of the mercury operates a gauge of the Bourdon type—a flat spiral made of hollow tubing of elliptical cross-section, which tends to straighten under pressure, like the paper " blow-out " toys which work on the same principle—showing a pointer moving over a graduated dial, or an inked pen for a permanent record. Fig. 12 illustrates a recording thermometer of this type. The range is −40° C. to 600° C., and the readings can be transmitted up to 120 feet.

(b) **Vapour pressure thermometers.** (i) *Industrial recording thermometers* similar in action to the mercury in steel type, using suitable organic liquids at low temperatures and mercury for higher temperatures, the vapour pressure operating the Bourdon gauge, are made. The range of any one thermometer is narrow, but they are very sensitive. (ii) *At very low temperatures*, in the neighbourhood of the normal boiling points of the permanent gases, the vapour pressure of a liquefied gas is the property used to estimate the temperature. At very low temperatures indeed, the vapour pressure of helium is used ; the pressure is measured by a suitable manometer (which is usually a vacuum gauge at very low temperatures), and no actual " thermometer " apart from this is used. The temperature on the absolute thermodynamic scale is obtained from the formula connecting vapour pressure and temperature.

(c) **Radiation and optical pyrometry,** for very high temperatures. Both these methods apply, in different ways, accurate quantitative observations of the well-known facts that as the temperature of a very hot body rises, it glows more brightly (the basis of " radiation

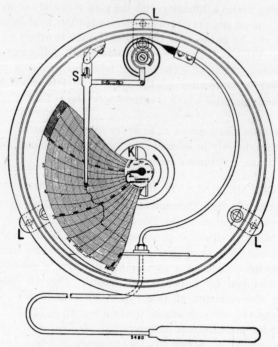

FIG. 12.—Recording mercury-in-steel thermometer.
By courtesy of the Cambridge Instrument Co., Ltd.

pyrometers ") and also changes in colour, from a dull red at about 600° C., through orange at about 1100° C., to white, from 1400° C. upwards (the basis of " optical pyrometry "). A knowledge of the laws of radiation is needed before the action of these instruments can be explained at all, and a full account is given in Chapter IX.

(*d*) **Magnetic thermometry.** The magnetic susceptibility of paramagnetic substances varies with the temperature, and this method has been used at the lowest extremes of temperature. There is some difficulty about relating the susceptibility scale, called the *Curie Scale*, to the absolute thermodynamic scale at these low temperatures, and readings are often expressed simply on the Curie Scale.

(*e*) **Bimetallic thermometers**, chiefly used as recording instruments, are described on p. 98.

THE INTERNATIONAL TEMPERATURE SCALE

The fundamental scale of temperature is the absolute thermodynamic centigrade scale, with the ice point and steam point as 0° C. and 100° C. respectively. The scale of the helium gas thermometer is the nearest approach to this scale. In 1927, the International Committee of Weights and Measures agreed upon a scale which is as close to the absolute thermodynamic scale as present knowledge permits.

The problem in devising a scale is two-fold. First, reproducible fixed points must be agreed upon ; and secondly, the means of interpolating temperatures between the fixed points (that is, suitable thermometers) must be prescribed.

The international fixed points are the following equilibrium temperatures, all under a pressure of one standard atmosphere. The symbol t is here used for temperatures on this scale.

Equilibrium between liquid and gaseous oxygen
(**Oxygen Point**) - - - - - - - $-182\cdot97°$ C.
$t_p = t_{760} + 0\cdot0126 (p - 760) - 0\cdot0000065 (p - 760)^2$
Equilibrium between solid and gaseous carbon dioxide $-78\cdot5°$ C.
$t_p = t_{760} + 0\cdot01595 (p - 760) - 0\cdot0000111 (p - 760)^2$
Freezing mercury - - - - - - - $-38\cdot87°$ C.
Equilibrium between ice and air-saturated water
at normal atmospheric pressure (**Ice Point**) - $0\cdot000°$ C.
Transition of sodium sulphate - - - - - $32\cdot38°$ C.
Equilibrium between liquid water and its vapour at the
pressure of one standard atmosphere (**Steam Point**) $100\cdot000°$ C.
$t_p = t_{760} + 0\cdot0367 (p - 760) - 0\cdot000023 (p - 760)^2$
Condensing naphthalene vapour - - - - $217\cdot96°$ C.
$t_p = t_{760} + 0\cdot058 (p - 760)$
Freezing tin - - - - - - - $231\cdot85°$ C.
Condensing benzophenone vapour - - - $305\cdot9°$ C.
$t_p = t_{760} + 0\cdot063 (p - 760)$
Freezing cadmium - - - - - - - $320\cdot9°$ C.
Freezing lead - - - - - - - - $327\cdot3°$ C.
Freezing zinc - - - - - - - - $419\cdot45°$ C.
Equilibrium between liquid sulphur and its
vapour at the pressure of one standard atmosphere (**Sulphur Point**) - - - - - $444\cdot60°$ C.
$t_p = t_{760} + 0\cdot0909 (p - 760) - 0\cdot000048 (p - 760)^2$
Freezing antimony - - - - - - - $630\cdot5°$ C.
Freezing silver (**Silver Point**) - - - - $960\cdot5°$ C.
Freezing gold (**Gold Point**) - - - - - $1063°$ C.
Freezing copper in a reducing atmosphere - - $1083°$ C.
Freezing palladium - - - - - - - $1555°$ C.
Melting tungsten - - - - - - - $3400°$ C.

The temperature t_p for a particular equilibrium at a pressure of p mm. mercury is deduced from the formulæ given, t_{760} being the temperature at standard pressure. The named temperatures (Oxygen, Ice, Steam, Sulphur, Silver, and Gold Points) are the primary standard temperatures.

The thermometers specified are :

(a) *from the ice point to* 660° C. : the platinum resistance thermometer using the formula $R_t = R_0 (1 + at + bt^2)$, where the constants R_0, a, and b are determined from observations at the ice, steam, and sulphur points.

(b) *from* – 190° C. *to the ice point* : platinum resistance thermometer, using the formula $R_t = R_0 \{1 + at + bt^2 + c(t - 100)t^3\}$, where the four constants R_0, a, b, and c, are found using the three fixed points above, together with the oxygen point.

(c) 660° C. *to the gold point* : measurement of the E.M.F. of a platinum – platinum-rhodium thermocouple, with one junction at 0° C., while the temperature of the other is defined by the equation $E = a + bt + ct^2$, where E is the E.M.F. and a, b, c are constants.

(d) *above the gold point* : the intensity of radiation of a given wave-length from a black body at $t°$ C. is compared with the intensity of the same radiation from a black body at the gold point.

It should be noted that there is no *standard* platinum resistance thermometer, since the behaviour of different samples varies.

Since 1927, the boiling points of nitrogen, neon, hydrogen, and helium have been determined on the thermodynamic scale with sufficient certainty for their use as fixed points in very low temperature work. A further account of the measurement of low temperatures is given on pp. 324 and 325.

Names and symbols. Absolute zero. The word " absolute " means " real, not merely relative or comparative ", and when applied to temperature measurements the term " absolute scale " should mean the one scale (that is, system of measurement) which is quite independent of the properties of any one particular substance. This is its strict meaning, and though the term is commonly used in another sense it should be clear that we cannot confer the attribute of absoluteness upon temperatures measured on some arbitrary system simply by adding 273 or any other number, for this merely changes the names of the temperatures without in any way altering the fact that they have been allotted in an arbitrary way to begin with.

The word " centigrade " refers to the naming of the ice point as 0° and the steam point as 100°. The same *notation* is employed for various *scales*. For example, we speak of a temperature of 50° C. on the mercury-in-glass scale, or a temperature of 50° C. on the platinum-resistance scale, or a temperature of 50° C. on the constant volume gas scale, or a temperature of 50° C. on the absolute thermodynamic scale. This last point is important ; here is a temperature stated in the centigrade *notation* and measured on the absolute thermodynamic *system*.

The symbol chiefly used in this book, except for one section of Chapter VII, to denote a temperature on any scale using the centigrade notation is $\theta°$ C. Usually it will be assumed that this refers to the absolute thermodynamic centigrade scale, and that the thermometers concerned have been calibrated to give readings on this scale ; if any particular arbitrary scale is used this will be stated. The symbol $t°$ C. may also be used where there is no need to reserve the English letter to denote *time*.

It will be seen later that there is an *absolute zero* of temperature, that is, a true and not arbitrarily chosen zero in the same sense that the pressure in a perfect vacuum is the absolute zero of pressure. The temperature of the absolute zero on the absolute thermodynamic centigrade scale is $-273·2°$ C. to the nearest $1/10°$. On the constant volume hydrogen centigrade scale this temperature is $-273·03°$ C.

For many purposes it is convenient to measure temperatures upwards from absolute zero. The ice point is then 273·2° on the absolute thermodynamic centigrade scale starting at absolute zero, and the steam point is 373·2° on the absolute thermodynamic centigrade scale starting at absolute zero. The terms " absolute scale " and " absolute temperature " are used to indicate temperatures measured on the absolute thermodynamic scale starting at absolute zero. The names " Kelvin scale " and " temperature in degrees Kelvin " are used to remove the slight ambiguity mentioned below. The symbol $T°$ K. is used to denote a temperature on this scale ; to convert a temperature $\theta°$ C. on the absolute thermodynamic centigrade scale to its value on the Kelvin scale, the relation is $\theta°$ C. $\equiv (\theta + 273·2)°$ K.

On the constant volume hydrogen centigrade scale the temperature of the absolute zero is $-273·03°$ C. Thus, on the constant volume hydrogen scale starting at absolute zero the temperature of the ice point is 273·03°, and the temperature of the steam point is 373·03°. The terms " absolute scale " and " absolute temperature " are used to indicate temperatures measured in this way. It is a contradiction in terms to speak of " the absolute constant volume hydrogen scale ", for of course merely renumbering the same sequence of degrees cannot convert an arbitrary scale into an absolute one. But, if we understand the word " absolute " here to mean " starting at absolute zero " there is no real objection to using the term.

For all purposes except the most refined measurements, the temperature of absolute zero is taken as the approximate figure − 273° C. The temperatures of the ice point and the steam point are then 273° and 373° respectively. This scale, for which the name " tercentesimal scale " has been suggested, is best regarded as an approximation to the absolute thermodynamic scale ; the terms " absolute scale " and " absolute temperature " are used in connection with it. This seems consistent enough if it be supposed that these temperatures are obtained from the true absolute thermodynamic centigrade temperatures by superposing an approximate value for the absolute zero.

The symbol $T°$ A. or $T°$ abs. will be used to denote temperatures on the constant volume hydrogen scale measured up from absolute zero, and also for temperatures on the approximate scale measured up from − 273° C. Thus, if $\theta°$ C. denotes a reading on the constant volume hydrogen scale, the corresponding " absolute " temperature is $(\theta + 273·03)°$ A., while if $\theta°$ C. denotes a reading on the absolute thermodynamic centigrade scale the corresponding reading on the approximate absolute scale is $(\theta + 273)°$ A. The symbol K is reserved exclusively for the true Kelvin scale.

To sum up, the term " absolute temperature " is generally used to indicate the *notation* employed, that is, to denote temperature measured up from absolute zero. The measurement may or may not be made on the Kelvin absolute thermodynamic scale, so to distinguish these two possibilities the name " degrees Kelvin " (°K.) is used for the true absolute scale temperature, and " degrees absolute " (°A., or ° abs.) for temperatures measured by other means on any other scale numbered up from absolute zero.

QUESTIONS ON CHAPTER I

1. Explain the principles used in establishing a scale of temperature.

Give an account of *two* experiments you could perform, using quite distinct physical properties, in order to determine the temperature of a liquid bath (about 110° C.), without using a mercury or other liquid thermometer, but using normal laboratory equipment. (L.)

2. Describe a clinical thermometer, and point out how its construction makes it (*a*) sensitive, (*b*) quick acting, (*c*) self registering.

Give reasons for and against the use of mercury as a thermometric fluid. (C.)

3. Describe the construction and graduation of a mercury thermometer, no other thermometer being available. What procedure must be adopted in using the instrument in order to obtain the highest accuracy of which it is capable? Point out in what respects a gas thermometer is superior to a mercury thermometer. (L.)

4. Describe a constant-volume air thermometer, and explain how an interval of 1° C. is defined on the scale of this instrument.

The following readings were obtained with a constant-volume air thermometer :

	Level of mercury in closed limb.	Level of mercury in open limb.
Bulb in melting ice - · · ·	136 mm.	112 mm.
Bulb in steam at 76 cm. pressure ·	136	390
Bulb at room temperature · ·	136	160

Calculate the room temperature. (O. & C.)

5. What is meant by saying that the boiling-point of a certain liquid is 400° C.?

Describe a thermometer which would enable you to read such a temperature, and explain how its readings are obtained. (O.)

6. What do you understand by (*a*) the perfect gas scale of temperature, (*b*) the platinum resistance scale of temperature? Why do the scales give different numbers for the same temperature if that temperature is neither that of melting ice nor that of water boiling under standard pressure?

What experiments would you make to determine the corrections necessary to convert platinum scale temperatures to perfect gas scale temperatures? (C.S.)

7. Explain how a scale of temperature is defined, illustrating your answer by reference to a " liquid in glass " thermometer.

A thermometer is constructed with a liquid which expands according to the relation $V_t = V_0 (1 + at + bt^2)$, where V_0 is the volume at 0° C., V_t the volume at $t°$ C. on the scale of a gas thermometer, and a and b are constants. If $b = a/1000$, what will the liquid thermometer read when the gas thermometer reads 50° C.? (C.S.)

8. What is meant by the " fixed " points of a mercury thermometer? How may they be found, and what further experiments must be made before it can be stated that the temperature of a certain body is 15° C.?

(C.S.)

9. Define a degree centigrade on (a) the constant volume scale, (b) the constant pressure scale, for a gas. Show that if Boyle's Law holds for the gas the mean coefficient of increase of pressure at constant volume and the mean coefficient of expansion at constant pressure between 0° C. and 100° C. are equal, and that the constant volume scale and the constant pressure scale agree with one another.

Explain how temperatures are measured by means of a platinum resistance thermometer.

(C.S.)

[Reference to pp. 134-139 in Chapter IV should be made for part of this question.]

10. How is a centigrade temperature defined on (a) a constant-volume gas-thermometer, (b) a platinum resistance thermometer? Give an account of platinum resistance thermometry.   (O. & C.)

11. Describe two methods suitable for measuring high temperatures of the order of 1000° C.   (O. & C.)

12. What is meant by a scale of temperature, and on what does the definition of any particular scale depend?

If alcohol is to be used as a thermometric liquid, how would you determine what temperature on the alcohol scale of temperature corresponds to 50° C. on the gas scale?   (O. & C.)

13. Discuss the measurement of temperature, and explain how temperature is defined on the scale of a given type of thermometer.

When used to measure temperatures of about 300° C. the readings on the scale of an accurate mercury thermometer are about 2° higher than those of an accurate air thermometer. Why is this, and what reasons, if any, are there for adopting one scale rather than the other?

(O. & C.)

14. What is meant by the absolute scale of temperature? Describe some form of thermometer by which absolute temperatures can be measured. Show, in detail, how you would use it to measure the temperature at which pure lead solidifies, explaining how the temperature is to be calculated from the measurements you would have made.

(O.)

CHAPTER II

THE MEASUREMENT OF HEAT

WHEN a hot body and a cold body are placed in contact, it is observed that the hot body becomes cooler and the cold body becomes warmer, and that this continues until both are at the same temperature. To explain this, we say that *heat has passed from the hotter to the cooler body.* This is merely a suggestion as to the cause of the observed effect. It is not in itself an *observation*, still less a satisfactory definition of heat. At one time men believed that heat was a weightless material fluid, and that temperature corresponded rather to hydrostatic pressure. It is not intended at this point to anticipate the work of Chapter VI, but it seems best to state some of the familiar observations which lead us to believe that heat is really a form of energy.

Heat is produced by the expenditure of *mechanical energy* (as in the brake drums of a car, or the bearings of any machine), of *electrical energy* (when an electric current flows in a conductor), of *chemical energy* (when coal is burned, or a mixture of hydrogen and oxygen exploded) and in several similar ways. Recent calculations suggest that the heat emitted from the sun is really derived from a chain of reactions between atomic nuclei in which *atomic energy* is converted into heat. It is rather easier to produce heat than to employ it satisfactorily for the generation of other forms of energy ; but heat is converted into mechanical energy in the steam engine and the internal combustion engine, is converted into electrical energy in the thermocouple, is absorbed in such chemical actions as give products with a greater store of chemical energy than the original substances. We say then that heat is one of the several different forms of energy.

This is begging the question, and merely substituting one name for another, if we are not already quite clear as to the meaning of energy. **The energy of a body, or system of bodies, is its capacity for doing work.** Work is done when a force moves the body to which it

29

is applied, and is measured by the product (*force × distance moved in the direction of the force*). The units chiefly used are **one foot-pound** (ft. lb.), which is the work done when a force of one pound-weight moves its point of application one foot ; **one erg**, which is the work done when a force of one dyne (1/981 gm. wt.*) moves its point of application one centimetre, distances in the direction of the force being understood in each case ; and **one joule**, which is 10^7 (ten million) ergs. Energy is measured in units of work, just as a bank balance, which is a capacity for spending money, is reckoned naturally in units of currency. There is a wilful confusion in popular speech between the words *energy* and *power*; we call a station which generates electrical *energy* from heat *energy* a " *power station* ". **Power means rate of working,** and is commonly expressed in **horse-power** (1 h.p. is a rate of working of 550 ft. lb. per second), **watts** (1 watt is a rate of working of one joule per second), or **kilowatts** (1 kw. is a rate of working of one thousand joules per second).

There is no compelling reason why we should not measure heat in ergs or joules or foot-pounds, and *where this is most convenient it is done*. One of the chief domestic sources of heat is electricity, The electric meter records in mechanical units the energy supplied to the electric heater. The Board of Trade Unit, or kilowatt-hour, is the energy supplied at the rate of one kilowatt (1,000 watts) for one hour (3,600 seconds), and thus equals 3,600,000 joules, and we pay, at so much a " unit ", for the actual energy used.

Heat units. A 300-watt electric immersion heater, when connected to a mains supply at the correct voltage, is converting 300 joules of energy into heat each second, and is thus producing heat at a uniform rate. Take a large copper vessel (called a calorimeter) of about one litre capacity, pour into it about 500 grams of water, insert the immersion heater, and note the times taken for the temperature to rise 5°, 10°, 15°, 20° C., stirring well. These times are found to be roughly in the ratio 1 : 2 : 3 : 4—that is, the quantities of heat put in are in the ratio 1 : 2 : 3 : 4—or in the same proportion as the rises in temperature. Hence, for a fixed mass of water, the heat supplied is proportional to the rise in temperature.

Now select a certain temperature rise, say 10°. Use in turn masses of 300, 600, 900 grams of water, and note the times taken

* " *g* " dynes = 1 gm. wt., where *g* stands for the acceleration of gravity at the place considered.

for the required temperature rise to occur. These times are roughly in the ratio 1 : 2 : 3, suggesting that, for a fixed temperature rise, the heat supplied is proportional to the mass of water used.

Combining the two sets of results, it appears that the heat supplied is proportional to both the mass of water and the temperature rise, or

quantity of heat supplied $\propto$ *mass of water* $\times$ *temperature rise.*

Unit quantity of heat on any system is taken as the quantity of heat required to raise the temperature of unit mass of water through one degree, the actual degree interval being specified for precise work. Water is taken as the standard substance on account of its universal availability, because it is already taken as the standard for many other purposes, and because the quantity of heat required per unit mass to produce a temperature rise of one degree is not *greatly* different at different temperatures.

In choosing water as the standard substance for this and other purposes, the possibility of " heavy water " composed of heavy isotopes of hydrogen and oxygen was naturally not foreseen ; fortunately " ordinary water " as obtained from freshwater lakes and from the tap-water of various cities appears to be extremely uniform in its properties. The relative abundance of the different isotopes ($^1H : {}^2H = 6900 : 1$, and $^{16}O : {}^{18}O : {}^{17}O = 506 : 1 : 0.2$) in ordinary water can now be stated with some precision, and it is found to be very constant. So ordinary water is a quite definite standard substance, and recent discoveries have not jeopardised its character in this respect.

In the Metric System, the unit quantity of heat is called the calorie. This is the quantity of heat required to raise the temperature of 1 gm. of water through one centigrade degree— from 14·5° C. to 15·5° C. for accurate work, when we speak of the 15° C. calorie. Some experimenters have used the 20° C. calorie, the chosen degree being from 19·5° C. to 20·5° C., while in experiments involving large ranges of temperature the " mean calorie ", which is 1/100 of the quantity of heat required to raise 1 gm. of water from 0° C. to 100° C., is used.

The work discussed in this book will not in general require these fine distinctions, but it is well to be aware of them. We shall always assume that the quantity of heat required to raise the temperature of 1 gm. of water through one centigrade degree is the same wherever that degree is chosen. It might be asked whether after all it would not be better to measure heat in energy units. This would ensure perfect consistency, and it is often done ; but in practice it is not always a simple measurement to make. Accepted values for the Mechanical Equivalent of Heat (symbol J), the number of energy units equivalent to one heat unit, are :

$$1 \ 15° \text{ calorie} \quad = 4·1852 \times 10^7 \text{ erg.}$$
$$1 \text{ mean calorie} = 4·1832 \times 10^7 \text{ erg.}$$

There is in addition the unit adopted by international agreement, called the "International Steam Table Calorie" (I.T. calorie), such that

$$1 \text{ I.T. calorie} = 4·1868 \times 10^7 \text{ erg.}$$

In some branches of science the name "calorie" is used for the kilocalorie, which is the quantity of heat required to raise the temperature of one kilogram of water through one centigrade degree. This is not at present done in Physics.

In the British System, the British Thermal Unit (B.Th.U.) is the quantity of heat required to raise the temperature of 1 lb. of water through one Fahrenheit degree. The therm, which equals 100,000 B.Th U., is a larger unit used chiefly in calculating gas bills, which are now made out so that the consumer pays for the heat provided instead of for the volume of gas which has passed through the meter. Engineers also use the pound-degree-centigrade unit, which is the quantity of heat required to raise the temperature of 1 lb. of water through one centigrade degree ; this is 9/5 B.Th.U.

The heat supplied to, or gained by, a mass of water, measured in any of the above units, is then equal to the product mass of water × temperature rise.

Thus,

heat gained = mass of water × temperature rise.

It is clear that the quantity of heat removed when 1 gram of water cools one C. degree equals one calorie, otherwise it would be possible to accumulate or destroy heat indefinitely by alternately heating and cooling a mass of water for a sufficient number of times. Hence we can write for the quantity of heat removed when any mass of water cools through any temperature range,

heat lost = mass of water × temperature fall.

Water equivalent and heat capacity of a body. The rough demonstration experiments outlined on p. 30 left out of account the fact that the copper container was in every case being heated, and therefore taking in a certain quantity of heat. The effect is thus as if there had been a little extra water in the vessel. We can find directly the mass of water to which the vessel is equivalent (called its **water equivalent**) in the following way. Take

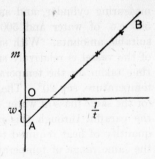

Fig. 13.

masses of 200 gm., 300 gm., 400 gm., of water in turn, heat with the immersion heater for exactly the same time, and note the rise in temperature at the end of each heating. Let m be the mass of water in any experiment, t the rise in temperature observed, and w the water equivalent of the vessel. Then the heat supplied is $(m + w) t$ calories, which, as it is the same each time, will be denoted by the constant a. Hence $(m + w) = a/t$, and a graph of m against $1/t$ is a straight line AB cutting the m-axis when $m = -w$, so that w is determined from the intercept OA in Fig. 13. The **heat capacity**, or **thermal capacity**, of a body is defined as the quantity of heat required to raise the body through one degree. As w calories are needed to raise w grams of water through one degree, the value of the thermal capacity (*in calories per centigrade degree*) will be the same numerically as the water equivalent (*in grams of water*). This is not *strictly* true, for the quantity of heat required to raise w gm. of water through one degree depends on the temperature at which that degree is situated ; but it is consistent with the assumption of p. 31.

Specific heat. In the experiment of the last section, a large copper can, weighing perhaps 300 gm., will be found to have a water equivalent of about 30 gm., or a heat capacity of about 30 calories per centigrade degree. It is evident that one gram of copper requires very much less heat to raise it one centigrade degree than does one gram of water. We will discuss this point further, with reference to a liquid first.

Place the immersion heater into equal masses of paraffin and water in turn ; for experiments of this type, it suffices to use a measuring cylinder, and as the specific gravity of paraffin is 0·8, 500 c.c. of water and 500/0·8, or 625 c.c. of paraffin would be suitable amounts. With such large masses, the thermal capacity of the vessel is relatively small. In each experiment, observe the time taken for the temperature to rise through the same range of temperature, say 20°. The time for the paraffin is about half that for the same mass of water, so the quantity of heat required to raise the paraffin through this range of temperature is about half the quantity of heat required to raise the same mass of water through the same range of temperature. Or, applying this to each degree rise of each gram of paraffin, 1 gm. of paraffin requires about half as much heat to raise its temperature one centigrade degree as does 1 gm. of water. But 1 gm. of water requires one calorie to raise its temperature through one centigrade degree, hence 1 gm. of paraffin requires about half a calorie to raise its temperature through one centigrade degree. This introduces the idea of specific heat.

The specific heat of a substance is usually defined in two ways :

(1) The specific heat of a substance is the ratio of the quantity of heat required to raise the temperature of a certain mass of the substance through a certain range of temperature to the quantity of heat required to raise the temperature of the same mass of water through the same range of temperature.

According to this definition, specific heat is a ratio between two quantities of heat, and is thus a number with no units. Further, if one quantity of heat is one-tenth or one-half the other, this ratio is quite unaffected by the units employed for measuring the quantities of heat, provided the same units (calories, B.Th.U., ergs, joules, or any other) are used for both of them. Thus the value of the specific heat does not depend on the system of units chosen, and is the same in all systems.

(2) The specific heat of a substance is the quantity of heat, measured in calories, required to raise the temperature of one gram of the substance through one centigrade degree ; or, in British units, the quantity of heat, measured in B.Th.U., required to raise the temperature of one pound of the substance through one Fahrenheit degree. According to this definition, the units in which specific heat is expressed should be " calories per gram per centigrade degree ", with a corresponding British system version.

There has been much discussion as to the relative merits of these two definitions. It appears from the argument used at the end of the paraffin experiment, that the result is numerically the same whichever definition is employed, at least to the accuracy required in this book. But they are not really alternatives at all, since they define two different things. Definition 1 deliberately compares the thermal behaviour of the substance with that of water ; it defines the specific heat of the substance relative to that of water, and the value of the specific heat of water itself depends on the temperature range chosen. It is the *relative specific heat*.

Definition 2 deals with the quantity of heat energy gained during a certain temperature change by a certain mass of the substance. It so happens that the unit in which the heat energy is measured is defined with reference to water, but it can be realised in terms of the absolute unit of energy, the erg, and could equally well be defined as a number of ergs. There is thus no comparison, either explicit or implicit, between the substance and water in this definition. It defines what may be termed the *absolute specific heat* of the substance.

It is urged frequently that the term " specific " should be reserved to denote comparative or relative quantities, " specific gravity " (but not " specific volume " or " specific resistance ") serving as precedent. If this be widely accepted, then definition 1 is that of specific heat, while the quantity of definition 2 is best renamed entirely, as " thermal capacity of unit mass ", for which some such name as " calorance " or " thermivity " may yet be coined.

In Kaye and Laby's " Tables ", some specific heats are given as numbers, others are specified as " relative to water at 15° C.", and the specific heats of gases are expressed in the units " calories per gram per centigrade degree ".

In this book, the term " specific heat " is used in the text to denote the absolute specific heat, or thermal capacity of unit mass, *any appropriate units of energy and mass being used*. When numerical values are stated without the units being specified, these are to be understood as " cal. per gm. per C. degree ".

The specific heat of a substance must not be regarded as a constant, for the specific heat of all substances varies with the temperature. For example, in the case of diamond, the specific heat at −186° C. is 0·0025, at 22° C., 0·122, and at 827° C., 0·429 ; the specific heat of copper is 0·91 at 0° C., and 0·95 at 100° C.

In many cases, for example with ferromagnetic materials and alloys like brass, there is a sharp and very considerable rise in specific heat in the neighbourhood of temperatures associated with changes in internal structure. We should therefore distinguish between the specific heat of a substance at a given temperature, and the *mean specific heat* over the range between two given temperatures, which is the quantity usually found by experiments and required in calculations. Unless the contrary is stated, the mean value over the appropriate range is referred to.

Let a quantity of heat Q calories be supplied to a body of mass m gm., and raise its temperature from θ_1 °C. to θ_2 °C. Let s be the *mean specific heat* between these two temperatures. Then the number of calories required, on the average, to raise 1 gm. of the substance through one centigrade degree is $\dfrac{Q}{m(\theta_2 - \theta_1)}$, so

$$s = \frac{Q}{m(\theta_2 - \theta_1)}.$$

This can be turned round and written as

$$Q = ms(\theta_2 - \theta_1),$$

or, in words,

$$heat\ gained = mass \times specific\ heat \times temperature\ rise.$$

Similarly, when a body loses heat and the temperature falls,

$$heat\ lost = mass \times specific\ heat \times temperature\ fall.$$

Again, let a small quantity of heat δQ be supplied to a body of mass m at temperature θ° C., and raise its temperature to $\theta + \delta\theta$° C. Let s be the mean specific heat over this small range of temperature.

Then

$$\delta Q = ms\,\delta\theta,$$

$$\therefore\ s = \frac{1}{m}\frac{\delta Q}{\delta\theta};$$

and in the limit, when δQ and $\delta\theta$ are both exceedingly small,

$$s = \frac{1}{m}\frac{dQ}{d\theta}.$$

This gives the specific heat *at the temperature* θ° C.

To raise the temperature of a body of mass m and specific heat s through *one* degree requires ms calories. Thus

$$thermal\ capacity = mass \times specific\ heat.$$

There is one further point, which is chiefly of interest in dealing with gases. Consider unit mass of gas, contained in a vertical cylinder with a movable piston on which weights may be placed to alter the pressure on the gas. Supply sufficient heat to raise the temperature of the gas by 1° C., at the same time keeping the volume constant by increasing the load on the piston. The quantity of heat supplied is called the **specific heat at constant volume**. Now start the operation afresh, with the same initial conditions. Supply sufficient heat to raise the temperature of the gas 1° C., but this time without altering the weights on the piston. The quantity of heat supplied is called the **specific heat at constant pressure**. The gas expands, raising the weights, and so *doing work upon an external body*. The specific heat of the gas at constant pressure must be *greater* than the specific heat at constant volume, for in addition to raising of the temperature of the gas, *the energy required to do the work to raise the weights must also be furnished*. The specific heat of a gas thus depends on the conditions under which the heat is supplied. Constant volume and constant pressure are only two out of innumerable sets of conditions, so the specific heat of a gas may have any one of innumerable different values.

These considerations do not arise in dealing with solids and liquids in *ordinary* conditions; the specific heat determined is that at constant pressure, and the value at constant volume can if necessary be calculated from this. The specific heat at constant pressure is as much as 5 per cent. greater than that at constant volume for some metals. Though the expansion is very small, the work which must be done against the elastic forces between the atoms in order to produce even a small given extension by mechanical means is appreciable ; and the same amount of energy must be furnished as heat to provide the same amount of work when the same extension occurs as the result of thermal expansion. It is because all measurements are made at constant pressure in all practical cases, rather than because of the magnitude of the difference, that the specific heat at constant pressure is the only one considered for a solid.

Latent heat. When a solid is melted, the change of state takes place at a definite temperature under given fixed conditions. Experiments using a constant source of heat make it evident that heat must be supplied in order to melt the solid. The reverse change demands the removal of heat. The quantity of heat required to change unit mass of a substance from the solid to the liquid state without change of temperature is called the latent heat of fusion of the substance.

When a liquid is vaporised, heat must be supplied. In the case of ordinary evaporation, heat is drawn from the surrounding liquid. When the liquid is boiling, at a fixed temperature under a given pressure, the heat supplied causes the liquid to vaporise at a fixed temperature. The quantity of heat required to change unit mass of a substance from the liquid state into vapour without change of temperature is called the latent heat of vaporisation (or evaporation) of the substance.

The word " latent " means " hidden ", and the idea is that the heat which is supplied to melt a quantity of ice, for example, is really stored in the resulting water. As will be seen later, this heat has really been used in doing the mechanical work necessary to change a rigid solid body into a fluid ; and similarly the latent heat of evaporation is really expended in doing mechanical work in converting a fluid of definite volume into the gaseous state.

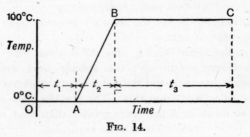

Fig. 14.

A very rough experiment, which assumes a bunsen burner to be a constant source of heat, may be used to give an idea of the values of the latent heat of fusion and the latent heat of vaporisation of water-substance, usually called the " latent heat of ice " (though the heat is latent in the resulting *water*) and " the latent heat of steam " respectively.

Two or three cubes of ice are placed in a thin copper can, which is immediately placed over a bunsen burner the flame of which is shielded from draughts. The temperature is read at intervals of one minute until this reaches 100° C., when it may be read at five-minute intervals until the can boils dry. A graph of temperature against time is plotted, and the times t_1, t_2, t_3, for the parts OA (melting of the ice), AB (raising of the water from 0° C. to 100° C.)

and BC (conversion of all the water into steam at $100°$ C.), are obtained from the graph (Fig. 14).

Then, as the bunsen is assumed to supply heat at a constant rate,

$$\frac{\text{Heat to melt ice at } 0° \text{ C.}}{\text{Heat to raise same mass of water 100 centigrade degrees}} = \frac{t_1}{t_2}.$$

Applying this to one particular gram of the ice,

$$\frac{\text{Heat to melt one gram of ice at } 0° \text{ C.}}{\text{Heat to raise one gram of water through 100 centigrade degrees}} = \frac{t_1}{t_2}.$$

But 100 calories are needed to raise the temperature of 1 gm. of water through 100 centigrade degrees ; therefore

Heat required to change 1 gm. of ice at $0°$ C. into water at $0°$ C.

$= 100 \dfrac{t_1}{t_2}$ calories.

Similarly,

$$\frac{\text{Heat to convert water at } 100° \text{ C. to steam at } 100° \text{ C.}}{\text{Heat to raise the same mass of water from } 0° \text{ C. to } 100° \text{ C.}} = \frac{t_3}{t_2}.$$

Whence the quantity of heat required to convert 1 gm. of water at $100°$ C. into steam at $100°$ C. $= 100 \dfrac{t_3}{t_2}$ calories.

We could have reworked the arguments for one particular pound of the substance, substituting 180 Fahrenheit degrees for 100 centigrade degrees, obtaining,

Heat required to melt 1 lb. of ice at $32°$ F. $= 180 \dfrac{t_1}{t_2}$ B.Th.U.

Heat required to turn 1 lb. of water at $212°$ F. into steam at $212°$ F.

$$= 180 \frac{t_3}{t_2} \text{ B.Th.U.}$$

The numerical value of the latent heat, if measured in the appropriate consistent _heat_ units, is independent of the system of mass chosen, but does depend on the scale of temperature used. It is usual to express latent heats as " so many *centigrade units* ", or " so many *Fahrenheit units* " ; or, when the metric system is being used, as " so many *calories per gram* ".

The results of an experiment of this kind, though extremely rough, should be of the right order. For example, actual values of t_1, t_2, and t_3 might be about 5 minutes, 6 minutes, and 35 minutes respectively, giving for the latent heat of ice, $100 \times 5/6 = 83$ cal./gm., and for the latent heat of steam, $100 \times 35/6 = 581$ cal./gm.

Latent heat calculations. The quantity of heat taken in to melt a given mass of solid without change of temperature is equal to (*mass × latent heat of fusion*). Similarly, the quantity of heat given out when a given mass of liquid solidifies without change of temperature is (*mass × latent heat of fusion*).

The quantity of heat taken in to convert a given mass of liquid into vapour without change of temperature is (*mass × latent heat of evaporation*). Similarly, the quantity of heat given out when a given mass of vapour condenses without change of temperature is (*mass × latent heat of evaporation*).

Numerical values for the latent heats of ice and steam. The value obtained in 1939 by Osborne in America for the latent heat of fusion of ice is 79·69 I.T. calories per gram at 0° C. A very slightly higher value is obtained if it is expressed in terms of the 15° calorie. In all simple calculations the value 80 calories per gram is used in this book.

The latent heat of steam depends on the temperature of the boiling point. The higher the boiling point, the lower the value of the latent heat. Above the critical temperature, which for any substance is that temperature above which it cannot exist in the liquid state at all (for water about 374° C.), since the liquid cannot exist, there can be no latent heat ; and the value approaches zero as this temperature is approached. Equations for the variation of the latent heat of steam with temperature over limited ranges have been given by several observers. Regnault's equation, for the range between 63° C. and 194° C., gives the latent heat L_t at $t°$ C. as $L_t = 606·5 - 0·695t$. The mean of the two most recent values for the latent heat of steam at 100° C., given by Kaye and Laby, is 538·6 I.T calories per gram. In all elementary calculations the value 540 calories per gram is accurate enough.

Cooling. So far in this chapter we have considered rough experiments designed to introduce new ideas rather than to furnish accurate quantitative measurements. Various possible sources of error, and means of eliminating or correcting for them, must now be considered. One of the most troublesome sources of error is the loss of heat to, or gain of heat from, the surroundings. This can be reduced by suitable design of the apparatus, but can rarely be completely eliminated.

The loss of heat through the surrounding air from the surface of the calorimeter takes place chiefly by convection if the calorimeter is polished. The rate of loss depends very greatly on whether the air surrounding the calorimeter is not disturbed by other means, when it is called " natural convection ", or whether the calorimeter is exposed to a steady current of air, which is called " forced convection ".

For natural convection, the rate of loss of heat is proportional to the 5/4th power of the temperature difference between the hot body and the surroundings. This law has been tested experimentally and found to hold for quite large temperature differences up to hundreds of degrees for medium-sized cylinders.

For forced convection or ventilated cooling in a strong draught, the rate of loss of heat is proportional to the temperature difference between the hot body and the steady stream of air flowing past it. This is known as Newton's Law of Cooling. This also is true for quite large temperature differences for genuine forced convection ; it is not, as is frequently stated, only applicable for small temperature differences.

The application of Newton's Law to the cooling of a calorimeter surrounded by still air appears to be hallowed by custom. Before criticising this, it is well to remember that the calorimeter is usually surrounded by an outer jacket to impede convection of any kind, and that convection is not the only means by which heat is lost. It is certain that, if the temperature difference is small, the error made in using Newton's Law for the cooling of the calorimeter is small ; though it is known to hold only approximately, it is good enough to estimate the small cooling correction with sufficient accuracy in most experiments.

It may be applied for the purpose of small corrections to the natural convection loss of a calorimeter, provided the temperature excess is small ; the limiting excess is often said to be about 30 centigrade degrees, but in this case Newton's Law gives only about 43 per cent. of the rate of loss calculated by the 5/4-power law.

Notice that the law refers to *rate of loss of heat,* and not merely to rate of fall of temperature. It does of course follow that the rate of fall of temperature, if it occurs, is proportional to the rate of loss of heat ; but it does not follow that the emission of heat is necessarily accompanied by a fall in temperature. For example, a wire carrying an electric current will reach a steady temperature at which the rate of emission of heat equals the rate at which heat is generated in the wire, or the regular fall in temperature of a liquid may be interrupted by a long period at a steady temperature, during which heat is being lost to the air and supplied at the same rate by the latent heat evolved as the liquid solidifies.

To test Newton's Law of Cooling. It is futile to set out to test a law which is stated to be true for a strong draught by observing the cooling of an unventilated body in still air. Such an experiment might provide useful information ; for example, it would show how large a temperature excess would be permissible if the error made in using Newton's Law to calculate the cooling is to be less than, say 20 per cent., or should enable us to deduce the true law of cooling under these conditions. But it would not be an attempt to *verify* Newton's Law. The experiment must be done in the draught from an open window, or in the neighbourhood of an electric fan.

A small copper calorimeter is placed on a badly conducting stand (such as a slab of cork) on a bench by an open window, and is about one-third filled with warm water. The temperature of the draught of air directed towards the calorimeter is taken ; this is called θ_0. The temperature of the water in the calorimeter, which should be well stirred with the thermometer, is taken at intervals of one or two minutes for about an hour.

A graph (Fig. 15) of temperature against time is plotted, and the line $\theta = \theta_0$ is drawn in. Several points as at P on the curve are taken, and the tangent to the curve is drawn at each of these points, to cut the θ_0 line at Q. The perpendicular PR to the line is also drawn. As the ordinate for P gives θ, the length of PR represents the temperature excess $(\theta - \theta_0)$. The rate of fall of temperature at P is given by the slope of the graph at P, represented by PR/RQ. Now, if Newton's Law of Cooling be true, as the rate of loss of heat is

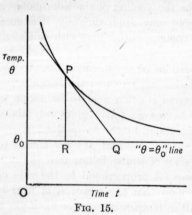

FIG. 15.

proportional to the temperature excess, in this case the rate of fall of temperature is proportional to the temperature excess. So, for the temperature represented by any point P,

$$\frac{PR}{RQ} = PR \times \text{a constant};$$

or, as PR cancels, the length RQ is constant.

The length of the intercept RQ is measured in each case, and if it is found that the lengths are the same for each position of P, Newton's Law of Cooling is obeyed.

Analytical discussion of Newton's Law of Cooling. Let m be the mass of the body, θ its temperature at any instant t, θ_0 the air temperature, and s the specific heat of the material of the body. Let the small change in temperature $-\delta\theta$ (written with a negative sign, because it is a fall) take place in the small interval of time δt, and let the corresponding heat change be $-\delta H$. Then,

$$-\delta H = -ms\,\delta\theta,$$

and the average rate of loss of heat over this interval is

$$-\frac{\delta H}{\delta t} = -ms\frac{\delta\theta}{\delta t};$$

or, in the limit, when the interval δt is taken to be extremely small,

$$-\frac{dH}{dt} = -ms\frac{d\theta}{dt}.$$

Newton's Law of Cooling states that the rate of loss of heat is proportional to the temperature excess, and in these symbols is written

$$-\frac{dH}{dt} = k(\theta - \theta_0),$$

where k is a constant for a given body under given conditions, its value depending chiefly on the area and nature of the surface, and the nature and pressure of the surrounding gas.

Substituting for $-\dfrac{dH}{dt}$, we can write $-\dfrac{d\theta}{dt} = \dfrac{k}{ms}(\theta - \theta_0)$,

or $$-\frac{d\theta}{dt} = c(\theta - \theta_0),$$

where c is another constant which is written for k/ms. It follows from the law that the rate of fall of temperature is proportional to the temperature excess; and the equation $-\dfrac{d\theta}{dt} = c(\theta - \theta_0)$ is that most often used in dealing with problems on the law, but it is *not a statement of the law*.

EXAMPLE. The temperature of a body falls from 30° C. to 20° C. in 5 minutes. The air temperature is 13° C. Find the temperature after a further 5 minutes.

There are two ways of doing this type of problem ; the first method is to work in terms of the *average rate of fall in temperature* and the *average temperature excess* over each five-minute interval ; the second method uses strict calculus. Both assume Newton's Law to hold.

First method. Let x be the final temperature.

For the first five minutes :

$$\text{average temperature} \qquad = \frac{30+20}{2} = 25° \text{ C.}$$

$$\text{average temperature excess} = 25 - 13 = 12 \text{ C. degrees.}$$

$$\text{average rate of fall of temp.} = \frac{10}{5} = 2 \text{ C. degrees/min.}$$

Since *average rate of fall of temp. = c × average temp. excess,*

$$2 = c \times 12. \dots\dots\dots\dots\dots\dots\dots\dots\dots\dots\text{(i)}$$

For the second five minutes :

$$\text{average temp.} \qquad = \frac{20+x}{2} °\text{C.}$$

$$\text{average temp. excess} = \left(\frac{20+x}{2} - 13\right) = \left(\frac{x}{2} - 3\right) \text{ C. degrees.}$$

$$\text{average rate of fall of temp.} = \frac{20-x}{5} \text{ C. degrees/min.}$$

and $$\frac{20-x}{5} = c\left(\frac{x}{2} - 3\right). \dots\dots\dots\dots\dots\dots\text{(ii)}$$

From equations (i) and (ii),

$$\frac{20-x}{10} = \frac{x/2 - 3}{12},$$

$$17x = 270,$$

and $$x = 15.88° \text{ C.}$$

Second method. Let $x°$ C. be the final temperature and let t stand for the time *from the start*.

As $$-\frac{d\theta}{dt} = c(\theta - \theta_0), \quad \frac{d\theta}{\theta - \theta_0} = -c\,dt.$$

Integrating both sides,

$$\log_e(\theta - \theta_0) = -ct + \text{a constant.}$$

We shall use the abbreviation " ln " to denote logarithms to the base e, using " log " for ordinary logarithms to the base 10, from now on.

When $\qquad t = 0,\ \theta = 30°$ C., and $\theta_0 = 13°$ C. always,

$\qquad \therefore$ the integration constant $= \ln(30 - 13) = \ln 17$.

Substituting this value, and putting $\theta_0 = 13$, the equation becomes

$$\ln(\theta - 13) = -ct + \ln 17$$

or, $\qquad\qquad \ln\left[\dfrac{\theta - 13}{17}\right] = -ct.$

This equation gives the value of θ at any instant t.

Now, $\qquad\qquad$ when $t = 5$ min., $\theta = 20°$ C.

$\qquad\qquad\qquad$ when $t = 10$ min., $\theta = x°$ C.

$$\therefore\ \ln\left[\frac{20 - 13}{17}\right] = -c \times 5,$$

$$\ln\left[\frac{x - 13}{17}\right] = -c \times 10.$$

$$\therefore\ \ln\left[\frac{x - 13}{17}\right] = 2\ln\left[\frac{7}{17}\right].$$

Now, logarithms to the base e are converted to logarithms to the base 10 by multiplying by 0·4343. This need not be written down, as the number cancels.

Hence $\qquad\qquad \log\left(\dfrac{x - 13}{17}\right) = 2\log\left(\dfrac{7}{17}\right).$

$$\therefore\ \log(x - 13) = 2\log 7 - \log 17$$
$$= 1\cdot6902 - 1\cdot2304$$
$$= 0\cdot4598.$$

Taking antilogarithms of both sides,

$$x - 13 = 2\cdot883$$
and $\qquad\qquad\qquad x = 15\cdot88°$ C.

The agreement of the two methods is close enough in this example, which shows that the much simpler first method, using *average* values, is here satisfactory. It does not follow that such close agreement always happens in all examples.

Further investigation of cooling. Newton's Law of Cooling is so regularly employed for the correction of cooling losses, and so frequently used to solve examples in which no mention is made of forced convection conditions, that it is easy to gain the impression that its validity is unlimited. This impression should be shattered by the following experiment.

Boiling water is placed in a calorimeter which stands on a cork support. The air temperature θ_0 is noted. The water is stirred and the temperature taken with a thermometer, which can be read to $1/10°$, at intervals of 2 minutes. The mean rate of fall of temperature, r, the mean temperature, $\theta°$, and the mean temperature excess $(\theta - \theta_0)°$ are calculated for each 2-minute interval, the table of results appearing as below.

Air temperature $12.4°$ C.

Time in min.	Temp. (°C.).	Mean rate of fall ($r°$/min.).	Mean temp. ($\theta°$ C.).	Mean temp. excess $(\theta - \theta_0)°$.	$\log r$.	$\log (\theta - \theta_0)$.
0	87·5					
		6·6	80·5	68·1	0·8195	1·8331
2	73·9					
		4·5	69·4	57·0	0·6532	1·7559
4	64·9					
		3·4	61·5	49·1	0·5315	1·6911
6	58·1					
⋮	⋮	⋮	⋮	⋮	⋮	⋮

First, a graph of r against $(\theta - \theta_0)$ is plotted. The points lie well on a definite smooth curve. This is far from being even roughly approximate to a straight line, so it is obvious that the rate of fall of temperature is *not* proportional to the temperature excess.

Next, as the curve indicates that there is some definite relation between r and $(\theta - \theta_0)$, the problem is to find it. Let $r = c(\theta - \theta_0)^n$, where c is a constant. Then $\log r = n \log (\theta - \theta_0) + \log c$. Or, if y stand for $\log r$, x for $\log (\theta - \theta_0)$ and b for $\log c$, $y = nx + b$.

Thus the graph of y against x should be a straight line, (not passing through the origin), and the slope dy/dx gives the value of n.

When the graph of $\log r$ against $\log (\theta - \theta_0)$ is plotted, the majority of the points will lie close to a straight line ; the exceptions will probably be one or two of the points for the highest temperatures, and the reason for this is probably that radiation is just beginning to contribute appreciably to the total loss. The slope of this line is then found. The value of n is usually between about 1.3 and 1.6, showing that the true law of cooling for a calorimeter *under these conditions* is something like $r = c(\theta - \theta_0)^{1.5}$ or, as the rate of loss of heat is proportional to the rate of fall of temperature,

$$- dH/dt = k(\theta - \theta_0)^{1.5}.$$

(The theoretical value of n is of course 1.25 for natural convection.)

CALORIMETRY

The measurement of quantities of heat is called **calorimetry**. There are numerous methods, which can be classified into two groups.

A. Thermometric calorimetry, in which a change of temperature is recorded.   Five distinct methods are available.

(1) *Method of mixtures*, in which the heat to be measured is transferred to a known mass of water. This is the best-known method, one of the simplest to use, and when precautions are taken is an accurate method.

(2) *Method of cooling*, which simply depends on the fact that the rate of loss of heat from a hot body under constant conditions follows a regular law.

(3) *Method of constant heat supply*, which has already been discussed in the rough experiments with an electric heater and a bunsen burner (pp. 34 and 38).

(4) *Electrical method*, in which the quantity of energy concerned is really measured in electrical units.

(5) *Method of continuous flow*, in which heat is supplied electrically at a steady rate to a steadily flowing stream of liquid.

B. Latent Heat calorimetry, in which the quantity of heat to be measured is caused to melt a mass of solid the latent heat of fusion of which is known, or to evaporate a mass of liquid of known latent heat of evaporation, or in which a known quantity of heat is supplied by the condensation of a measured mass of vapour of known latent heat.   We shall discuss examples of the various methods, but not in this order.

THERMOMETRIC CALORIMETRY

Specific heat of a solid by the method of mixtures.   A thin copper calorimeter, of mass w and specific heat s, contains W grams of water at a temperature θ_1 °C.   A known mass m of the solid is heated to a suitable high temperature θ_2 °C. and dropped into the calorimeter, and the final highest temperature of the mixture θ_3 °C., observed after thorough stirring.   Then, if no heat is lost to the surroundings, all the heat lost by the hot body in cooling to the final temperature has been gained by the water and calorimeter in rising to the final temperature.

Let x be the specific heat of the solid. The heat lost by m grams of solid of specific heat x in cooling from $\theta_2°$ C. to $\theta_3°$ C. is $mx(\theta_2 - \theta_3)$ cal. The heat gained by W grams of water rising from $\theta_1°$ C. to $\theta_3°$ C. is $W(\theta_3 - \theta_1)$ cal. The heat gained by w grams of copper of specific heat s in rising from $\theta_1°$ C. to $\theta_3°$ C. is $ws(\theta_3 - \theta_1)$ cal.

Then, as $\quad heat\ lost = heat\ gained$,
$$mx(\theta_2 - \theta_3) = W(\theta_3 - \theta_1) + ws(\theta_3 - \theta_1).$$

The only unknown in this equation is x, which can thus be calculated. We shall always leave equations of this type at this stage.

Precautions and corrections come under three headings :

(a) *During the heating of the specimen*, it is important to ensure that the specimen does reach the temperature recorded by the thermometer as $\theta_2°$ C. For this, prolonged heating is necessary, with the thermometer in contact with the specimen. Also, some kind of protection is needed if the body is heated in a water or steam bath, so that it is kept dry.

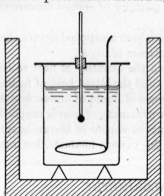

(b) *During transference to the calorimeter*, which should be done as quickly as possible, care must be taken to avoid splashing water out of the calorimeter.

(c) *During mixture*, the calorimeter should stand in an outer container, supported by badly conducting spikes of cork, strips of cardboard set edgeways, by fine threads, or some other similar method, as in Fig. 16. The outer can surrounds the calorimeter with a layer of still air, and should itself be surrounded

Fig. 16.—Calorimeter and outer case.

by a constant-temperature water jacket, so that the losses which do occur are regular. Lagging the calorimeter by packing cotton wool or felt round it should reduce convection if the material is dry ; otherwise it merely increases the heat capacity by an uncertain amount. The outside of the calorimeter and the inside of the outer can should be highly polished to reduce *radiation* losses, though it is doubtful whether much loss by radiation takes place with the small temperature excesses realised in the experiment. *Continuous stirring* during the rise in temperature is extremely important, and the water equivalent of the stirrer and the thermometer itself should be determined. The stirrer may be a piece of thick copper wire, which is considered as part of the calorimeter. The heat capacity per c.c. of mercury and of glass are very nearly the same, and the allowance for the thermometer's heat capacity can be taken as $0.45v$, where v c.c. is the volume of thermometer immersed. The calorimeter should be fitted with a lid provided with holes for the thermometer and stirrer, to check *evaporation*.

So far we have considered the reduction of heat losses by attention to design and method. We have now to correct for the cooling which unavoidably occurs in spite of every care. The *cooling correction* is most simply done as follows, using a modification of the method devised by Regnault and based on Newton's Law of Cooling. Experience will show that the correction is really not necessary unless the solid is so poor a conductor of heat that the process of attaining the steady final temperature takes some minutes; for even if the rate of loss of heat is considerable, the total loss in a very short time will be small. A suitable substance to use as an exercise is rubber.

Before introducing the solid, allow the water in the calorimeter to attain the temperature of the surroundings. At the moment when the hot solid is introduced into the calorimeter the temperature is taken, and thermometer readings are observed at half-minute intervals (stirring all the while) until the temperature ceases to rise. Stirring and thermometer readings are continued for a period at least as long as the " rise in temperature " period, and a graph of temperature against time is plotted (Fig. 17).

The air temperature (θ_0) line AB is drawn. At the highest point C of the curve, a horizontal line CE is drawn, and a perpendicular CD is dropped to AB. From any point F on CE a perpendicular FGH to AB is drawn, cutting the graph at G. The fall f_2 represented by FG gives the cooling in the time represented by DH; it is required to find the fall f_1 which occurs during the time represented by AD.

From Newton's Law of Cooling, which we assume to hold, $-d\theta/dt = c(\theta - \theta_0)$ or $-d\theta = c(\theta - \theta_0)dt$; and over any finite time interval δt, the drop $-\delta\theta$ is given by $-\delta\theta = c(\theta - \theta_0)\delta t$.

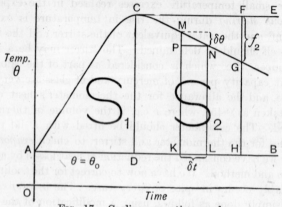

Fɪɢ. 17.—Cooling correction graph.

Considering the portion of the curve from M to N, KM represents $(\theta - \theta_0)$, KL represents δt, the area $KM \times KL$, or $KLMN$, represents $(\theta - \theta_0)\,\delta t$, and MP the fall $-\delta\theta$.

The fall in temperature over the interval MN is thus $c \times KLMN$, or

$c \times (area\ of\ the\ strip\ between\ the\ curve\ and\ the\ \theta_0\ line)$.

This is true wherever we take the strip, and applies also for the *fall of temperature below the true " no-loss " value* for the part of the curve AC which is actually rising. So, calling the area between AC and AD, S_1, and the area between CG and DH, S_2,

$$f_1 = c\,S_1, \qquad f_2 = c\,S_2,$$

$$\therefore \frac{f_1}{f_2} = \frac{S_1}{S_2}, \quad \text{and} \quad f_1 = f_2\frac{S_1}{S_2}.$$

The rule for finding the correction to be added to the *observed* maximum temperature (that at the point C) to give the *true temperature* is, then, to note the fall $f_2{}^\circ$, measure the areas S_1 and S_2 by counting squares, and the required correction $f_1{}^\circ$ is given by

$$f_1 = f_2\frac{S_1}{S_2}.$$

This proof may appear easier if reworded as an analogy to *velocity-time curves*. On a velocity-time graph, the area between any portion of the curve and the time-axis represents, on the appropriate scale, the distance travelled during the interval concerned. On a " velocity-of-cooling "-time graph, the area under the curve should similarly represent the " distance " cooled during the interval concerned. Now, we deduce from Newton's Law of Cooling that the velocity of cooling is proportional to the temperature excess. Hence a graph of *temperature excess* against time (which is the graph of Fig. 17 with the origin shifted up to A) shows the way in which the *velocity of cooling* depends on the time, though the scale is here reduced by a factor $1/c$ (for temperature excess $= 1/c \times$ rate of fall of temperature), which means that the " distance cooled " is c times the area beneath the curve, instead of being *equal* to the area.

Hence, $$f_1 = c\,S_1, \quad \text{and} \quad f_2 = c\,S_2,$$

whence $$\frac{f_1}{f_2} = \frac{S_1}{S_2}, \quad \text{and} \quad f_1 = f_2\frac{S_1}{S_2}.$$

The method of mixtures may be used satisfactorily to find the specific heat of a liquid ; the best way to proceed is to have the liquid in the calorimeter and introduce a heated solid of known specific heat. It cannot be employed in this simple way for gases, because of their extremely small density, but Regnault determined the specific heat of many gases *at constant pressure*, by passing a continuous stream of gas for a long time through the calorimeter, allowing it then to escape, and determining the mass indirectly.

Regnault's determination of the specific heat of a gas at constant pressure (C_p). The gas is stored in the reservoir V (Fig. 18) which is surrounded by a water bath, the constant temperature of which is observed by a thermometer T. The stream of gas passes through the stop-cock S and the regulator R (shown enlarged at the top of the figure), which is adjusted during the experiment to keep the reading of the manometer M constant. The gas passes through a spiral tube immersed in a bath of heated oil the temperature of which is observed by a thermometer ; the heated gas then passes through the tube at C into a metal vessel inside an ordinary calorimeter, escaping finally by the tube D ; the rise in temperature of the thermometer during the experiment is observed. From the temperature θ_2 of the oil bath, the initial and final temperatures θ_1 and θ_3 of the calorimeter, the mass of water in the calorimeter, and the water equivalent of its metal parts, the fall in temperature of the gas and the total heat supplied to the calorimeter are obtained. The mass of gas is found by measuring the pressures

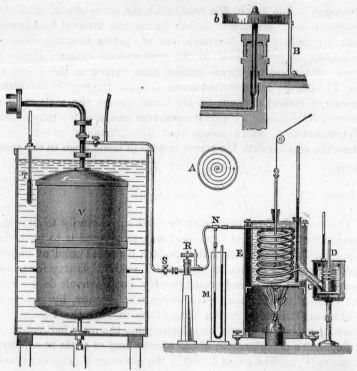

Fig. 18.—Regnault's apparatus for specific heat of a gas at constant pressure.

p_1 and p_2 of the gas in V (by means of a manometer which is not shown) at the beginning and end of the experiment, and also the corresponding temperatures denoted by T. From a knowledge of the temperature and pressure, and the value of the density of the gas under some standard conditions, the initial and final densities ρ_1 and ρ_2 gm./c.c. are found. The original mass of gas in V is then $\rho_1 v$ gm. (where v stands for the volume of V in c.c.), the mass left in at the end is $\rho_2 v$ gm., and the mass of gas which has passed through the calorimeter is $(\rho_1 - \rho_2) v$ gm.

The "cooling correction" is more than usually important; actually more heat is gained from the adjacent heater, though it is carefully screened, than is lost to the atmosphere. The experiment is done in three stages, occupying equal periods of time, say ten

minutes. During the first period, the change in temperature of the
calorimeter when no gas is passing is observed. The gas is then
passed through for an equal period, and the rise in temperature
observed. The flow of gas is then stopped, and the change in
temperature during the third equal period found. The reason
why *two* separate " correction " timings are required is interesting.
The *loss from the calorimeter to the atmosphere* is supposed to follow
Newton's Law of Cooling, for the temperature excess is small. The
gain to the calorimeter from the heater, by conduction and radiation,
is practically constant. So the rate of change of temperature $d\theta/dt$,
during the first ten minutes can be written $-d\theta/dt = c(\theta - \theta_0) - C$, an
expression with *two* unknown constants c and C. The observations
during the third ten minutes give a second similar equation,
and the two together are solved to find c and C. A third similar
equation is now used for the heating period ; and if $\bar{\theta}$ stand for the
average temperature of the calorimeter during this period, the
average rate of change of temperature during this period, $-d\bar{\theta}/dt$
is given by $-d\bar{\theta}/dt = c(\bar{\theta} - \theta_0) - C$, and the correction required is
found by multiplying the average rate of change by the time.

The specific heat at constant pressure (always denoted by the
symbol C_p) is then calculated in the ordinary way.

Latent heat of fusion of ice by the method of mixtures. The
calorimeter is weighed, about two-thirds filled with water at about
30° C., and weighed again. It is placed in its enclosure on a
non-conducting stand, and the temperature taken. Small pieces
of dry ice are added one by one, and the water is stirred until each
piece has melted before the next piece is added. When the temperature has fallen to about 5° C., the thermometer is read. The calorimeter is then weighed to find the mass of ice added.

Let W be the mass of water, w the mass of the calorimeter, υ the
specific heat of copper, m the mass of ice melted. Let θ_1 °C. and
θ_2 °C. be the initial and final temperature of the calorimeter, and
L cal./gm. the latent heat of fusion of ice.

The heat lost by the water in cooling from θ_1 °C. to θ_2 °C. is
$W(\theta_1 - \theta_2)$ cal. Heat lost by the calorimeter cooling through the
same range is $ws(\theta_1 - \theta_2)$ cal.

The heat gained by m gm. ice melting at 0° C. is mL cal. ; heat
gained by m gm. melted ice (" *ice-water* ") in rising from 0° C. to
θ_2° C. is $m\,\theta_2$ cal.

Now, assuming no heat to have escaped during the experiment, we can write

$$heat\ lost = heat\ gained\ ;$$
$$\therefore\ W(\theta_1 - \theta_2) + ws(\theta_1 - \theta_2) = mL + m\,\theta_2,$$

whence L is determined.

The chief error is probably due to the ice chips not being completely dry. They should be kept on a filter paper, pressed lightly between filter paper, and transferred quickly to the calorimeter on a bone or glass spatula. Watson recommends the use of a single large piece of ice, held below the surface of the water by a stirrer carrying a wire-gauze cage. A single piece of ice has a much smaller total surface than the same mass in small chips, and thus can be more easily freed of moisture.

The " cooling correction " is to some extent eliminated in this experiment, for when the calorimeter is above air temperature it is losing heat to the surroundings, and when below air temperature it is gaining heat. If θ_1 is as much above the temperature of the surroundings as θ_2 is below, the average rate of loss in the first part is equal to the average rate of gain in the later stages. If the temperature were to fall at a steady rate, as much time would be spent below the surrounding temperature as above it, and loss and gain would exactly cancel. It is almost impossible to ensure a really steady rate of fall, so that in practice the compensation is not exact.

A further source of error is the condensation of dew on the outside of the calorimeter.

The calculation is simple in the case of ice, for we are able to obtain it at its melting point, and the product is water, the specific heat of which is known. The method of mixtures can of course be applied to substances other than ice. For example, molten metal at a known temperature may be poured into the calorimeter, and the heat gained by the calorimeter and contents then equals that given out (a) *by the molten metal in cooling to the melting point*, plus (b) *the latent heat given out by solidification at the melting point*, plus (c) *that given out by the solid in cooling to the final temperature*. It is thus necessary to know the specific heat of both the solid and the liquid, as well as the melting point, in addition to the observations actually taken during the experiment.

Latent heat of evaporation of water (the " latent heat of steam ") by the method of mixtures. In this experiment, a measured mass of steam is condensed in a calorimeter containing cold water, and the heat given out is measured. There are two chief reasons why the experiment as here described does not permit very great accuracy. First, it is extremely difficult to ensure that the steam passing into the calorimeter is " dry ", that is, free from condensed water droplets. Also, owing to the large value of the latent heat of evaporation, a large rise in temperature may be caused by a relatively small mass of steam, which it is often difficult to weigh accurately.

The calorimeter is weighed, two-thirds filled with water, and weighed again. It is placed in its outer can, and the temperature taken. A current of dry steam is blown on the surface of the water until a rise in temperature of about 30° is obtained. The steam passes from the generator through a water trap (Fig. 19) designed to obstruct the passage of water condensing in the delivery tube from the boiler, and any " dew-drop " on the end of the outlet tube should be carefully removed with a piece of filter paper. The final temperature of the calorimeter is taken after stirring, and the calorimeter and contents weighed again.

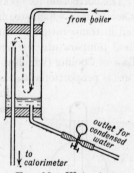

FIG. 19.—Water-trap.

Let m be the mass of steam condensed, W the mass of water, w the mass of the calorimeter, and s the specific heat of copper ; let the initial and final temperatures be θ_1 °C. and θ_3 °C., and the boiling point (found after reading the barometer and consulting the graph on p. 6) θ_2 °C. Let L be the latent heat of steam at this temperature. Then, assuming that no heat has escaped during the experiment, the heat lost by the steam in condensing, and by the resulting water (" steam-water ") in cooling to the final temperature equals the heat gained by the calorimeter and water in rising to the final temperature.

Heat lost by m gm. steam condensing at θ_2 °C.
$$= mL \text{ cal.}$$
Heat lost by m gm. steam water cooling from θ_2 °C. to θ_3 °C.
$$= m(\theta_2 - \theta_3) \text{ cal.}$$

Heat gained by W gm. water rising from θ_1 °C. to θ_3 °C.

$$= W(\theta_3 - \theta_1) \text{ cal.}$$

Heat gained by w gm. copper rising from θ_1 °C. to θ_3 °C.

$$= ws(\theta_3 - \theta_1) \text{ cal.}$$

As $heat\ lost = heat\ gained,$

$$mL + m(\theta_2 - \theta_3) = W(\theta_3 - \theta_1) + ws(\theta_3 - \theta_1),$$

and from this equation the value of L is calculated, as all other quantities are observed.

In view of the large uncertainty caused by the doubtful dryness of the steam, it may be wondered whether the observation of the true boiling point and the application of the cooling correction are really necessary ; but there is no reason to suppose, until it has been determined, that the cooling correction is small.

The correction for cooling may be done as follows. Note the time x sec. during which steam is blown on the surface, and then note the fall in temperature $\delta\theta$ during the next $x/2$ seconds. The corrected final temperature is then $(\theta_3 + \delta\theta)$ °C. This follows from Newton's Law of Cooling (which is assumed), for if the rate of fall of temperature is proportional to the temperature excess, the rate of fall at the final temperature θ_3 °C. is twice the average rate of fall. The correction required

= average rate of fall × time
= ½ final rate of fall × time
= final rate of fall × ½ time
= *the observed fall in temperature at the end of the experiment during half the time of the experiment.*

Care must be taken not to get too high a final temperature, for this, besides rendering Newton's Law of Cooling extremely inappropriate, greatly increases evaporation from the surface.

The method of mixtures was used by Berthelot, using an improved form of apparatus (Fig. 20) in which the steam passed down a tube T through the boiling water in the generator A (so that it emerged *dry*, but possibly *superheated*) and was condensed in a

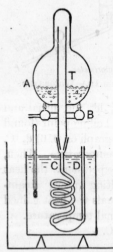

FIG. 20.—Berthelot's apparatus for latent heat of evaporation.

separate vessel *CD* inside the calorimeter, which could be removed and weighed on a delicate balance so that the small mass of steam condensed could be measured directly. The superheating difficulty is to some extent overcome by placing an electric heater inside the generator, instead of using a gas ring *B* below it.

Specific heat of a liquid by the method of cooling. The factors upon which the rate of loss of heat from the *surface* of a body can possibly depend, when the body is supported by non-conducting material in an enclosure, are :

    (1) the temperature of the surface ;

    (2) temperature of the surroundings ;

    (3) area of the surface ;

    (4) nature of the surface ;

    (5) nature and pressure of the surrounding gas ;

    (6) nature of the surface of the enclosure ;

    (7) volume and shape of the enclosure, which determine to some extent the relative importance of conduction and convection through the gas.

It must also depend, in the general case, on the rate at which heat is supplied to the *surface* from *within the body*, that is, whether the body is a good conductor or not. For this reason the method to be described is unsatisfactory for solids, as Regnault showed experimentally. But with a liquid in a thin metal can, we shall assume that, owing to efficient stirring or natural convection currents in the liquid, this difficulty does not arise.

Now, whatever be the laws by which the rate of loss of heat depends on these factors (in particular, whether Newton's Law of Cooling applies or not), *if all these factors are exactly the same for two bodies, then the rate of loss of heat from those two bodies must be exactly the same.* This is the principle of the " method of cooling " for finding the specific heat of a liquid such as paraffin.

Two thin aluminium cans, of as nearly the same dimensions and state of surface as possible, about 2 cm. diameter and 5 cm. long, are weighed. One is nearly filled with water, and the other with paraffin. Each is supported from a large cork or board *A* by means of corks which protrude through *A* and carry thermometers. After assembly, the two cans are immersed in a large water bath maintained at a suitable high temperature, until the two thermometers read, say 80° C. approximately. The board *A* is removed from the

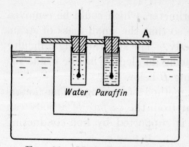

FIG. 21.—Method of cooling.

bath, the cans quickly dried, and then placed in an enclosure surrounded by a large outer vessel of cold water (Fig. 21). Readings of the two thermometers are started at once, and are continued at intervals of about two minutes until both have fallen considerably, say both to below 40° C. The cans are then removed, and weighed to find the mass of water and of paraffin.

A graph of temperature against time is plotted for each can, as Fig. 22. As it is important to consider the cans at the same temperatures, we then proceed as follows. Choose two suitable temperatures θ_1 °C. and θ_2 °C., and draw lines parallel to the time axis to cut the curves at A, B, and C, D. Drop perpendiculars AA', etc., on to the time axis. Then $A'C'$ represents the time t_1 sec. for the paraffin to cool from θ_1 °C. to θ_2 °C., and $B'D'$, the time t_2 sec. for the water to cool through the same range. Let m_1 and m_2 be the masses of the cans containing respectively paraffin and water, s the specific heat of the metal, and x the specific heat of the paraffin. Let M be the mass of paraffin and W the mass of water.

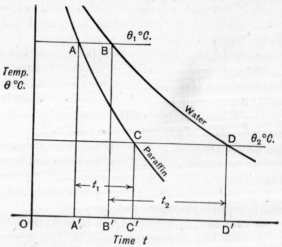

FIG. 22.—Cooling curves for water and liquid.

Heat lost by paraffin and container cooling from θ_1 °C. to θ_2 °C.

$$= (m_1 s + Mx)(\theta_1 - \theta_2) \text{ cal.}$$

Rate of loss of heat $= \dfrac{(m_1 s + Mx)(\theta_1 - \theta_2)}{t_1}$ cal./sec.

Also heat lost by water and container cooling from θ_1 °C. to θ_2 °C.

$$= (m_2 s + W)(\theta_1 - \theta_2) \text{ cal.}$$

Rate of loss of heat $= \dfrac{(m_2 s + W)(\theta_1 - \theta_2)}{t_2}$ cal./sec.

As the two rates of loss of heat are equal,

$$\frac{(m_1 s + Mx)(\theta_1 - \theta_2)}{t_1} = \frac{(m_2 s + W)(\theta_1 - \theta_2)}{t_2},$$

and
$$\frac{m_1 s + Mx}{t_1} = \frac{m_2 s + W}{t_2};$$

when the mean value of the specific heat between θ_1 °C. and θ_2 °C., x, is calculated.

In this experiment, the chief difficulty is that the water and paraffin cannot be stirred. Other defects are that very slight variation in the conditions for the two cans causes erroneous results, and that it is difficult to observe a rapidly falling thermometer accurately. It is often recommended that a single large calorimeter be used instead of the two small cans, and two experiments, the first with water and the second with the liquid, done separately, with proper stirring. The heat capacity of the container is a smaller fraction of the total heat capacity in this case. The advantage of the method of cooling is that it avoids transference and mixing.

LATENT HEAT CALORIMETRY

Bunsen's ice calorimeter. The density of water at 0° C. is nearly 1 gm. per c.c., and that of ice about 0·92 gm. per c.c. The addition of 80 calories to a mixture of ice and water causes the melting of one gram of ice, and a decrease in volume of

$$\left(\frac{1}{0\cdot92} - 1\right) = 0\cdot087 \text{ c.c.}$$

Measurement of the change in volume by sufficiently delicate methods should thus permit the accurate measurement of small quantities of heat. This is the principle of Bunsen's ice calorimeter,

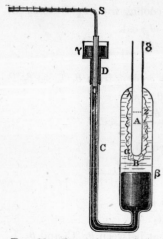

FIG. 23.—Bunsen's ice calorimeter.

though as usually used, this instrument is calibrated in such a way as to avoid using an assumed value for the latent heat of fusion of ice.

The calorimeter (Fig. 23) consists of a glass test tube A fused into a larger cylindrical bulb B, which has a glass stem CD fitting into an iron collar at D. The stem and the lower part of the bulb are filled with pure boiled mercury, and the bulb above the level β contains pure boiled water. A calibrated capillary tube S fits tightly into a cork in the collar D. A shell of ice $\alpha\lambda$ is frozen on the outside of A, by passing a stream of very cold alcohol through A, evaporating ether in A, or other means. Then the whole bulb is immersed in a vessel of pure ice and water, and left for a long time until the whole apparatus is at 0° C. Purity of the surrounding ice-water mixture is very important, as impurities lower the freezing point, and there is the risk then that steady freezing of the water in B will occur.

In an experiment, a little pure water is first placed in A, and the instrument is left surrounded by ice and water until the reading of the mercury index in S is practically steady. A mass W of water at a known temperature θ° C. is then introduced, and the number of divisions n through which the mercury thread moves back is observed. The heat given up by W gm. water cooling from θ° C. to 0° C. is $W\theta$ cal.; hence the number of calories supplied when the mercury moves back *one* division is $W\theta/n$ cal.

A mass M of the substance of which the specific heat x is required is heated to a steady temperature θ_1° C., and then rapidly placed in the water in A. As water just above 0° C. is slightly denser than at 0° C., the heat given up by the substance to the water in A is conveyed downwards. The number of divisions through which the mercury thread moves back is observed, and the quantity of heat Q to which this corresponds worked out from the previous calibration.

This equals the heat given up when M gm. of substance of specific heat x cools from $\theta_1°$ C. to $0°$ C., hence

$$x = Q/M\theta_1.$$

The mercury thread is never quite steady, and allowance has to be made for the gradual creep of the thread. This is done by observing the average rate of creep over some long time before and after the experiment, and multiplying this by the time the experiment has taken.

The Bunsen ice calorimeter has been very useful in determinations of the specific heats of substances of which only small quantities are available. It does not depend for its operation upon an accurate knowledge of the latent heat of ice. An important precaution is to see that the water in B is quite free from air. There is no question of any " cooling correction ", since the whole calorimeter is always at a steady temperature.

Dewar's liquid oxygen calorimeter. This method has been used for the determination of mean specific heats between various temperatures and the boiling point of oxygen ($-183°$ C.).

Liquid oxygen is contained in a vessel B (Fig. 24) fitted with a delivery tube by which the gas generated may be collected over water. A short flexible tube connects the upper end of B with the tube C containing the specimen, which can be introduced into B by raising this

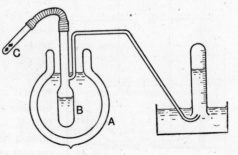

Fig. 24.—Liquid oxygen calorimeter.

tube to the vertical position. A vacuum vessel A containing liquid oxygen surrounds B. A mass m of substance of specific heat x at a known temperature $\theta°$ C. is introduced, the volume of oxygen collected is measured, and the volume v which this would occupy at $0°$ C. and 760 mm. pressure, if dry, is calculated. From the known density ρ of oxygen under these conditions, the mass $M = v\rho$ evaporated is found. If L be the latent heat of evaporation of oxygen (its actual value is about 58 cal./gm.), the heat given to the oxygen is ML calories. This is lost by m gm. of a substance of specific heat x cooling from $\theta°$ C. to $-183°$ C., whence

$$mx(\theta+183)=ML \quad \text{and} \quad x=\frac{ML}{m(\theta+183)}.$$

Here it is impossible to stop a gradual evaporation of the liquid, due to a very slow gain of heat from the surroundings; the average rate of this evaporation is observed, and multiplied by the duration of the experiment to give the correction to be subtracted from the observed volume. In most cases the calorimeter is calibrated by the use of a mass of lead of known specific heat, when the actual value of L is not required.

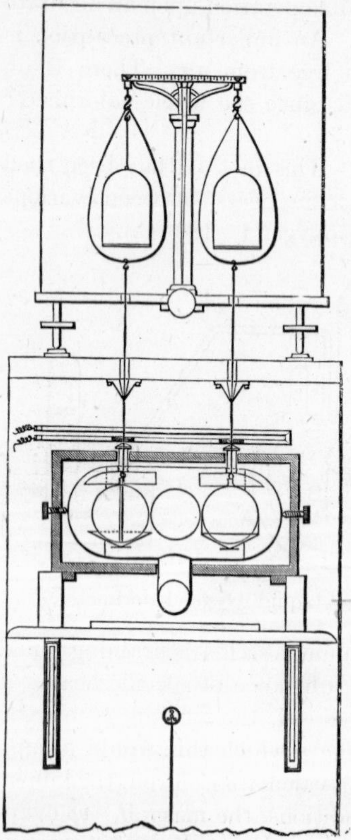

FIG. 25.—Joly's differential steam calorimeter.

Joly's differential steam calorimeter. This apparatus was designed to determine the specific heat of a gas at constant volume. Two hollow copper spheres, as nearly as possible equal in all respects, are suspended by fine wires from the arms of a sensitive balance in a chamber into which steam at 100° C. can be passed. The wires pass through plugs of plaster of Paris in the roof of the chamber, and just above these are two small electric heaters, so that moisture condensing in the opening is either absorbed or evaporated and cannot obstruct free motion of the wire. Shields to prevent water condensed on the roof from falling on the spheres are attached to the top of the chamber, and trays of thin metal are fixed below the spheres to catch water condensed on the spheres. Fig. 25 shows the apparatus in detail.

Both spheres are at first evacuated and counterpoised on the balance. One sphere is then filled with the gas under test at a pressure of about 22 atmospheres, replaced in the steam chamber, and counterpoised again. The difference in weight gives the mass m of gas enclosed. The steady temperature θ_1° C. of the steam chamber is then observed. Steam is now passed into the chamber for about five minutes, after which condensation on the spheres is complete. The temperature θ_2° C. of the steam is observed by a delicate high-range thermometer. The balance is then counterpoised again, and the further change in weight w is found. The mass of steam which condenses in providing the heat needed to raise the two equal copper spheres themselves from θ_1° C. to θ_2° C. is the same, so w gives the difference between the two masses condensed, that is, the mass of steam the condensation of which is due to the enclosed gas.

The specific heat of a gas at constant volume is always denoted by the symbol C_v. The heat supplied to raise the temperature of m gm. of gas of specific heat C_v from θ_1° C. to θ_2° C. is thus wL calories, where L is the latent heat of steam at temperature θ_2° C.

Hence

$$mC_v(\theta_2 - \theta_1) = wL,$$

and

$$C_v = \frac{wL}{m(\theta_2 - \theta_1)}.$$

A test for leakage during the experiment is made at the end, and corrections are made for : (a) the expansion of the sphere containing the gas, both on account of its own rise in temperature, and because of the rise in pressure of the gas inside ; this effect means that the gas *has not really been at constant volume*, and has expanded and done some external work, so that the value of C_v is a little too high on this account, and the correction can be calculated ; (b) unequal thermal capacities of the two spheres, which can be compensated for in a second experiment in which the two spheres exchange duties. Numerous other corrections of a minor character are needed.

ELECTRICAL CALORIMETRY

When the terminals of a battery or of the mains supply are connected by a conducting wire, a current of electricity passes through the wire, and we say that it is caused by an electrical *pressure difference* or *potential difference* (P.D.) The unit of potential difference is called the **volt**. The unit of current is called the

ampere. The *resistance* of the conductor, according to **Ohm's law,** is given by the relation

resistance in ohms = P.D. in volts/current in amperes.

Energy has to be expended (or work done) in order to send the current through the wire ; the source of this is the chemical action in the battery, or the work actually being done by the turbines which drive the dynamo supplying the mains. The volt is so defined that

rate of working in watts = (P.D. in volts × current in amperes) ;
hence,

energy expended in joules = watts × sec. = volts × amp. × sec.

A common type of difficulty exists here ; there is a small difference between the value of the volt as thus defined and the legal standard (the *international volt*), and between the theoretical and international standard values of the ampere. If international volts and amperes are used in this equation, the result does not give the energy in true joules. To shift the difficulty one stage further on, the *international joule*, a little larger than the true joule, is used. This point is important, in that it affects the accuracy of all electrical determinations.

In the ordinary way, the energy expended is converted into heat. The number of joules required to produce one calorie is known as the result of many careful experiments, some of which are described later. This number is called the **Mechanical Equivalent of Heat** (symbol J), or, when it is applied to an electrical rather than a purely mechanical supply of energy, the **Electrical Equivalent of Heat** (symbol J, or more usually nowadays J' ; it is proposed to use J in this chapter and J' in later discussions of recent work). The values $4·186$ joules = 1 calorie, which is a little above the most recent determinations, but in general use or, for rougher calculations $4·2$ joules = 1 calorie, will be used in this book for J.

Thus, when a current of I amp. under a P.D. V volt flows for t sec., the energy expended is VIt joules, and the heat developed is

$$H = \frac{VIt}{J} \cdot \text{calories.}$$

Using Ohm's Law,

$$V = IR \quad \text{and} \quad H = \frac{I^2Rt}{J} \text{ cal.,}$$

so that for a given conductor, the heat evolved in a given time is proportional to the square of the current. Further, for a given current, the heat produced in a given time is proportional to the resistance ; thus when the current passes through thick copper leads of very small resistance to thin wires of nichrome, constantan, or platinum of very high resistance, nearly all the heat is developed in the thin wires.

It is important to realise that to *measure* the energy supplied it is not sufficient just to measure the current ; two of the three quantities *current, potential difference, resistance*, must be found.

Investigation of the cooling of a calorimeter. The advantage of this method is that a small steady temperature excess of any desired value can be maintained, and the temperatures determined accurately.

A small copper calorimeter is fitted with a lid through which pass two thick copper leads fitted at their tops with terminals, and connected at their lower ends by a resistance, R ohms. Holes in the lid admit a thermometer E and stirrer F The calorimeter is about half filled with water and placed on an insulating stand in an outer can.

The electrical circuit, also shown in Fig. 26, consists of an ammeter, a 12-volt accumulator, and a variable resistance or rheostat X, by which the value of the current is altered, and there is also a key to break the circuit. The current is switched on, and the calorimeter eventually reaches a steady temperature, *at which the rate*

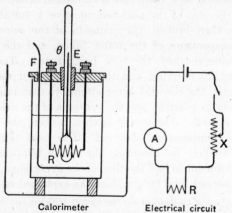

Calorimeter   Electrical circuit

Fig 26.—Electrical investigation of cooling.

of loss of heat to the surroundings equals the rate at which heat is supplied electrically. Then observe the value of the current, I, the temperature of the water in the calorimeter, $\theta°$ C., and the air temperature, $\theta_0°$C. Then *rate of loss of heat = rate of supply of heat* $= \dfrac{I^2 R}{J}$ cal./sec., and, if the law of cooling is $-\dfrac{dH}{dt} = k(\theta - \theta_0)^n$, then

$$I^2 R / J = k(\theta - \theta_0)^n.$$

Now, R, J, and k are the same always, so I^2 is proportional to $(\theta - \theta_0)^n$. A series of results is taken for different values of the current ranging from 0·3 amp. to about 2 amp., and a graph of I^2 against $(\theta - \theta_0)$ plotted. The value of the index n is obtainable as on p. 46, by plotting a fresh graph of log I^2 against log $(\theta - \theta_0)$ and finding the slope of the line. If it is intended to test Newton's Law of Cooling, the first essential is, of course, to see that the necessary forced convection conditions are attained.

Electrical determination of the value of " J ". The calorimeter of the previous experiment is used, with a sensitive thermometer graduated in tenths of a degree. The calorimeter and stirrer are weighed, and the calorimeter is two-thirds filled with water before weighing again. The resistance R is then placed in the water, and the circuit connected up (Fig. 27). This is the same as in the previous experiment, except for one matter. The voltage drop across R has to be measured, so a voltmeter is connected *across the terminals of R.** The rheostat X is adjusted to give a suitable current. The circuit is then broken, the contents of the calorimeter well stirred, the temperature of the water taken, and the experiment begun by closing the key, the time being noted. The current is passed for, say 20 minutes, and the ammeter and voltmeter are read at intervals, the rheostat being altered to maintain the values as nearly steady as possible, and the contents of the calorimeter are continuously stirred. The circuit is then broken, the time noted, and the final temperature observed. The final temperature is corrected for cooling, by observing the fall in temperature at the end of the experiment in half the time of the experiment, and adding this to the observed final temperature, as explained on p. 56.

* It is advisable *first* to connect up the circuit without the voltmeter, and make sure that a suitable current will pass, and *after this* to connect the voltmeter across the terminals of R.

Let w be the mass of calorimeter
and stirrer, s the specific heat of
copper, W the mass of water. Let
θ_1 °C. be the initial temperature,
θ_2 °C. the final temperature after
time t sec., and $\delta\theta$ the cooling after a
further $t/2$ sec. The corrected rise in
temperature is then $(\theta_2 + \delta\theta - \theta_1)$ °C.
The heat developed is

$(W + ws)(\theta_2 + \delta\theta - \theta_1)$ **calories.**

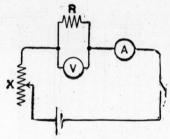

FIG. 27.—Electrical circuit for calorimetry experiments.

A correction has to be made to the
ammeter reading, because this gives the total current in the circuit, a
small part of which flows through the voltmeter. If V is the voltmeter reading and S its resistance, this current, to be subtracted from
the ammeter reading, is V/S amp. Let I be the *corrected* current.

Then, energy supplied in joules is VIt joules.

As $(W + ws)(\theta_2 + \delta\theta - \theta_1)$ calories are furnished by VIt joules, the
number of joules required to produce one calorie, J, is

$$\frac{VIt}{(W + ws)(\theta_2 + \delta\theta - \theta_1)} \text{ joules/cal.}$$

Determination of the specific heat of a liquid. The calorimeter,
apparatus, circuit, and observations are the same as for the previous
experiment, except that the calorimeter contains M gm. liquid of
specific heat x, instead of W gm. water, and the value of J is known.
With the same symbols as before, heat supplied electrically is
VIt/J cal. Heat gained by M gm. liquid of specific heat x and
w gm. copper of specific heat s rising from θ_1 °C. to $(\theta_2 + \delta\theta_1)$ °C.,
is $(Mx + ws)(\theta_2 + \delta\theta - \theta_1)$ calories. Equating the heat supplied to
the heat gained,

$$(Mx + ws)(\theta_2 + \delta\theta - \theta_1) = \frac{VIt}{J},$$

whence x is calculated.

Measurement of the latent heat of evaporation of a liquid. The
evaporation of a measured mass of liquid at the boiling point by
the application of a measured quantity of heat is the basis of this
method, which was used by Henning to find the latent heat of steam
with high accuracy.

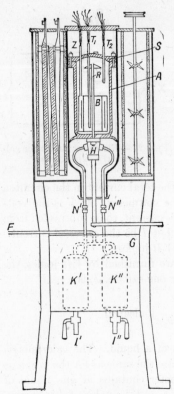

Fig. 28.—Henning's apparatus for latent heat of evaporation.

Reproduced from "Heat and Thermo-dynamics" by courtesy of Dr. J. K. Roberts and Messrs Blackie & Son, Ltd.

Fig. 28 is a diagram of the apparatus. Water is boiled in the cylinder A by means of an electric heater B, from which leads to the current and voltage measuring instruments pass at Z. T_1 and T_2 are electrical thermometers giving the temperatures of the liquid and the vapour. The steam generated, passing down the tube R (which is fitted with a splash guard) can leave by either of two paths N' or N'', from the tap at H, to be condensed in vessels K' or K'' which are surrounded by cold water in the vessel G. During the measurements everything is steady, and before this state is reached the steam is condensed in K''; when steady conditions are reached, the steam is diverted to K', and timing started. The current and voltage are observed, and after a measured time interval the steam is switched back to K''. The mass of steam condensed in K' is run off at I' and weighed. The cylinder A is surrounded by an air-space in the centre of a well-stirred electrically heated oil bath which is maintained as nearly as possible at the temperature of A, so that loss to (or gain from) the surroundings is very small. The small "cooling correction" is eliminated by doing a second experiment in which all the temperatures are the same, the time is the same, but the rate of supply of electrical energy is different. Now, if the temperatures are the same, the rate of loss or gain of heat is the same, and therefore the value of the correction *for the same time* is the same.

Let t sec. be the duration of the experiment, and voltage V_1 and the current I_1 amp. in the first run, and V_2 and I_2 in the second.

Let the masses of water condensed in the two cases be m_1 gm. and m_2 gm. Let L be the latent heat of steam, and h the heat loss in each case.

Then,
$$\frac{V_1 I_1 t}{J} = m_1 L + h,$$

and
$$\frac{V_2 I_2 t}{J} = m_2 L + h.$$

$$\therefore \frac{(V_1 I_1 - V_2 I_2) t}{J} = (m_1 - m_2) L,$$

so
$$L = \frac{(V_1 I_1 - V_2 I_2) t}{(m_1 - m_2) J} \text{ cal./gm.}$$

Advantages of the method are : (1) steady temperatures, which can therefore be found accurately ; (2) it is applicable to any liquid ; (3) by altering the pressure in the apparatus, a wide range of boiling points is obtained, and the variation of the latent heat with temperature may be studied. A similar principle, but with greater refinement of measurement, was used by Osborne, Stimson, and Ginnings in 1939 with the electrical apparatus described on p. 243.

Vacuum calorimeter of Nernst and Lindemann. This apparatus is remarkable for three elegant simplifications : (1) the substance, if a metal, is itself the " calorimeter " ; (2) the same coil of platinum serves both as heater and platinum resistance thermometer ; (3) the whole apparatus is enclosed in a vacuum, so that exchange of heat with the surroundings is very small indeed.

Fig. 29 shows the treatment of a metal specimen ; the shaded parts—the outer cylinder and the central plug on which the platinum coil (insulated by paraffined paper) is wound—are made of the material under test. Materials other than metals are contained in a silver vessel, the platinum wire being wound upon a silver tube projecting into the vessel. The calorimeter is suspended by the connecting leads in a vessel which has an outlet through which it may be evacuated, and the whole is surrounded by a constant temperature bath of, say, liquid air contained in a Dewar flask (p. 360), or other liquids for different temperatures. After the specimen has attained the temperature of the bath, the vessel is evacuated and thus thermally insulated.

The mass m of substance used is found. Then during an experiment, a current is passed through the heater for time t sec. and the

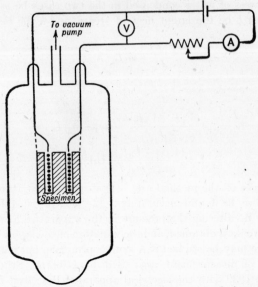

Fig. 29.—Nernst and Lindemann's vacuum calorimeter.

P.D. V maintained constant by varying the rheostat; I_1 and I_2, the initial and final values of the current are measured, and the initial resistance $R_1 = V/I_1$ and the final resistance $R_2 = V/I_2$ calculated by applying Ohm's Law, the small rise in temperature $\delta\theta$ being deduced from the change in resistance. From the average value I of the current, the heat supplied, VIt/J cal., is found. Then, if x be the specific heat, $$VIt/J = mx\,\delta\theta + h,$$

where h is a small correction for heat lost by *radiation*, the only means of heat transference possible through the vacuum. Very small rises of temperature can be employed, so that the value of the specific heat at a particular temperature, instead of the mean value over a considerable range, is found.

The apparatus was chiefly used for measurements at low temperatures, where the values are needed for theoretical reasons. Most low-temperature calorimeters have been based on this design, though for extremely low temperatures two separate coils, a heating coil of *constantan* and a *lead* resistance thermometer, are used instead of the single platinum one.

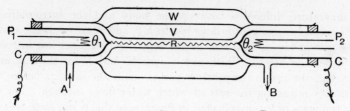

Fig. 30.—Callendar and Barnes' continuous flow calorimeter.

Continuous flow calorimeter of Callendar and Barnes. The heating wire R (Fig. 30) stretched between thick copper conductors CC, goes along the axis of a narrow tube through which a continuous stream of water passes, flowing in at A and out at B. The temperatures $\theta_1°$ C. at A and $\theta_2°$ C. at B are determined by the platinum resistance thermometers P_1 and P_2. The flow tube is surrounded by a vacuum jacket V which reduces the heat loss considerably, and a constant temperature jacket W which ensures that this loss is steady. The current I through the wire is measured very accurately by noting the potential drop across a standard resistance in series with R, and comparing this with the E.M.F. of a standard cell. The potential difference V across R is also determined by the potentiometer in terms of the E.M.F. of the standard cell, the accuracy in these two measurements being of the order of one part in ten thousand. When a steady flow of cold water at constant inflow temperature passes through the apparatus, and a constant current is maintained through R, a steady state is reached at which θ_1 and θ_2 are constant, and the temperature of every part of the apparatus remains steady. The heat capacity of the apparatus then does not enter into the calculation, since no heat is being absorbed by any part of it.

The water flowing through the apparatus in t seconds is collected and its mass m found. Let the average value of the specific heat of water between the temperatures $\theta_1°$ C. and $\theta_2°$ C. be s, and let the heat lost from the apparatus in t sec. be h cal. Then the energy dissipated in t sec. is VIt joules, and the heat evolved is

$$ms(\theta_2 - \theta_1) + h \text{ calories};$$

so
$$\frac{VIt}{J} = ms(\theta_2 - \theta_1) + h. \quad \ldots\ldots\ldots\ldots\ldots\ldots(1)$$

Now, the rate of loss of heat from the flow tube is constant for a given temperature difference between the body and the surroundings. If a second experiment is done in which θ_1 and θ_2 are made the same, the rate of loss of heat will be the same, and the heat lost in t sec. will be h as before. With new values V' and I' for the P.D. and current, the rise in temperature can be made the same as before by suitably adjusting the rate at which water flows through. Let m' be the mass of water collected in t sec. (note this is the *same time* as for the previous experiment). Then,

$$\frac{V'I't}{J} = m's(\theta_2 - \theta_1) + h. \quad \dots\dots\dots\dots\dots\dots(2)$$

h is eliminated by subtracting the two left-hand sides and the two right-hand sides of equations (1) and (2), giving, if s is known, the expression for J,

$$J = \frac{(VI - V'I')t}{(m - m')s(\theta_2 - \theta_1)} \text{ joules/cal.}$$

If J is known, the value of s is found, using

$$s = \frac{(VI - V'I')t}{J(m - m')(\theta_2 - \theta_1)} \text{ cal./gm./ °C.}$$

Now, if we use the 15° C. calorie, the value of s is 1 between 14·5° C. and 15·5° C., whence the value to be adopted for J is settled by an experiment between these temperatures. The value obtained by Callendar and Barnes was 4·183 joules per 15° C. calorie. Working with different initial temperatures, and using small rises in temperature, they thus determined the variation of the specific heat of water with temperature. Their results have been confirmed by later workers. The variation of specific heat with temperature is quite appreciable. In terms of the 20° C. calorie, the values are 1·0094 at 0° C., 0·9982 at 37·5° C. (minimum value), rising to 1·0074 at 100° C.

Each of the individual measurements in the experiment can be made with high accuracy. The temperatures can be determined to one ten-thousandth of a degree, and the currents and potential differences to about one part in ten thousand. Nevertheless, the absolute accuracy of this experiment is limited to that with which the E.M.F. of the standard cell used is known in true volts, which was probably not to within one part in ten thousand at the time of this experiment.

This experiment is regarded as the classical example of continuous flow calorimetry and it may be well to conclude with a note on the advantages of the method. These are : (1) As the temperatures are steady, very accurate slow-reading platinum thermometers can be used ; these would be useless for changing temperatures. Hence small ranges of temperature can be employed. (2) The heat capacity of the apparatus is not involved, since no part of it experiences a rise in temperature. (3) The " cooling correction " is eliminated by doing two experiments. (This is actually not complete in its compensation in practice.)

The method works equally well for gases, which if passing slowly down the flow tube are under "constant pressure" conditions. Callendar and Swann, using apparatus very similar to that of Fig. 30, found the value of C_p, the *specific heat at constant pressure*, for several gases.

VARIATION OF SPECIFIC HEAT WITH TEMPERATURE

Dulong and Petit's Law (1819), originally stated that the product of atomic weight and specific heat(called the **atomic heat**) is the same for all elements, and approximately equal to 6·4. Later, calculations suggested that the atomic heat should *theoretically* have a value of between 6·0 and 6·2 if calculated on the specific heat at constant pressure, and 5·96 if calculated for the specific heat at constant volume, and *should be practically independent of the temperature*. But the specific heat *does* vary with the temperature ; and the elements can be divided roughly into two classes : those for which the variation with temperature is *small*, and the atomic heat is somewhere near the calculated value, and those for which the variation with temperature is *large* at about ordinary temperatures, with values of the atomic heat at these temperatures which are far too low. Carbon is an example of the second class (cf. figures for the diamond on p. 36).

The results of Nernst and Lindemann's experiments showed that all solid crystalline elements *at a sufficiently high temperature* have atomic heats which are closely equal to 5·92 ; and that *at sufficiently low temperatures*, all solid crystalline elements behave as carbon does at ordinary temperatures, the specific heat falling rapidly as the temperature is reduced below a certain value, and tending to the value zero as the absolute zero of temperature ($-273\cdot2°$ C.) is approached. The reason why carbon and the other exceptions do not fit in with Dulong and Petit's Law at ordinary temperatures is simply that for these substances ordinary temperatures are " low ". They do obey the law if they are hot enough.

Why should this law, which appears so simple, be followed in such a " half-and-half " fashion? Do the very laws of mechanics themselves, on which these calculations are ultimately based, vary with the temperature? The problem was successfully attacked by Debye, using the ideas of the *quantum theory*, which had been introduced by Planck in order to deal with similar inconsistencies between ordinary theoretical calculations and the observed results in certain radiation problems. It is not proposed in this book to discuss this theory at length, and the student should refer to one of the advanced treatises for information about it.

According to the kinetic theory, the atoms in a solid are in a state of continual vibration. The average energy of vibration is proportional to the absolute temperature. When a quantity of heat energy is supplied to a body, the energy of each individual atom is increased, and the rise in the *average* energy is manifested as a rise in temperature. Working along these lines, it should be possible to calculate the quantity of heat energy which must be supplied to unit mass of a substance in order to cause a rise in temperature of one degree, and so obtain a theoretical value for the specific heat. If we take the atomic weight in grams of different elements, this weight always contains the same number of atoms, and hence the average increase in energy of an individual atom when a certain quantity of heat is supplied to one gram-atom is the same for all elements ; that is, the atomic heat should be the same for all elements.

But more than at first appears lies behind the term " average energy ".

Common-sense suggests that, if the energy supplied to a body *can* be shared equally among all its atoms, then this should happen. Thus a given supply of heat should always cause a definite rise in the energy of each individual atom, a definite increase in the average atomic energy, and hence a definite temperature rise which is the same whatever the initial temperature. Thus the specific heat and atomic heat should *not* vary with the temperature.

When a consistent chain of argument leads, as this does, to a false conclusion, the initial premises must be suspect. Here common-

TABLE OF SPECIFIC HEATS

Substance.	Temperature (°C.).	Specific Heat.
SOLIDS		
Aluminium - - -	− 240	0·0092
	0	0·21
	600	0·282
Copper - - -	− 250	0·0035
	0	0·091
	97·5	0·095
Iron - - - -	− 133	0·077
	0	0·105
	97·6	0·114
Lead - - - -	− 250	0·0143
	0	0·030
	300	0·034
Glass - - - -	18	0·19
Rubber - - -	15–100	0·27–0·48
LIQUIDS		
Mercury - - -	20	0·033
Alcohol - - -	0	0·55
Paraffin - - -	20–60	0·51–0·54
Glycerine - - -	18–50	0·58
Saturated brine - -	15	0·72
	C_p (sp. ht. at constant pressure)	C_v (sp. ht. at constant volume)
GASES		
Air - - - -	0·24	0·17
Hydrogen - - -	3·42	2·40
Argon - - -	0·127	0·075
Carbon dioxide - -	0·20	0·165

From Kaye and Laby's " Physical and Chemical Constants ",
(9th edition, 1941) (Longmans, Green & Co. Ltd.).

sense has made an important assumption—that it is possible to divide a quantity of energy exactly into any number of equal shares. But supposing energy is itself conveyed in discrete indivisible quanta of finite size, this cannot happen.

The quantum theory explanation finds expressions for the statistical distribution of the quanta supplied among the atoms eligible to receive them, and arrives at a value for the average rise in the energy of the atoms in this way. This value does vary with the temperature, and leads to specific heat values which vary as experiments find. For each substance there is a temperature above which there is little difference between the quantum theory and " common-sense " predictions, and we have seen that at high temperatures the simpler treatment does agree fairly with experiment.

In the table on p. 75 are figures showing the way in which the specific heats of some of the common metals vary with the temperature.

QUESTIONS ON CHAPTER II

1. Give definitions of the specific heat and the latent heat of fusion of a solid. Explain whether or not the numerical values of these quantities will change if your measurements are made in pounds and degrees Fahrenheit instead of grammes and degrees centigrade.

Describe how you would measure the latent heat of vaporization of alcohol, showing how you would make your calculations from your observations. (O.)

2. Explain the difference between specific heat and thermal capacity.

In an experiment, 30 gm. of granite were placed in a test-tube that was heated by standing in boiling water. The granite was transferred to a calorimeter weighing 50 gm. in which there were 35 gm. of water at 10° C. The temperature of the water rose to 25° C. Find (a) the specific heat of granite, and (b) the thermal capacity of the granite used. What errors are likely to have been introduced during the experiment? If you were performing the experiment how would you seek to minimise the errors? (Specific heat of copper = 0·1.) (Scot.Leav.Cert.)

3. Describe an experiment to determine the specific heat of a solid which is soluble in water, carefully explaining how you would calculate your result.

A piece of aluminium of mass 0·5 lb. and specific heat 0·25 is left for a time in a gas oven heated by a steady burner. The aluminium is then taken out and immediately dropped into 5 lb. of water contained in a copper can of water equivalent 0·05 lb. The temperature of the water rises from 59° F. to 81·5° F. Neglecting any steam produced at first, calculate the approximate temperature of the gas oven. (J.M.B.)

4. Define " latent heat of evaporation ".

10 grams of ice in a closed vessel are melted by sending in steam slowly at 100° C. Find the quantity of water present when the last of the ice has just melted.

(Latent heat of water = 80 cal./gm. ; of steam = 536 cal./gm.) (O.S.)

5. Specific heats are frequently determined by using a thermos flask instead of a copper calorimeter. Describe how you would find the specific heat of lead shot in this way, explaining carefully why the

procedure is different from that suitable to an experiment using a copper calorimeter. (O.S.)

6. Describe how you would measure the latent heat of evaporation of petrol and the latent heat of fusion of naphthalene. (O.S.)

7. Draw a labelled diagram to illustrate an experiment for determining the latent heat of vaporization of water. Do *not* describe the experiment, but state the probable sources of error, and show how the result would be calculated from the experimental data.

Water in a vacuum flask is boiled steadily by passing an electric current through a coil of wire immersed in the water. When the potential difference across the coil is 5·25 volts and the current through it is 2·58 amp., 6·85 gm. of water evaporate in 20 min. When the potential difference and the current are maintained at 3·20 volts and 1·57 amp. respectively, 2·38 gm. of water evaporate in 20 min., all the other conditions being the same. Calculate the latent heat of vaporization of water in joules per gm. (J.M.B.)

8. The temperature of a furnace is found in the following way : A copper sphere of mass 100 gm. is left in the furnace until it has attained the temperature of the latter. It is then dropped into a copper calorimeter of mass 150 gm., containing 200 gm. of water, initially at 16° C. The final common temperature is 38° C., and on weighing the whole there is a loss of 1·2 gm. of water. Calculate the temperature of the furnace. (Specific heat of copper, 0·1 ; latent heat of steam at 100° C., 536 calories per gm.)

Describe in detail an accurate method of determining the temperature of the furnace. (O. & C.)

9. What is meant by the specific heat of a substance?

Describe how you would determine the specific heat of a solid such as copper (a) at room temperature, (b) at a temperature between 0° C. and – 20° C., discussing possible errors and corrections. (O. & C.)

10. Define " latent heat of evaporation ", and describe how you would attempt to find its value as accurately as possible in the case of water.

Indicate also a method for the case of a liquid which is available only in limited quantities. (O. & C.)

11. Describe and explain a method of determining the latent heat of steam, and point out any precautions which are necessary in order to obtain an accurate result.

A copper calorimeter weighing 100 gm. contains a mixture of 10 gm. of ice and 100 gm. of water at 0° C. Steam at 100° C. is passed into the mixture until the final temperature of the calorimeter and its contents is 10° C. Determine the mass of steam which has been passed into the calorimeter.

(Latent heat of steam = 540 cal./gm. Latent heat of ice = 80 cal./gm. Specific heat of copper = 0·1.) (C.W.B.)

12. Explain the uses and the advantages of some accurate form of ice calorimeter. Show how quantities of heat can be calculated from the observed readings of the instrument. (O.)

13. What are the principal sources of error in the determination of specific heat by the method of mixtures? Explain briefly how the errors are minimised.

Equal volumes of water and paraffin are allowed to cool under the same conditions in the same calorimeter and the time-temperature readings are given in the following table :

Time (min.)	0	1	2	3	4	5
Temp. water (°C.)	60·4	57·6	55·3	53·4	51·8	50·5
Temp. paraffin (°C.)	60·2	55·9	52·2	49·1	46·2	43·6

Draw graphs of temperature (ordinates) and time (abscissae) for both liquids. If the thermal capacity of the calorimeter is 10·5 cal. deg.⁻¹ C., the mass of the water 85·5 gm. and that of the paraffin 68·4 gm., calculate the mean specific heat of paraffin between 51° C. and 57° C.

(J.M.B.)

14. Steam at 100° C. is passed into 100 gm. of a mixture of ice and water in a calorimeter of water equivalent 5 gm. When the ice has just all melted the weight is found to have increased by 5 gm. due to condensed steam. Assuming no loss or gain of heat from the surroundings, find (a) what weight of ice was present when the condensation of steam began, (b) the rise in temperature if the passage of steam is continued until a further 5 gm. has condensed.

Explain why in an actual experiment if the passage of steam were continued the weight would still go on rising even after the temperature of the mixture had reached the boiling point of water.

(Latent heats of steam and water = 540 and 80 calories per gram respectively.)

(C.)

15. Describe and explain how the mean specific heat of a solid over a range of temperature between 0° or room temperature and about 100° C. can be accurately determined by two methods, the first of which depends on the melting of ice, and the second on the condensation of steam.

(C.W.B.)

16. Describe in detail how you would determine the specific heat of a liquid by the method of cooling, showing how to calculate the result from the measurements you would make.

(O.)

17. Describe the Bunsen ice-calorimeter and discuss its merits.

The capillary tube of such a calorimeter has an internal diameter of 0·4 mm. When a piece of metal of mass 0·5 gm. heated to 100° C. is dropped into the calorimeter, the mercury meniscus moves 4 cm. What is the specific heat of the metal? (Specific gravity of water at 0° C. = 1·000, that of ice at 0° C. = 0·917 ; latent heat of fusion of ice = 80 calories per gram.)

(O. & C.)

18. Describe Bunsen's ice calorimeter and explain how you would use it to find the specific heat of a diamond.

4 gm. of a substance at 50° C. dropped into the ice calorimeter caused the mercury thread in the capillary tube to move through 5·4 cm. The cross-sectional area of the tube was 0·005 sq. cm. 1 gm. of ice occupies

1·09 c.c. and the latent heat of fusion of ice is 80 calories per gm. Calculate the specific heat of the substance. (O.)

19. State Newton's Law of Cooling, and describe how you would attempt to verify it experimentally.

Two solid spheres, of radii r_1 and r_2, are made of the same material and have similar surfaces. The spheres are raised to the same temperature and are then allowed to cool under identical conditions. Compare (a) their initial rates of loss of heat, (b) their initial rates of fall of temperature. (O. & C.)

20. Deduce an expression for the heat which the passage of a steady current develops in a conductor.

A resistance coil through which a variable current can be passed is immersed in a calorimeter containing water. Explain how you would use the apparatus to investigate Newton's law of cooling. (O. & C.)

21. State Newton's law of cooling, and explain how you would test it experimentally.

A copper calorimeter of mass 100 gm., containing 150 c.c. of a liquid of specific heat 0·6 and specific gravity 1·2, is found to cool at the rate of 2° per minute when its temperature is 50° above that of its surroundings. If the liquid is emptied out, and 150 c.c. of a liquid of specific heat 0·4 and specific gravity 0·9 are substituted, what will be the rate of cooling when the temperature is 40° above that of the surroundings? (Specific heat of copper = 0·1.) (O. & C.)

22. State Newton's law of cooling, and describe an experiment by which you could verify it.

A calorimeter containing first 40 and then 100 grams of water is heated and suspended in the same constant-temperature enclosure. It is found that the times taken to cool from 50° to 40° in the two cases are 15 and 33 minutes respectively. Calculate the water-equivalent of the calorimeter. (O. & C.)

23. State Newton's law of cooling, pointing out the conditions under which it is likely to hold.

Describe how you would carry out an experiment to test it, and explain carefully the purpose of the parts of your apparatus and how you would use the observations you would make. (O.)

24. What is meant by the latent heat of vaporization of a substance? 2 gm. of iron wire at 15° C. are dropped into liquid oxygen maintained at its boiling-point in a thermos flask. The volume of oxygen, measured at 16° C. and 80 cm. of mercury pressure, driven off is 432 c.c. Find the latent heat of vaporization of oxygen.

The specific heat of iron may be taken as 0·09, the boiling-point of oxygen as - 184° C., and the density of oxygen at normal temperature and pressure 0·0014 gm. per c.c. (O. & C.)

25. A thermos flask contains liquid oxygen at its boiling-point. 25·2 gm. of mercury at room temperature, 21·5° C., are allowed to enter the liquid oxygen, and the gaseous oxygen produced is found to have a volume of 3068 c.c. under room conditions (the barometric

height is 74 8 cm. of mercury). Calculate the latent heat of fusion of mercury, assuming that a surface of liquid oxygen remains in the flask.

(Specific heat of liquid mercury - - 0·034 cal. per gm. per °C.
Specific heat of solid mercury - - 0·030 ,, ,, ,,
Freezing point of mercury - - - - 38·8° C.
Latent heat of evaporation of oxygen . 58 cal. per gm.
Boiling point of oxygen - - - - - 182·9° C.
Density of oxygen at s.t.p. - - - 1·429 gm. per litre.) (L.)

26. A current of 4 amperes passes through a coil of wire immersed in 100 gm. of turpentine contained in a calorimeter. If the potential difference between the ends of the wire is 1·5 volts, calculate the rise in temperature of the calorimeter and its contents which takes place in three minutes.

(Water equivalent of calorimeter = 10 grammes ; specific heat of turpentine = 0·42 : $J = 4·2$ joules per gramme-calorie.) (C.W.B.)

27 A cylinder of copper has an electric heating filament inside it, so that it may be heated by passing a current. After the temperature had been raised the current was switched off and the copper allowed to cool. The following observations were made of the temperature at 20-second intervals .

86·0°, 70·0°, 60·0°, 51·7°, 44·5°, 38·5° C.

The current was again switched on and adjusted to 3·5 amperes in order to keep the cylinder at a constant temperature of 53° C.

If the specific heat of copper is 0·095 cal. per gm. per deg. C., and the mass of the cylinder 200 gm., what is the resistance of the heating filament?

(Take the value of J as 4·2 joules per calorie. Graph paper is available.) (L.)

28. What are (a) the advantages and (b) the difficulties of the continuous flow method of calorimetry?

Describe in some detail how this method may be used to determine the latent heat of steam at atmospheric pressure. (J.M.B.)

CHAPTER III

EXPANSION OF SOLIDS AND LIQUIDS

INCREASING the temperature of a rod causes it to expand, that is, to increase in length and thickness. The observed expansion in length must be proportional to the length of the rod ; for if a rod one metre in length expands by one millimetre, two such rods placed end to end to make a rod two metres long expand by two milli-metres. It is found that, at least within the accuracy of ordinary observations and within the range of temperature of most ordinary experiments, the expansion is nearly proportional to the temperature rise. The expansion also depends on the material of the rod ; when equal lengths are heated through the same difference in temperature, it is found that the expansion of iron is about two-thirds that of brass and about half that of zinc. In the light of these facts, rules for dealing with the linear expansion of a rod can be stated.

Let the length of a rod at $0°$ C. and $t°$ C. be l_0 and l respectively. Then $l = l_0(1 + \alpha t)$, where α is a " constant " for the particular material concerned, called the **coefficient of linear expansion** (C.L.E.) of the material. The formula given above is only approximately true ; for most substances a formula containing t^2 and t^3 fits the results of accurate observation more closely—or we can say that α itself varies with the temperature. The value defined by the above equation is really the *mean value between* $0°$ C. *and* $t°$ C. *of the coefficient of linear expansion.*

In most problems on expansion we require the change in length when a rod is heated between two temperatures neither of which is $0°$ C.

Let l_0 be the length at $0°$ C., l_1 the length at $t_1°$ C., and l_2 the length at $t_2°$ C.

It is easy to show that, if α itself is small, and does not vary greatly with the temperature, there is no very considerable difference between

  (a) the mean C.L.E. between $0°$ C. and $t_1°$ C. ;
  (b) the mean C.L.E. between $0°$ C. and $t_2°$ C. ; and
  (c) the mean C.L.E. between $t_1°$ C. and $t_2°$ C. ;

81

providing that the temperature difference $(t_2 - t_1)$ is not too great. If we accept the equality of α for both (a) and (b),

$$l_1 = l_0(1 + \alpha t_1)$$

and

$$l_2 = l_0(1 + \alpha t_2) \; ;$$

so

$$\frac{l_2}{l_1} = \frac{1 + \alpha t_2}{1 + \alpha t_1}. \quad \dots\dots\dots\dots\dots\dots\dots(i)$$

If we also write α for (c), we can say

$$l_2 = l_1[1 + \alpha(t_2 - t_1)]. \quad \dots\dots\dots\dots\dots(ii)$$

Simplifying equation (i),

$$l_2/l_1 = (1 + \alpha t_2)(1 + \alpha t_1)^{-1}.$$

Now, if we expand $(1 + \alpha t_1)^{-1}$ by the binomial theorem,

$$(1 + \alpha t_1)^{-1} = 1 - \alpha t_1 + \alpha^2 t_1^2 - \alpha^3 t_1^3 \dots,$$

continuing with higher powers of αt_1 ; and if αt_1 is so small that $\alpha^2 t_1^2$ and higher powers of αt_1 can be disregarded, $(1 + \alpha t_1)^{-1} = (1 - \alpha t_1)$, as a close approximation.

$$\therefore \; l_2/l_1 = (1 + \alpha t_2)(1 - \alpha t_1),$$

or,

$$l_2/l_1 = [1 + \alpha(t_2 - t_1) - \alpha^2 t_1 t_2].$$

Again, as $\alpha^2 t_1 t_2$ is a small quantity of the same order as $\alpha^2 t_1^2$,

$$l_2/l_1 = [1 + \alpha(t_2 - t_1)],$$

or,

$$l_2 = l_1[1 + \alpha(t_2 - t_1)],$$

which is equation (ii).

Equation (i) simplifies to (ii) as an approximation if both αt_1 and αt_2 are so small that their squares and higher powers can be neglected, and for all practical purposes we shall use the formula $l_2 = l_1[1 + \alpha(t_2 - t_1)]$, using whatever value of the c.l.e. is given as the mean value between $t_1°$ C. and $t_2°$ C. The notation is simplified by letting l_0 stand for the *original length*, l for the length at the higher temperature, and t for the *temperature rise*, when this equation will be written $l = l_0(1 + \alpha t)$. In any experiment between two definite temperatures to determine α, there is of course no doubt as to what is being found ; it is definitely the mean c.l.e. between these two temperatures.

We can assign a meaning to the term " actual coefficient of expansion at $t°$ C." Let a small rise in temperature from $t°$ C. to $(t + \delta t)°$ C. cause an increase in length from l to $l + \delta l$. Then

$l + \delta l = l(1 + \alpha \delta t)$, where α is the mean coefficient over this small interval.

$$\therefore \quad \alpha = \frac{1}{l}\frac{\delta l}{\delta t};$$

or, in the limit, when δl and δt are extremely small,

$$\alpha = \frac{1}{l}\frac{dl}{dt},$$

which gives the *actual* C.L.E. *at* $t°$ C.

The *zero coefficient of expansion* is $\alpha = \frac{1}{l_0}\frac{dt}{dl}$, where l_0 is the length at 0° C.

It should be noticed that the difference between the values of the mean coefficient determined over different temperature ranges is a matter of *experimental observation*.

The difference in value between the actual coefficient and the zero coefficient is a matter of *arithmetical reckoning* ; as neither of these two values is independent of the temperature, we cannot say that either is the " right " way of reckoning.

Supposing $\frac{1}{l_0}\frac{dl}{dt}$ is a constant, α_z ; then integrating gives $l = l_0(1 + \alpha_z t)$, where l_0 is the value at 0° C. ; the length increases by *equal amounts* for equal temperature increases, or by the law of " simple interest ".

Supposing $\frac{1}{l}\frac{dl}{dt}$ is a constant, α_a ; integrating gives $l = l_0\,e^{\alpha_a t}$, where again l_0 is the value of l when $t = 0$; the length increases by *equal fractions of the existing length* for equal temperature rises, or by the law of " compound interest ".

Expanding $e^{\alpha_a t}$, the second equation gives

$$l = l_0\left(1 + \alpha_a t + \frac{\alpha_a^{\,2} t^2}{2} + \text{higher powers of } \alpha_a t\right);$$

but *if* $\alpha_a t$ *is so small that* $\alpha_a^{\,2} t^2$ *and higher powers can be neglected*, this approximates to $l = l_0(1 + \alpha_a t)$, whence no distinction between α_z and α_a need be made in practice for all ordinary purposes.

To sum up :

(1) We shall define the coefficient of linear expansion of a material as *the increase in length of unit length for unit temperature rise*.

(2) We shall always use the values provided in problems as the

mean values between the temperatures concerned ; and remember that in experiments we are determining the *mean values between the initial and final temperatures.*

(3) We shall use the formula $l = l_0(1 + \alpha t)$, where l_0 denotes the original length, l the final length, t the rise in temperature, and α the mean coefficient of expansion over this range.

(4) We shall be prepared to distinguish *if necessary* between *mean values* and the *actual value at any temperature*, and between the coefficient based on the *increase in length of unit length at the low temperature*, and that based on the *increase in length of unit length at* 0° C., meanwhile remembering that for all practical purposes, except for very large temperature changes, these distinctions are so small as to be unnecessary.

TABLE OF COEFFICIENTS OF LINEAR EXPANSION,
per C. degree.

Aluminium	0 0000255	Most glasses, about	0·000008
Copper	0·0000167	Pyrex	0 000003
Lead	0 0000291	Fused silica	0·0000006
Platinum	0·0000089	Many woods,	
Zinc	0·0000263	along grain, about	0·000004
Brass	0·0000189	across grain, about	0·00005
Iron (cast)	0·0000102	Invar steel, with 36%	
Wrought iron,		nickel	0·0000009
steel, about	0·000012	Other kinds of invar steel, with co-efficients $-0·0000003$ to $0·0000025$ are made.	

The value of the coefficient of expansion does not depend on the unit of length used ; one centimetre heated one degree expands α cm., 1 ft. heated one degree expands α ft., and so on. But as one Fahrenheit degree is 5/9 centigrade degree, the Fahrenheit coefficients are obtained from the above by multiplying by 5/9.

It will be noticed that the values of the coefficients of linear expansion for all materials are very small, of the order of ten to twenty parts in a million for most metals, and also that the values both for fused silica and invar steel are considerably less than one part in a million.

Determination of the coefficient of linear expansion of brass (mean value between air temperature and 100° C.) From the value of α given in the table, it can be seen that the expansion of a rod one metre long is of the order of one millimetre for a rise in temperature of

80 centigrade degrees. Such a change is very difficult to measure with accuracy. There are two methods of attack in simple experiments in which one end of the rod is fixed and the other free to move. The first is to *magnify* the displacement of the free end of the rod by some mechanical or optical device, and the second is to use refined measuring instruments to observe the expansion *directly*. One simple experiment of each kind will be described, and its defects discussed.

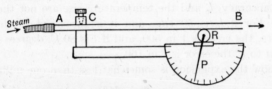

Fig. 31.—Simple expansion apparatus.

Roller-lever method. In Fig. 31, AB is a hollow tube of the metal, firmly clamped at C. The free end moves over a cylindrical roller R (a very fine needle) to which is attached a thin pointer P moving over a protractor scale graduated in degrees. R rolls freely on a glass plate, and firm contact between the tube and the roller is secured by hanging a weight on a loop of thread over the tube. The distance CR (l_0) is measured, and the air temperature $t_1°$ C. taken, and the initial reading θ_1 of P on the protractor scale observed. Steam is now passed through the tube, until it has been issuing freely from the end B for some time, and the pointer P is quite steady, when the final reading θ_2 is taken. The barometer is read, and the true temperature of the steam, $t_2°$ C., determined from the graph of p. 6. Finally, the diameter d of the roller R is determined at several points using a micrometer screw gauge reading to $1/100$ millimetre, and the average taken. The calculation then proceeds as follows.

In order to rotate the roller once if it were fixed in a bearing, the rod would have to expand through one circumfe ence, πd, of the roller. But as the roller is free, it rolls forward through one circumference, by a distance πd; hence the expansion of the tube for one rotation of the roller is $2\pi d$, twice as much as one would at first suppose. The angle turned through by the roller is $(\theta_2 - \theta_1)$ degrees, and this is $\dfrac{\theta_2 - \theta_1}{360}$ revolution.

The expansion is then $2\pi d \dfrac{(\theta_2 - \theta_1)}{360}$ cm.

The temperature rise, t, is $(t_2 - t_1)$ C. degrees.

Now α is the increase in length for unit length for unit temperature rise, that is, $\alpha =$ expansion/(length $\times$ temp. rise).

So
$$\alpha = \frac{2\pi d(\theta_2 - \theta_1)}{l_0(t_2 - t_1) \times 360}.$$

As to accuracy, l_0 and the temperature rise are not the *deciding* factors. For if l_0 is 50 cm., and it is measured to the nearest millimetre, the error is 1 in 500, and if t is 80 C. degrees and it is measured to $\frac{1}{2}°$ the error is 1 in 160.

We know the expansion is somewhat less than one millimetre, so

$$0 \cdot 1 = d(\theta_2 - \theta_1) \times \frac{2\pi}{360} = \frac{d(\theta_2 - \theta_1)}{57} \text{ approx.,}$$
$$\therefore \ d(\theta_2 - \theta_1) = 5 \cdot 7.$$

Increasing $(\theta_2 - \theta_1)$ so that it may be more accurately measured means decreasing d, with a larger proportional error. If $d = 0 \cdot 1$ cm., with an error of one part in a hundred, $(\theta_2 - \theta_1)$ is 57°, and, involving *two* measurements *each* of which may be in error by half a degree, has an error of one part in 57. If the roller diameter is halved, the proportional error in d is doubled, while the value of $(\theta_2 - \theta_1)$ is 114°, and its error is halved to one part in 114. In the first case, the total error in finding $d(\theta_2 - \theta_1)$ is $\frac{1}{100} + \frac{1}{57}$, or $0 \cdot 0275$; in the second case it is $\frac{1}{50} + \frac{1}{114}$, or $0 \cdot 028$. There seems no way of reducing this error much below $0 \cdot 028$. The total error is 1 in 500 (or $0 \cdot 002$, as a decimal) for l_0, 1 in 160 (or $0 \cdot 0063$) for t, and $0 \cdot 028$ for $d(\theta_2 - \theta_1)$, giving a total of $0 \cdot 002 + 0 \cdot 0063 + 0 \cdot 028$ or, $0 \cdot 036$, which is $3 \cdot 6$ per cent.

We have here left out of account several *incalculable* uncertainties : the average temperature of the tube is somewhat below the temperature of the steam, the stand itself expands, and the roller may possibly slip slightly. These add a large uncertainty to the result.

It is interesting to compare the accuracy of this experiment with the relatively simple experiment which follows. The ingenious roller device simply means that we have to measure a small length (the diameter of the roller) with a precision instrument, and then

superimpose a large protractor error. It is far better in principle
to measure the expansion *directly*. A similar criticism applies to
all mechanical lever and optical lever devices ; the *sensitiveness*
is increased by increasing the *long arm* of the lever, but the *accuracy*
is limited by the certainty with which the *short arm* of the lever
can be measured.

Using a micrometer screw gauge. The specimen is in the form
of a thin tube, closed at both ends, with side tubes for the passage
of steam. The tube is lagged with asbestos rope, and its lower
end rests on a glass plate. At the top, an ebonite platform supports
the three legs of a spherometer, the central micrometer screw of
which can be screwed down to make contact with the expansion
tube. As it is difficult to see exactly when contact is made, the
spherometer and specimen are included in an electric circuit containing a high resistance and a galvanometer (a voltmeter enables
the resistance to be dispensed with). Fig. 32 illustrates the
apparatus.

Measurements of the cold length of the tube, the air temperature,
and the high temperature, are made as before. To measure the
expansion, the spherometer is screwed down so that the galvanometer
just indicates contact, read, and
then screwed back several turns
to allow for the expansion.
After steam has been passing
steadily through for some time,
the spherometer is screwed up
to make contact again, and the
reading taken. This is repeated
after some minutes more, and if
any increase is noted, repeated
again until the reading is steady,
showing that expansion is complete.

The calculation $\alpha = $ expansion/
(original length $\times$ temp. rise) is
performed as before.

While the accuracy of measur-
ing l_0 and t is the same as in the
last experiment, the expansion,

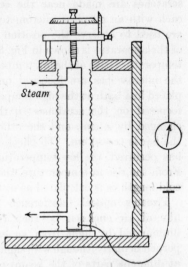

Fig. 32.—Micrometer screw expansion apparatus.

which is of the order of a millimetre, is certainly determined to within 0·01 mm., that is, to one part in a hundred. The maximum possible error due to the measurements is then $0·002 + 0·0063 + 0·01 = 0·0183$, say 1·8 per cent. Lagging the tube, and the method of assembly of the apparatus, reduce uncertainties as to incomplete heating and expansion of the stand.

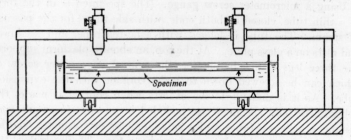

Fig. 33.—Comparator.

Comparator method. This is a standard precision method for specimens in the form of a bar or tube. The specimen is held horizontally so that it can expand freely at both ends. Two scratches are made near the ends. Two travelling microscopes each with an eyepiece micrometer, mounted on heavy stone slabs, are used to observe the position of each mark. The arrangement of the apparatus is shown in Fig. 33. The bar is placed in a constant temperature bath at the low temperature, and the length l_0 measured ; the microscopes are focussed on the scratches. Then the bar is placed in a bath at the high temperature, and the microscopes again focussed on the scratches ; if the reading of one microscope has changed by x cm., and the other by y cm., the total expansion of the bar is $(x+y)$ cm. To check that no expansion of the support has occurred, the low-temperature reading is repeated at the end. From the rise in temperature, the expansion, and the value of the cold length, α is calculated as in the simple experiments.

Fizeau's optical interference method. When a thin parallel film of air enclosed between two parallel transparent plates is illuminated by light from an extended source falling practically perpendicularly (though with slight variations in the angle of incidence at different parts of the beam) on the film, an *interference pattern*, consisting of concentric coloured rings, or, if monochromatic light of one wave-length λ is employed, of concentric bright and dark rings, is observed. The bright rings occur when the *optical path difference* between the waves reflected at the top and the bottom of the thin air film is a whole number of wave-lengths, so that the two are exactly " in step ", and the dark rings occur when the optical path difference is $\frac{1}{2}$, $1\frac{1}{2}$, $2\frac{1}{2}$ ... etc. wave-lengths, so that the " crest " of one wave emerges in step with the " trough " of another, and the two waves annul one another. The full explanation of the production of the rings is more difficult than is often supposed, and will not be attempted here. But the principle of the experiment can be understood from the following argument.

Number the bright rings, 1, 2, 3, 4 ... out from the centre. Suppose that slight differences in obliquity cause optical path differences of λ, 2λ, 3λ, 4λ, ... etc., when these rings appear in the positions A, B, C, D, ... respectively. Now suppose that the thickness of the film is reduced. The whole pattern expands, and for a certain new value of the thickness, ring 1 appears at B, ring 2 at C, ring 3 at D, and so on. That is, the optical path difference at B has been reduced from 2λ to λ, that at C from 3λ to 2λ, that at D from 4λ to 3λ, and, as the wave which is reflected at the bottom of the film has traversed it *twice*, it can be seen that *the change of thickness of the film must be exactly half a wave-length*, or λ/2. Thus, if the centre of one bright band is displaced by such a distance that it falls in the position previously occupied by the adjacent bright band, the film thickness has been reduced by half a wave-length ; fractions of a band separation are of course estimated. The wave-length of the yellow lines of sodium is about 0·000059 cm., and of the green line from the mercury arc about 0·000055 cm. We thus have a method of measuring directly small displacements to at least 1/30,000 cm., even counting only to the nearest whole band shift. The method was applied by Fizeau and subsequent experimenters to the determination of the coefficient of expansion of crystals.

The specimen P (Fig. 34), in the form of a flat polished plate of measured thickness (a few millimetres) rests on a flat metal plate AB, which also supports an optically worked glass plate CD very close to the upper surface of P. The interference pattern due to the thin film of air

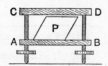

Fig. 34.—Fizeau's expansion method.

between P and CD is observed at the low temperature. The shift of the bands as the thickness of the air film changes when the whole apparatus is heated through a known temperature rise is observed ; this is due to the difference between the expansion of the crystal and that of the screws supporting CD, for which allowance must be made.

Superficial and cubical expansion. The coefficient of superficial expansion is the increase in area of unit area for unit temperature rise. We shall denote this by α_s.

The coefficient of cubical expansion is the increase in volume of unit volume for unit temperature rise. We shall call this α_c.

Substances which have the same properties in all directions are called *isotropic*. Many crystals, and substances such as wood, do not have the same properties in different directions, and these are said to be *anisotropic*.

For an isotropic solid, if α be the coefficient of linear expansion, $\alpha_s = 2\alpha$, and $\alpha_c = 3\alpha$ approximately, and sufficiently closely for all practical purposes.

Consider a cube of unit side heated through a rise of t degrees :

	Length of side.	Area of face.	Volume of cube.
At low temperature	1	1	1
$t°$ higher - -	$(1 + \alpha t)$	$(1 + \alpha t)^2$ $= 1 + 2\alpha t + \alpha^2 t^2$	$(1 + \alpha t)^3$ $= 1 + 3\alpha t + 3\alpha^2 t^2 + \alpha^3 t^3$
Now, if α is of the order 10^{-5} and t of the order 10^2, αt is of the order 10^{-3}, and, neglecting		$\alpha^2 t^2$ of order 10^{-6}	$\alpha^2 t^2$ of order 10^{-6} and $\alpha^3 t^3$ of order 10^{-9}
we can write -	$1 + \alpha t$	$1 + 2\alpha t$	$1 + 3\alpha t$
The *increase* per unit for $t°$ rise is then - -	αt	$2\alpha t$	$3\alpha t$
and the increase per unit for $1°$ rise is	α	2α	3α

Hence $\alpha_s = 2\alpha$, and $\alpha_c = 3\alpha$, approximately.

For anisotropic solids, the coefficients of expansion may be different in different directions. Suppose unit cube of such a material to have coefficients of linear expansion α_1, α_2, and a_3 along three edges at right angles to one another; the volume at $t°$ C. is $(1 + \alpha_1 t)(1 + \alpha_2 t)(1 + \alpha_3 t)$. By multiplying out, and neglecting the products $\alpha_1 \alpha_2 t^2$, etc., and $\alpha_1 \alpha_2 \alpha_3 t^3$, the volume is $[1 + (\alpha_1 + \alpha_2 + \alpha_3) t]$ for all practical purposes, whence $\alpha_c = \alpha_1 + \alpha_2 + \alpha_3$.

X-ray methods for crystals. The atoms or ions in a crystal are arranged in a regular pattern in space, and can be regarded as set in a series of parallel planes, the distance between successive planes being called the lattice spacing. There are, of course, several different directions in any given type of crystal along which these lattice planes can be found.

The lattice spacing d for a given set of lattice planes in a crystal is determined by observing the angle θ at which X-rays of wavelength λ are regularly reflected. Then $n\lambda = 2d \sin \theta$, where n is a whole number.

It is found that d increases with the temperature, and can be represented by the formula $d = d_0(1 + \alpha t)$, where α is the coefficient of expansion of the lattice-spacing. The values of α obtained from measurements of d at different temperatures agree closely with direct measurements made on single crystals for the same directions.

Expansion of a hollow vessel. Consider a cube of unit side; let the c.l.e. be α. For a rise in temperature of $t°$ C., each side becomes $(1 + \alpha t)$, and the volume inside is $(1 + \alpha t)^3$, approximately equal to $(1 + 3\alpha t)$. But this is just what happens when we consider a solid cube of the same material, hence the *volume of the hollow space inside the cube increases just as if the hollow space itself were made of the material of the cube.* This of course applies to a vessel of any shape.

Expansion and elasticity. Increasing the temperature is one way of lengthening a rod; it can also be extended by a pull in the direction of its length. If the rod returns to its original length when the pull is removed, the stretching is said to be *perfectly elastic.* It is found experimentally that for a given specimen the force is directly proportional to the extension it produces, provided this does not exceed the limits of perfect elasticity. For a given material, the force per unit area (called the stress) is proportional to the elongation per unit length (called the strain) and the ratio stress/strain is called **Young's Modulus** for the material, denoted here by the symbol E;

that is, $\dfrac{\text{stress}}{\text{strain}} = E$, or stress $= E \times$ strain.

This is one way of expressing **Hooke's Law**; it applies equally well for compression (which is a negative extension).

Now suppose a bar of length l_0, area of cross-section A, is heated through $t°$. The expansion is $l_0 \alpha t$ and the *strain* $l_0 \alpha t / l_0 = \alpha t$. Let this now be clamped at the ends and cooled down again to the original temperature. The result is just the same as if it had, without heating, been pulled out mechanically, and the force required to keep it extended will be the same as that which would be required to produce the extension. Since *strain* $= \alpha t$, therefore *stress* $= E\alpha t$, and

$$total \ force = stress \times area = A E \alpha t.$$

A similar argument applies for the force required to stop expansion —we can imagine a bar whose hot length is $l_0(1 + \alpha t)$ to have been compressed by an amount $l_0 \alpha t$ so that its length is reduced to l_0, the force required being $\dfrac{A E \alpha t}{(1 + \alpha t)}$.

SOME PRACTICAL APPLICATIONS OF EXPANSION

Many of the more obvious examples of the effects of expansion, and the steps taken to use or to counteract these effects, are probably familiar to the student. Allowance for expansion in the laying of railway lines and the erecting of steel bridges, the shrinking of metal tyres on cartwheels and similar methods of assembling metal parts in engineering, are a few of the many well-known examples. In accurate measurements of length, allowance has to be made for the fact that the scale expands and is accurate at one temperature only. We shall describe in detail a few important practical applications, some of which are fairly recent. Nearly all of these employ two expansible materials, and either seek to defeat expansion by expansion, or use the fact that a bimetallic strip (consisting of two metals of different coefficients of expansion brazed side by side) bends when heated, or find an ingenious application for the very small expansibility of fused quartz or invar steel (36 per cent. nickel).

Compensation of clocks and watches. The hands of a clock are attached to wheels which come midway in a train of gears between the driving wheel actuated by the spring or weights, and the escapement which controls the rate at which the whole train of wheels runs down. In the pendulum clock each beat of the pendulum moves a claw-shaped pallet arm so that one tooth of the last wheel of the train (called the " scape wheel ") can pass. It follows that, if the pendulum beats more rapidly than it should, the whole train of wheels will run too fast, and the clock will gain ; while if the pendulum beats too slowly, the clock will lose.

The pendulum usually consists of a metal rod with a heavy disc (the " bob ") at the lower end. It is, strictly speaking, a " rigid pendulum ", but for our purposes it will be imagined to be a " simple pendulum ", with a bob of negligible dimensions suspended at the end of a wire of negligible mass. The length of a simple pendulum is the distance between the point of support and the centre of gravity of the bob. For a simple pendulum of length l, the time T of one complete small-amplitude swing (two beats) is given by the formula $T = 2\pi\sqrt{l/g}$, where g is the acceleration of gravity at the place concerned.

We will first consider the effect of a rise in temperature on the period of the pendulum.

Let l_0 be the cold length, T the correct period, then

$$T = 2\pi\sqrt{\frac{l_0}{g}}.$$

At a temperature $t°$ higher, the new length is $l_0(1 + \alpha t)$ and the new period

$$T + \delta T = 2\pi\sqrt{\frac{l_0(1 + \alpha t)}{g}} = 2\pi\sqrt{\frac{l_0}{g}} \cdot (1 + \alpha t)^{\frac{1}{2}},$$

or, $$T + \delta T = T(1 + \alpha t)^{\frac{1}{2}} ;$$

as αt is very small, $(1 + \alpha t)^{\frac{1}{2}} = (1 + \frac{1}{2}\alpha t)$ approximately.

$$\therefore \ T + \delta T = T(1 + \tfrac{1}{2}\alpha t) = T + \tfrac{1}{2}\alpha t T.$$

$$\therefore \ \delta T = \tfrac{1}{2}\alpha t T,$$

and $$\frac{\delta T}{T} = \tfrac{1}{2}\alpha t.$$

$\dfrac{\delta T}{T}$ gives the *fractional* increase in period.

If $t = 10$ C. deg.   and $\alpha = 0\!\cdot\!000018$ (*brass*),

$$\frac{\delta T}{T} = 0\!\cdot\!00009.$$

Note that this is independent of the actual length of the pendulum.

For the effect on the clock, suppose that T is one second. This simplifies the argument, and is legitimate since $\delta T/T$ is the same whatever the length.

Then $\delta T = 0\cdot00009\,T = 0\cdot00009$ sec.

That is, each swing of the pendulum takes $1\cdot00009$ sec. instead of 1 sec., and the clock loses $0\cdot00009$ sec. in every $1\cdot00009$ sec., or for all practical purposes, $0\cdot00009$ sec. in every second. Hence,

in one hour it loses $60 \times 60 \times 0\cdot00009$ sec.,

in one day it loses $24 \times 60 \times 60 \times 0\cdot00009$ sec.,

in 30 days it loses $30 \times 24 \times 60 \times 60 \times 0\cdot00009$ sec., which is 234 sec., or 3 min. 54 sec.

So the error is sufficiently great to need some means of compensation.

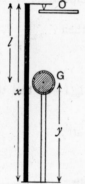

FIG. 35.—Principle of compensated pendulum.

All methods of compensation follow the same general principle, and the simplest to understand is that of Harrison's Gridiron. Fig. 35 shows the principle, while the actual construction of such a pendulum is shown in Fig. 36 (b). The distance l between the point of support O, and a fixed point here supposed to be the centre of gravity G has to remain constant. Two rods, x cm. of a material of C.L.E. α_1, and y cm. of a material of higher C.L.E. α_2 are used. If l, which is $(x - y)$, is to remain the same at all temperatures, the expansion of the first rod downwards for a rise in temperature t must balance the expansion of the second rod upwards,

so
$$x\alpha_1 t = y\alpha_2 t,$$

or
$$\frac{x}{y} = \frac{\alpha_2}{\alpha_1}.$$

If x is of iron ($\alpha_1 = 0\cdot000012$) and y is brass ($\alpha_2 = 0\cdot000018$),

$$\frac{x}{y} = \frac{0\cdot000018}{0\cdot000012} = \frac{3}{2}.$$

In the actual gridiron pendulum of Fig. 36, the downward expanding members are of iron, and the upward expanding members of brass, the total lengths of iron and brass being in the ratio 3 : 2.

At the present time, it is possible by the use of invar steel to design a pendulum rod the change of length of which with temperature is practically zero.

In the watch escapement, the pallets are at one end of a lever the other arm of which engages a pin on the mount of a small flywheel called the **balance wheel**, which is controlled by a hair-spring. Two factors determine the rate at which the balance wheel oscillates, the stiffness of the hairspring, and the moment of inertia of the balance wheel which depends (among other things) on its diameter. A rise in temperature weakens the hairspring and increases the diameter of the balance wheel, both changes causing the oscillations to be slower. The former is the more important effect. The usual method of compensation is, as shown in Fig. 37, to make the balance wheel rim in two or more segments of a bimetallic strip with brass on the outside and steel on the inside, and weighting the rim suitably. As brass has the greater coefficient of expansion, the end of each segment curls inwards when the temperature rises, thus reducing the moment of inertia sufficiently to compensate both for radial expansion and weakening of the spring.

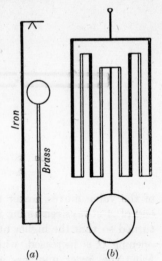

Fig. 36.—Gridiron pendulum. (a) Effective *relative* proportions of iron and brass, (b) actual design.

" **Regulo** " gas-oven thermostat (Fig. 38). The head H carries a dial D on which a series of numbers is clearly marked. When the dial D is turned, it causes the spindle A to rotate. The screwed portion of the spindle A is in mesh with the screwed boss of the valve V, and when A rotates, the disc

Fig. 37.—Compensated balance-wheel.

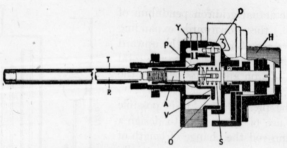

Fig. 38.—" Regulo " thermostat.

By courtesy of Radiation, Ltd.

of the valve moves nearer to or further away from its seating, the end of A always remaining in contact with the rod R. When D is turned so that the higher numbers on the dial are visible, the valve opening O is increased, whilst, when the movements of the head bring the lower numbers into view, the opening of the valve is lessened. Thus, by turning the dial, the setting of the valve can be altered, and it is the setting of the valve that determines the particular temperature maintained.

An expanding tube T, the tail end of which is closed, is fixed into the " Regulo " head. This tube extends across the inside of the oven near the top, and expands or contracts with changes of the temperature within the oven. The automatic lengthening and shortening of this tube causes the closing and opening of the valve in the head, and controls the gas supply to the oven.

To utilise the movement of the brass tube, there is fixed inside it a rod R of special non-expanding metal (probably *invar*), one end of the rod being attached to the tail end of the tube. The other end of the rod is free, but the brass piece A, which carries the disc valve, is pressed up against it by the spring S. When the brass tube becomes hot and lengthens, it carries the rod with it, and because the rod does not expand, the disc valve is moved so that the opening O is gradually reduced. The gas is led to the inside of the " Regulo " head at P, and it has to pass through the opening O on its way to the oven. It is at O that the gas is automatically controlled.

When the *whole* of the gas supply to an oven is controlled automatically, the possibility arises that the gas may be momentarily cut off and brought on again. This would occur if the oven were heated to a high temperature, and the dial were then turned to a much lower mark. Under these conditions, the valve would be closed completely until the oven had cooled, when unburned gas would escape from the burner. This possibility is avoided by leading a portion of the gas through an alternative channel, Y, direct to the burner, so that some of the gas does not pass through the automatic valve. Such an alternative supply is known as a by-pass, and it is not controlled automatically.

"Sunvic" high-vacuum switch. The expansion of a wire when it is heated by the passage of an electric current through it is the basis of the operation of the high-vacuum switch, shown in Fig. 39. A and B are conductors carrying the heavy current in a circuit, C is a lever pivoted at the top of A, making or breaking the connection between A and B. S is a long strip of special steel, wound several times between the insulating bobbins TT; this strip is connected in a second circuit so that a small current can be sent through it when it is required to keep A and B connected, while when the current through S stops, connection between A and B is broken. This is because when S carries no current it is cool, contracts, operates the lever C against the spring D, and opens the contacts; when S carries a current it expands, slackens, and allows D to close the switch. The whole is maintained in the highest possible vacuum, so that it is impossible for

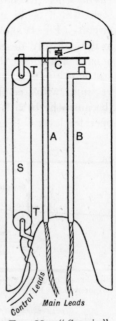

FIG. 39.—"Sunvic" vacuum switch.

an arc to be established when the contacts are separated, as would happen if such a switch were to operate in air.

Bimetallic thermostat control. The use of a compound strip made of two metals such as iron and brass, of widely different coefficients of expansion, has already been mentioned (p. 95). Such a strip when heated will bend into an arc with the more expansible metal on the outside of the curve. Fig 40 shows the "Sunvic" thermostat control. The two metal strips shown form part of an electric

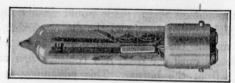

FIG. 40.—Bimetallic thermostat control switch.
Reproduced by courtesy of Sunvic Controls, Ltd.

circuit when the contact pieces touch. The upper one is a bimetallic strip which bends up when the temperature rises and breaks the circuit. Fig. 41 shows how this is connected, with the high-vacuum switch already described, to maintain a constant temperature in a bath heated by the heater (denoted by " load "). The thermostat is in the bath, and is connected in series with the wire S of the vacuum switch, so that when the thermostat control contacts open (because the bath is too hot), S takes no current, cools, contracts, operates lever C (Fig. 39), and switches off the load current. When

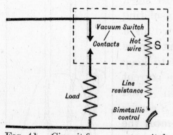

FIG. 41.—Circuit for vacuum switch operated by bimetallic control.

the bath cools down, the thermostat contacts shut, current again passes through S, and the load current passes as before. This thermostat is sensitive to temperature changes of one centigrade degree, provided the rate of change is not too great. The glass envelope is filled with hydrogen, which gives a fairly quick response to temperature changes, and at the same time preserves the contacts from dirt and corrosion.

Another model, with the bimetallic strip fixed the other way round so as to *close* the circuit when it is *heated*, is used as a fire alarm.

Bimetallic thermometers and thermographs. The change of curvature of a bimetallic strip when its temperature changes can be caused to actuate a pointer moving over a dial. The sheer simplicity of this arrangement commends it for simple domestic thermometers. It is, however, used for scientific instruments also, particularly for recording instruments, or thermographs. Fig. 42 shows a recording thermograph, in which the change of curvature of a helical bimetallic strip, which can be seen in the cage at the right,

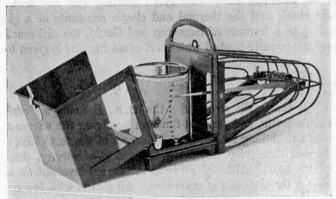

FIG. 42.—Bimetallic thermograph.
By courtesy of Messrs. Negretti and Zambra.

moves an inked pen which records on a chart on a clockwork-driven drum. The helix operates directly on the spindle of the pen arm, without any levers or links ; it exerts a powerful control which is ample to overcome the friction between the pen and the chart, and responds with very little lag (a most important point) to temperature changes. The thermograph needs no attention, apart from winding, and replacing the chart, and is used for such purposes as packing with the cargo of a ship to give a record of the temperature in the hold during the voyage.

Glassware. (a) *The fracture of glass vessels on heating* depends on several factors. Thick glass vessels, when subjected to *sudden* changes of temperature, can be relied on to break. This is because glass is a poor conductor of heat, and the part subjected to the heating is therefore maintained at a much higher temperature than the surrounding parts for an appreciable time, during which it expands and exerts forces (depending on its elastic constants) on the other parts which they are usually unable to stand, though this depends on the strength of the glass.

Breakage is avoided by (i) choosing thin glassware, as is done for laboratory apparatus, (ii) avoiding sudden temperature changes (boiling jam, for example, is poured into heated pots), and (iii) choosing glass of small coefficient of expansion and high thermal conductivity.

Several formulae have been given relating the resistance to thermal shock and the thermal and elastic constants of a glass. According to a formula of Hampton and Gould, the difference of temperature rapidly applied which will cause fracture is given by

$$t_1 - t_0 = \frac{P(1-\sigma)}{\alpha E} \cdot \frac{1}{f(x,\, t)},$$

where P is the tensile strength, α the C.L.E., E Young's Modulus, σ Poisson's Ratio, and $f(x,\, t)$ a function involving the nature and extent of the chilling medium, the thickness of the test piece, and the thermal diffusivity (involving thermal conductivity, density and specific heat). Although all these factors are involved, *the most important is the coefficient of expansion*. All glasses with low C.L.E. stand up well to thermal shock. Fused silica ($\alpha = 0\cdot0000005$ per C. deg.), and the new American glass " Vycor " ($\alpha = 0\cdot0000008$ per C. deg.) which contains 97 per cent. silica, can both be heated to white heat and plunged safely into cold water. " Pyrex " glass ($\alpha = 0\cdot0000033$ per C. deg.), even in the form of thick tubes, can be thrust into a blowpipe flame suddenly without risk of fracture. Ordinary soft glass ($\alpha = $ about $0\cdot0000085$ to $0\cdot0000095$ per C. deg.) of course needs very careful treatment.

The coefficient of thermal conductivity of fused silica is about twice that of ordinary glass ; while the great tensile strength of *very thin fibres* of fused silica is well known, the strength and elastic properties of this material in large specimens do not differ very much from those of ordinary glass.

(b) *Uses of fused silica vessels.* For all purposes where it is important that the volume of a vessel shall not change appreciably with the temperature, as with graduated vessels and also pyknometers and other pieces of apparatus for studying the expansion of liquids, fused silica is the material used.

(c) *The sealing of metal wires through glass.* Formerly platinum, which has a C.L.E. approximately the same as that of glass, was used for sealed-in conductors in appliances such as discharge tubes. Various less expensive methods are nowadays in use, the general principle being to use thin tubes of soft metal which can yield under the stresses set up, rather than to avoid the stress altogether. With fused silica several methods were tried ; plugs of invar steel ground into tapered seatings, molybdenum wire sealed through the material, and, more recently, seals in which a plug of lead (which when molten will " wet " the fused silica) carries the conductor.

Expansion in optical and electrical apparatus. Expansion difficulties arise in cases where at first one might not expect them. For example, the mirrors of reflecting telescopes are very accurately figured, but all this is to no purpose if the surface is distorted by expansion of different portions which may be at different temperatures. Low coefficient of expansion and high thermal conductivity are the two properties required, and of course they are *not* found in the *same* material. Fused silica has been employed for mirrors up to 25 inches in diameter ; the 200-inch reflector at Mount Palomar, California, has a mirror of " Pyrex " glass.

The electrical constants of inductance coils and condensers depend, among other things, on their dimensions—and thus change with expansion. For example, the inductance of a coil is proportional to the ratio *area of cross-section/length*, from which it would appear that the temperature coefficient should be the same as the coefficient of linear expansion. The capacity of an air condenser is proportional to *area of plates/separation*, and here it is possible by constructing the condenser of two different metals to arrange that the increase in area of the plates is balanced by the increase in their separation. Great ingenuity is required to maintain this compensation *during change* of temperature (as well as at different *steady* temperatures), as this involves the heat capacity of the different parts.

In the *hot-wire ammeter*, the current to be measured (or a known fraction of it) passes through a wire held under tension. The rate of development of heat is proportional to the square of the current, and so also is the steady temperature reached and the consequent expansion, which is made to operate a pointer moving over a scale.

EXPANSION OF LIQUIDS

The expansion observed when a liquid is heated is always less than the true expansion of the liquid itself, as the capacity of the containing vessel also increases. We must thus distinguish between the **real coefficient of expansion**, which is *the true increase in volume of unit volume for unit temperature rise*, and the **apparent coefficient of expansion**, which is the *observed increase in volume of unit volume for unit temperature rise, measured in an expansible vessel the expansion of which is disregarded.*

In all experiments which are conducted over a considerable range of temperature, the mean coefficient of expansion between the initial and final temperatures is found ; likewise, this is the value required in calculations of any practical use. As many liquids expand irregularly, the value of the mean coefficient of expansion depends on the range of temperature concerned, which should be specified. We may need to distinguish between the **zero coefficient**, in which the expansion is reckoned as a *fraction of the volume at* $0°$ C., and the coefficient reckoned as a *fraction of the volume at the low temperature*.

If V_0 be the volume at $0°$ C., V_t that at $t°$ C., and α_0 the zero coefficient,

$$V_t = V_0(1 + \alpha_0 t) \; ;$$

while if V_1 and V_2 be the volumes at $t_1°$ C. and $t_2°$ C., and α_m the mean coefficient between these two temperatures,

$$V_2 = V_1[1 + \alpha_m (t_2 - t_1)].$$

We shall find it convenient, to save space, to use as a general rule the equation $V = V_0(1 + \alpha t)$, where V_0 stands for the *original* volume at the low temperature, which *may* sometimes be $0°$ C., V the volume at the high temperature, t the *rise in temperature*, and α the mean coefficient of expansion between the temperatures concerned.

Approximate relation between real and apparent coefficient. Let α be the real coefficient, a the apparent coefficient, and g the coefficient of cubical expansion of the material of the vessel (usually glass), the hollow space inside which expands as if it were solid glass. Consider a small flask of volume exactly 1 c.c., which is full to the top with the liquid at the cold temperature. Let it be heated through exactly one degree. Then, if the vessel did not expand, the volume expelled would be α c.c. But, for $1°$ rise, the vessel expands g c.c., and this space must be filled before any overflow occurs. The observed overflow is then not α c.c., but $(\alpha - g)$ c.c.

That is, $\qquad a = \alpha - g,$

or, $\qquad \alpha = a + g.$

This result is not *strictly* correct, though it may be hard to see any flaw in the argument at first sight. Its detection is left to the ingenuity of the student, who should compare the result with that on p. 106. It is, however, true enough for all practical purposes.

Change in density with rise in temperature. Whatever happens to the containing vessel, one change can be connected definitely with the *real coefficient* of expansion, and that is the *change in density* of the liquid. This is a most important point, and it should be carefully noted now.

Consider a fixed mass M of liquid, occupying a volume V_0 at the cold temperature, and V at a temperature $t°$ higher.

Let ρ_0 be the density at the cold temperature, ρ that at the high temperature. Let α be the mean value of the real coefficient of expansion between the temperatures concerned.

Now,
$$\rho = \frac{M}{V} \quad \text{and} \quad V = V_0(1 + \alpha t) ;$$

so
$$\rho = \frac{M}{V_0(1 + \alpha t)} = \frac{M}{V_0} \cdot \frac{1}{(1 + \alpha t)} ;$$

but
$$\rho_0 = \frac{M}{V_0} ,$$

so
$$\rho = \frac{\rho_0}{1 + \alpha t} .$$

COEFFICIENTS OF EXPANSION OF LIQUIDS

Liquid.	α (per C. deg.)
Ethyl alcohol - -	0·0011
Aniline - - - -	0·00085
Benzene - - -	0·00124
Glycerine - - -	0·00053
Mercury - - -	0·00018
Paraffin oil - - -	0·0009
Pentane - - -	0·00159
Toluene - - -	0·00109
Turpentine - - -	0·00094

(The above figures, from Kaye and Laby's " Tables ", give the mean values for a range round 18° C.)

Methods of measuring the coefficient of expansion of a liquid. The value of the coefficient of expansion is comparatively large when compared with the coefficient of cubical expansion of a solid—as high as about 0·001 for liquids such as alcohol and paraffin. It should, therefore, be possible to measure a roughly by the simplest of methods—say by taking about 40 c.c. in a burette at room temperature, and heating this in a water jacket through about 50°, when the expansion of $40 \times 50 \times 0.001 = 2$ c.c. could be measured with an accuracy of 5 per cent. by reading the burette tube itself. With a bulb of known volume connected to a fine graduated tube, this could be transformed into a refined method, but the student's chief criticism then would be that the bulb and tube must be calibrated, an operation taking as much care and trouble as a whole determination by any other method. It is, however, valuable when a continuous range of readings have to be taken, as, for example, in studying the variation of density of water with the temperature. A vessel made for this purpose is called a dilatometer.

Fig. 43 shows a type of dilatometer designed for very accurate work. Its great advantage over the " weight thermometer " or " specific gravity bottle " method described below is that errors due to evaporation of the liquid are avoided.

Apart from the dilatometer, the most important methods of determining the mean coefficient of expansion of a liquid over appreciable temperature ranges all *compare the density* (*true or apparent*) *of hot liquid with that of cold liquid*. They are based on the three stock methods of finding specific gravities (that is, comparing densities) used in hydrostatics. These are :

1. The specific-gravity bottle method.

2. The sinker method, which depends on Archimedes' Principle.

3. The balancing-column method, in which the vertical heights of two columns exerting equal pressures are compared.

FIG. 43.
Dilatometer.

Specific gravity bottle method. The specific gravity bottle is the simplest and most familiar of the small closed vessels which enable a definite volume of liquid to be taken. Other such vessels, the pyknometer (Fig. 44) which has two fine capillary tubes CA and FB with a reference mark G, to which it may be very accurately and readily filled, and the **weight thermometer** (originally so named because when heated the rise in temperature could be estimated by weighing the overflow), a vessel with a single narrow capillary neck which is difficult to fill and exasperating to empty again, are often used for this experiment; but the exact type of vessel is of minor importance, provided it has a narrow outlet tube—unless it is desired to weigh the overflow directly, when the weight thermometer would be preferable.

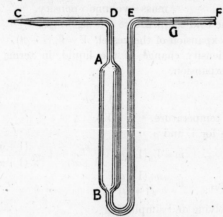

Fig. 44.—Pyknometer.

A clean dry specific gravity bottle is weighed. It is then filled with liquid at the air temperature, which is observed, and then the bottle is weighed again. It is then placed in a water bath, and heated slowly to a suitable high temperature (glycerine, paraffin, and mercury can of course be heated safely to 100° C.; but with alcohol it is unwise to heat much above about 55° C.). The bottle is left at this steady temperature for about ten minutes, and the temperature of the bath is recorded. The bottle is then removed, dried, and weighed again. From these readings the mass of liquid expelled, the mass left in at the end, and the rise in temperature are found. The formula for the mean value of the apparent coefficient of expansion of the liquid between the initial and final temperatures is then

$$a = \frac{mass\ expelled}{mass\ left\ in \times temperature\ rise}.$$

Let α be the real coefficient of expansion, a the apparent coefficient of expansion, and g the coefficient of cubical expansion of the glass of the vessel. Let m_0 be the mass of liquid filling the bottle at the low temperature, m the mass filling it at the high temperature, and ρ_0 and ρ the densities of the liquid at the cold and hot temperatures respectively. Let V_0 and V be the volumes of the vessel at these two temperatures. Let t degrees be the *rise* in temperature.

Now, since density $=$ mass/volume,

mass $=$ volume $\times$ density.

Then, for the cold temperature $m_0 = V_0 \rho_0$,
while, for the expansion of the vessel, $V = V_0(1 + gt)$,
and for the density change of the liquid, in terms of the *real* coefficient of expansion,

$$\rho = \frac{\rho_0}{1 + \alpha t}.$$

At the high temperature, $m = V\rho$.
Substituting for V and ρ,

$$m = V_0(1 + gt) \cdot \frac{\rho_0}{(1 + \alpha t)} = V_0 \rho_0 \frac{(1 + gt)}{(1 + \alpha t)},$$

or, as $m_0 = V_0 \rho_0$, $\qquad m = \frac{m_0(1 + gt)}{(1 + \alpha t)}.$

Cross-multiplying and simplifying,

$$m + m\alpha t = m_0 + m_0 gt.$$

$$\therefore \quad \alpha = \frac{m_0 - m}{mt} + \frac{m_0}{m} g.$$

This expression is for the real coefficient ; we require the apparent coefficient. But, if the expansion of the vessel is disregarded, this simply means we must put $g = 0$, when it is necessary to write a instead of α.

So, $\qquad a = \frac{m_0 - m}{mt}.$

Whence, in words,

$$a = \frac{mass\ expelled}{mass\ left\ in \times temperature\ rise}.$$

Substituting for a, in the original equation for α,

$$\alpha = a + \frac{m_0}{m} g,$$

whence α is not *exactly* equal to $a + g$, as was stated (for an approximation) on p. 102.

The error in using the formula $\alpha = a + g$, though appreciable, is rarely large enough to be important, though it increases for large

temperature rises and hence may have to be considered, if the
value of t is large. If $a = 0 \cdot 0010$, and $g = 0 \cdot 000025$, then, for a
rise of $100°$,

$$\frac{m_0}{m} = 1 \cdot 1, \quad \frac{m_0}{m} g = 0 \cdot 0000275.$$

So while $\left.\begin{array}{l} a + g = 0 \cdot 0010250 \\ a + \dfrac{m_0}{m} g = 0 \cdot 0010275 \end{array}\right\}$ a difference of about $0 \cdot 25$ per cent.

Sinker method. A hollow sealed glass sinker is loaded with
mercury so that it just sinks in the cold liquid, and is suspended from
a fine wire attached to the pan support of a balance. The base of
the balance and the top of the supporting table are bored to allow
the wire to pass freely through. A large vessel of the liquid of
which the coefficient of expansion is required is heated by an
electric immersion heater, which also serves as a stirrer (Fig. 45).

The sinker is weighed in air and in the liquid at the low temperature, which is observed. The liquid is heated up and well stirred,
the steady temperature noted, and the sinker is weighed again.
The upthrust on the sinker (weight in air minus weight in liquid)
is calculated in each case. From Archimedes' Principle, the up-

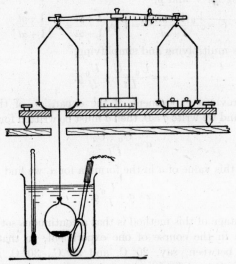

FIG. 45.—Sinker method.

thrust on the sinker equals the weight of the mass of liquid displaced. The calculation then follows the same lines as that for the specific gravity bottle method, the only difference being that the mass *displaced* by the glass shell of the sinker is found, instead of the mass *contained* by the glass shell of the bottle.

Let the temperature rise be t centigrade degrees. Let U_0 be the upthrust in cold liquid, U that in the liquid at the high temperature, V_0 and V, ρ_0 and ρ be the volumes of the sinker and densities of the liquid at the two temperatures, and let α, a, and g be the mean values of the real coefficient of the liquid, the apparent coefficient of the liquid, and the coefficient of cubical expansion of glass over the range of temperature of the experiment.

The mass of liquid displaced at the cold temperature is $V_0\rho_0$, so $U_0 = V_0\rho_0$.

For the expansion of the sinker, $V = V_0(1 + gt)$, and for the change in density of the liquid, in terms of the real coefficient,

$$\rho = \frac{\rho_0}{1 + \alpha t}.$$

The mass of liquid displaced at the high temperature is $V\rho$, so $U = V\rho$.

Substituting for V and ρ,

$$U = \frac{V_0(1 + gt)\rho_0}{1 + \alpha t} = V_0\rho_0 \frac{1 + gt}{1 + \alpha t} = U_0 \frac{1 + gt}{1 + \alpha t};$$

and, by cross-multiplying and simplifying,

$$\alpha = \frac{U_0 - U}{Ut} + \frac{U_0}{U} g.$$

As in the previous experiment, if the expansion of the sinker is disregarded and we write $g = 0$, then a must be written for α; whence

$$a = \frac{U_0 - U}{Ut}.$$

Substituting this value of a in the formula for α, we find

$$\alpha = a + \frac{U_0}{U} g.$$

One advantage of this method is that a continuous set of readings is obtainable in the course of one experiment, so that the mean values of a between, say, 20° C. and 30° C., 30° C. and 40° C., 40° C. and 50° C., can be found.

Careful stirring of the bath before each weighing is necessary, and the accuracy of the experiment can be increased by setting a weight which is a little too heavy on the balance pan, and allowing the liquid to cool a little and noting the temperature at which the balance is exactly counterpoised ; that is, finding the *temperature for a given weight*, rather than *the weight for a given temperature*. This is because weighing is a rather lengthy operation, and the temperature will in any event fall slightly while it is being done— in fact, a conscientious student with a sensitive balance usually finds that he cannot obtain a satisfactory weighing to the nearest milligram as the cooling keeps up with his adjustment of the rider.

Balancing column method. The pressure due to a column of liquid depends on three things only. These are, *the vertical height of the column, the density of the liquid* and *the acceleration of gravity*, the formula being $p = h\rho g$ dynes per sq. cm., or $p = h\rho$ gm. wt. per sq. cm. It is not affected at all by the area, length, size, or shape of the containing vessel, and so *change of the dimensions of the vessel likewise cannot affect it*. Hence, by balancing the pressures due to two columns of the same liquid at different temperatures, we have a means of comparing their true densities directly, and so determining the real coefficient of expansion *directly*. The experiment was first performed by Dulong and Petit. A simple demonstration model of their apparatus will be described, some of its defects noted, and then one of the accurate experiments on the same lines performed by Regnault will be discussed.

The simple apparatus consists of a large U-tube, about 100 cm. high, with the limbs about 60 cm. apart, made of glass tubing about 8 mm. in diameter. The U-tube is open to the air on both sides, and one limb is surrounded by a jacket through which steam from a boiler can be passed (Fig. 46).

Steam is passed through the jacket until the levels in both limbs are steady. No " cold measurements " are made, and nothing is done until this steady state of affairs is reached. It is seen that the level B of the liquid in the hot limb is appreciably higher than C, the level in the cold limb. There is considerable uncertainty as to the exact length of the heated portion, but we shall assume that only the liquid actually inside the jacket is heated to steam temperature, and that all the rest of the liquid is at the temperature of the surrounding air.

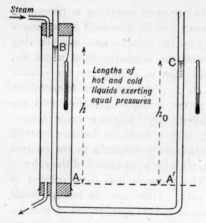

Steam

B

Lengths of
hot and cold
liquids exerting
equal pressures

h

C

h_0

A

A'

Fig. 46.—Balancing column method.

Imagine a horizontal line AA' to be drawn at the level of the lower cork in the steam jacket. Below this level, equal vertical heights of cold liquid balance one another in the two limbs. The columns AB of hot liquid and $A'C$ of cold liquid then exert equal pressures and balance one another. The vertical heights h and h_0 of AB and $A'C$ are obtained by measuring the vertical heights of A, B, and C above the horizontal bench. The air temperature and the temperature inside the steam jacket are recorded, and the temperature difference t is found.

Then, if ρ_0 be the density of the cold liquid and ρ that of the hot liquid, as *pressure = vertical height × density*, in gm. wt. per sq. cm., and the two columns exert equal pressures,

$$h\rho = h_0\rho_0 \quad \text{or} \quad h = h_0 \frac{\rho_0}{\rho};$$

but

$$\rho = \frac{\rho_0}{1+\alpha t}, \quad \text{or} \quad \frac{\rho_0}{\rho} = 1 + \alpha t.$$

So

$$h = h_0(1 + \alpha t)*,$$

and

$$\alpha = \frac{h - h_0}{h_0 t}.$$

Note again that this gives the *real coefficient of expansion directly*.

There are two chief criticisms of this very simple apparatus. There is much uncertainty as to the actual heated length. Also, $(h - h_0)$ appears in the formula for the calculation, and the percentage error in this may be much larger than would at first be expected.

---

* It should not be necessary to point out here that, *although lengths are being measured*, and the formula written down here appears similar to that on p. 81, we are *not* finding the coefficient of *linear* expansion of a liquid. But this confusion is not uncommon, with respect to this experiment, and also in correcting the barometer for the expansion of the mercury (p. 115), and the student is advised to make sure that he understands the *whole* of this argument—not merely the last step.

For example, with mercury $\alpha = 0.00018$; if $h_0 = 50$ cm. and $t = 80$ centigrade degrees, $(h - h_0) = 0.72$ cm.   Now, both h and h_0 require *two* measurements, each of which may be in error by 0.05 cm., so the maximum error in h and h_0 individually is 0.1 cm., a mere 0.2 per cent. of the individual lengths.   As the errors may conspire to make h too big and h_0 too small, the maximum error in the difference $(h - h_0)$ is 0.2 cm.   This is 20 parts in 72, or 28 per cent. —a large error.   For accuracy, then, the first requisite is that every part of the apparatus shall be at an accurately known temperature ; the second is that the difference in levels shall be determined directly by some precision measuring apparatus such as a cathetometer.   In addition, it is desirable that the upper surfaces should be at the same temperature, to eliminate surface tension errors.

The determination of the real coefficient of expansion of mercury is a matter of great importance.   If we know accurately the value of α for any *one* liquid, we can, by observing the value of a for this liquid in a given vessel, find the value of g for the vessel directly. This is far more satisfactory, especially in the case of glass, than taking the c.c.e. to be 3 times the c.l.e.   Henceforward this vessel may be used to find α for other liquids by measuring their apparent coefficients by it.   Also, mercury is the liquid commonly employed in pressure gauges and barometers, and accurate pressure measurements by these means are only possible if the density of mercury at different temperatures is accurately known.   An exhaustive series of experiments on mercury was carried out by Regnault, of which only one will be described.

In Regnault's apparatus (Fig. 47), the two limbs of the U-tube were connected at the top to vertical tubes A and B, by means of fairly narrow cross-tubes.   The tubes A and B themselves were both contained in the same water jacket at a known temperature.   The lower ends of the tubes were connected by a narrow flexible iron tube.   The hot limb was maintained in a bath of heated oil, and the cold limb in a water jacket at temperature t_0 C., which we will suppose to be $0°$ C. ; the only part of the apparatus about which there could be any temperature uncertainty was the lower cross-tube.   Referring to Fig. 47, h_1 and h_2 are the heights of the mercury in the adjacent upper tubes on the hot and cold sides respectively, at temperatures t_1 (density of mercury ρ_1) ; H is the length main-

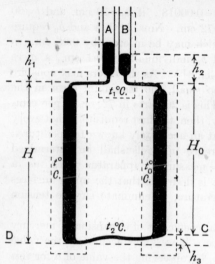

tained at temperature t (density ρ) ; H_0 the length in the cold bath at temperature t_0 (density ρ_0) ; and h_3 the small vertical difference in levels between C and D, at the surrounding temperature t_2 (density ρ_2). Then, if α be the real coefficient of expansion, equating pressures at the level D, in gm. wt. per sq. cm.,

$$h_1\rho_1 + H\rho = H_0\rho_0 + h_2\rho_1 + h_3\rho_2.$$

Substituting $\rho_1 = \dfrac{\rho_0}{1 + \alpha t_1}$, etc.,

$$\frac{h_1\rho_0}{1 + \alpha t_1} + \frac{H\rho_0}{1 + \alpha t}$$

FIG. 47.—Regnault's apparatus for real coefficient of expansion of mercury.

$$= H_0\rho_0 + \frac{h_2\rho_0}{1 + \alpha t_1} + \frac{h_3\rho_0}{1 + \alpha t_2}.$$

$$\therefore \frac{h_1 - h_2}{1 + \alpha t_1} + \frac{H}{1 + \alpha t} = H_0 + \frac{h_3}{1 + \alpha t_2},$$

whence α is calculated. The difference $h_1 - h_2$ is measured directly, and the only term involving the " uncertain " temperature t_2 involves the very small difference in levels h_3 and is thus small.

Expansion of water. Water at 0° C. when heated contracts as the temperature rises, the volume of a given mass being least at about 4° C. (the *density* then being *greatest*), above which point rise in temperature causes expansion. The exact temperature of maximum density, at a pressure of one atmosphere, is given as 3·98° C. An accurate knowledge of this temperature is important, since the litre is defined as *the volume occupied by one kilogram of pure, air-free water at the temperature of maximum density and 760 mm. pressure.* The litre (found experimentally to be 1000·028 c.c.) is the generally accepted practical unit of volume.

Hope's experiment (Fig. 48) is one of the classic demonstrations ; it is simple, and shows the existence of the maximum density temperature in a striking manner. A tall glass vessel full of water has a freezing bath of ice and salt halfway up, while sensitive thermometers A and B are fitted at the top and bottom. The readings of the two thermometers are noted at air temperature before the freezing mixture is applied. At first, the water in the neighbourhood of the freezing mixture is cooled, becomes denser than the water below, sinks to the bottom, and so the temperature read by the lower thermometer falls until it reaches about 4° C., the reading

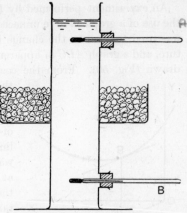

Fig. 48.—Hope's experiment.

of the upper thermometer meanwhile being little affected. The lower thermometer then remains at 4° C., while the upper one falls, at first gradually, then rapidly, to 0° C. If the readings of the two thermometers are taken at regular intervals, and a temperature-time graph plotted for each (Fig. 49), the point at which the two curves intersect gives the maximum-density temperature.

There are really three stages to the experiment; at first, convection takes the cooled liquid down to the bottom and continues until all the water below the freezing belt is at 4° C.; then the water above the belt cools by conduction to 4° C.; after this, the cooler water is the less dense, and so the upper part of the vessel is brought rapidly by convection to the freezing point.

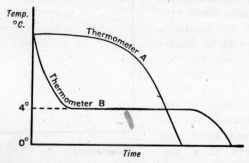

Fig. 49.—Thermometer readings in Hope's experiment.

An experiment performed by Despretz is an excellent example of the use of a graph to save unnecessary computation. A dilatometer was used to observe the change in apparent volume with temperature, and a graph ABC of apparent volume against temperature was drawn (Fig. 50). From the coefficient of expansion of the glass, the change in volume of the vessel was calculated, and plotted as the line OD. Now, the vertical height of any point of the curve above the line OD gives the true volume of the water; this vertical height is least at the point B where the tangent to the curve is parallel to OD; so this tangent is drawn, and the temperature corresponding to this point on the curve is the temperature of minimum volume and hence maximum density (shown where BD cuts OX).

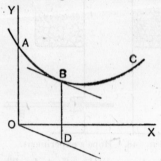

FIG. 50.—Temperature of maximum density from dilatometer readings.

Joule and Playfair found the temperature of maximum density accurately in the following way. If a graph of density against temperature is drawn in the neighbourhood of the maximum, the rate at which the slope changes is practically constant, so the curvature is nearly constant; hence, over a very small region in the neighbourhood of the maximum, the curve can be thought of as an arc of a circle, with the important consequence that *the curve is symmetrical about the maximum point for this small range*, as drawn in Fig. 51. Hence, if two temperatures t_1 and t_2 are found, one slightly below and the other slightly above the temperature of maximum density, at which the density is the same, then the temperature of maximum density is (to a high degree of approximation if the difference between the two temperatures is small) midway between these temperatures.

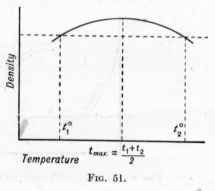

$$t_{max.} = \frac{t_1 + t_2}{2}$$

Temperature

FIG. 51.

Two long columns of water, a, a, were connected by a horizontal tube b at the bottom
and a horizontal cross-channel c at the top
as is indicated in Fig. 52. A small glass
float was placed in the trough. One column
was slightly below 4° C., the other was warmed
slightly above 4° C., and the temperatures of
the two columns at which the float was very
nearly stationary (showing no convection
currents, and hence equal density) were
observed. The difference in temperature
between the two columns was of the order
0·8° C. The temperature of maximum density was determined as 3·95° C.; this is
slightly below the present accepted temperature, 3·98° C.

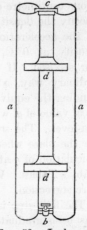

FIG. 52.—Joule and
Playfair's experiment.

Fig. 53 shows the way in which the density
of water varies with the temperature between 0° C. and 10° C.

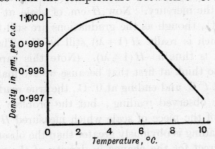

FIG. 53.—Variation of density of water with temperature.

The barometer correction. Several units are used for expressing
pressure measurements; dynes per square centimetre and bars
(1 bar = 10^6 dynes per square centimetre) are the absolute units,
but the most usual units are centimetres or millimetres of mercury,
" a pressure of 200 mm. mercury " (or sometimes just " a pressure
of 200 mm.") denoting that the pressure described will just support
a vertical column of mercury 200 mm. high. Now, the vertical
height is only one of the three factors on which the absolute pressure
of a liquid column depends, the others being the density of the
liquid and the value of the acceleration of gravity. If the unit

" one centimetre of mercury " is to mean anything precise, we must specify the density (or temperature) of the mercury, and the value of the acceleration of gravity ; and the standard figures are the density at 0° C. (13·5951 gm./c.c.), and the value $g = 980·665$ cm./sec./sec. If the height of the barometer is measured in the ordinary way, a correction must be made for the temperature (finding the equivalent height of mercury at 0° C.) and also for the local value of g, which depends on the latitude and the height above sea-level. The second correction is usually done once and for all for the place where the barometer is to be used ; formulae for the calculation of g at any latitude and altitude are given in Kaye and Laby's Tables. We shall concern ourselves only with the temperature correction.

The first step is to correct for the expansion of the scale, which has been graduated at one temperature, and is only accurate at that temperature. Suppose the scale is correct at 0° C. Let H be the observed height as read from the scale at $t°$ C., λ the coefficient of linear expansion of the material of the scale, and h the true height of the mercury. Now H cm. of scale at 0° C. expand to h cm. at $t°$ C., though as the graduations are still there we read this height which is really $H(1 + \lambda t)$ still as H. The true height of the column is thus $h = H(1 + \lambda t)$. (Note this carefully : there is a tendency to think at first that because we are making a correction starting at $t°$ C. and ending at 0° C., the true reading should be lower than the observed reading ; but the problem is to find the *length at $t°$ C.* of the piece of scale which measured H cm. *at 0° C.*, and the true reading is obviously greater than the observed reading.)

Next, to correct for the change in density of the mercury. Let h_0 be the height of the column of mercury at 0° C. which balances the height h of mercury at $t°$ C. Let ρ_0 and ρ be the densities at 0° C. and $t°$ C., and α the real coefficient of expansion of mercury.

Then $$h_0 \rho_0 = h\rho, \quad \therefore \quad h_0 = h\frac{\rho}{\rho_0}.$$

But $$\frac{\rho}{\rho_0} = \frac{1}{1 + \alpha t}, \quad \therefore \quad h_0 = \frac{h}{1 + \alpha t}.$$

Substituting for h, we get $h_0 = H\frac{1 + \lambda t}{1 + \alpha t}$,

$$h_0 = H(1 + \lambda t)(1 + \alpha t)^{-1} ;$$

or $h_0 = H(1 + \lambda t)(1 - \alpha t)$, approximately, neglecting $\alpha^2 t^2$ and higher powers of αt.

$$\therefore \; h_0 = H\{1 - (\alpha - \lambda)t\},$$

again approximating by neglecting $\alpha \lambda t^2$.

This gives the height of the column of mercury at 0° C. which exerts the same pressure as the column measured as H at $t°$ C., so h_0 is the required " corrected height ".

Note that α is the *real* coefficient of *cubical* expansion of the mercury, and λ is the coefficient of *linear* expansion of the material of the scale.

Applications of the expansion of liquids. The decrease in density with temperature rise is responsible for the transference of heat by convection, and such applications as central heating systems are well known. The liquid-in-glass thermometer has been described earlier. The liquid thermostat is really simply a modified thermometer. Fig. 54 shows a thermostat designed to regulate the supply of gas to the burner heating the bath in which the spiral bulb stands ; the spiral contains toluene, the expansion of which pushes up mercury in the vertical tube, shutting off the gas supply when the temperature is too high. This occurs at a temperature determined by the amount of liquid in the bulb and tube originally. The tap at the right is a by-pass to prevent complete extinction of the flame. A similar arrangement is used to make and break the current in electrically heated baths.

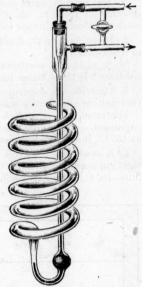

The freezing of ponds from the surface downwards depends on two facts. First, the water is densest at about 4° C. ; secondly, heat is abstracted from the top only. If we imagine the air above the pond to be at, say −10° C., convection will be maintained normally until the whole of the water in the pond is at 4° C. ; next, below this temperature, the

FIG. 54.—Liquid thermostat.
By courtesy of
Messrs. Griffin & Tatlock, Ltd.

coolest liquid stays at the top, and a thin layer of ice forms. The eventual thickness of the coating of ice is determined by the rate at which heat is lost through the coating of ice by conduction and the length of time for which this operates (see p. 344). It is often stated that " the rest of the water in the pond is at 4° C." ; this is, of course, true at the start of the freezing, but it ignores the fact that water, though a bad conductor, *does* transfer heat by conduction. The whole of the pond must eventually reach 0° C. by conduction, if the initial state of affairs persists long enough. Anyone who really believes that ice can only form at the top of a mass of water has only to leave a bucket of water out of doors on any frosty night ; he will find the ice coating on the top *and sides* of the vessel!

QUESTIONS ON CHAPTER III

1. Describe briefly a method of measuring accurately the coefficient of expansion of a solid (in the form of a rod).

A steel tape-measure is correct at 12° C. If it is used to measure a distance of 1,000 ft. when the temperature is 2° C., what error will be made? (Coeff. of linear expansion = 0·000012 per °C.)   (O. & C.)

2. Describe a method of measuring the coefficient of linear expansion of a substance.

Show that the coefficient of cubical expansion of a homogeneous substance is three times its coefficient of linear expansion.   (O. & C.)

3. Describe an accurate method for determining the coefficient of thermal expansion of a solid in the form of a rod.

The pendulum of a clock is made of brass, whose coefficient of linear expansion is $1·9 \times 10^{-5}$ per degree C. If the clock keeps correct time at 15° C., how many seconds per day will it lose at 20° C.?   (O. & C.)

4. A steel wire 8 metres long and 4 mm. in diameter is fixed to two rigid supports. Calculate the increase in tension when the temperature falls 10° C. (Linear coefficient of expansion of steel 12×10^{-6} per

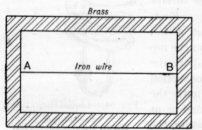

degree centigrade. Young's Modulus for steel 2×10^{12} dynes per sq. cm.)   (O. & C.)

5. Define Young's Modulus for the material of a wire.

The diagram shows an iron wire AB stretched inside a rigid brass framework and rigidly attached to it at both ends, A and B. The length of AB at 0° C. is 300 cm. and the diameter of the wire is 0·6 mm. What extra tension will be set up in the stretched wire when the temperature of the system is raised to 40° C.?

(Take the coefficient of linear expansion of iron as 0·000012 per deg. C. ; the coefficient of linear expansion of brass as 0·000018 per deg. C. ; Young's Modulus for iron as $2·1 \times 10^{12}$ dynes per sq. cm.)

(L.)

6. What is meant by the statement that the coefficient of linear expansion of iron is 0·000012 per degree C.? How would you show experimentally that for brass this quantity is about 0·000018 per degree C.?

If a strip of iron and a strip of brass are welded together to form a straight bi-metal strip at room temperature, what would happen if the strip were (a) raised to a high temperature, (b) lowered to a temperature below 0° C.?

Describe one application of the bi-metal strip in a device in common use. (L.)

7. Describe how you would determine accurately the absolute coefficient of thermal expansion of mercury. Why is a knowledge of this quantity important?

Benzene has a density of 0·90 gm./c.c. at 0° C. and a coefficient of cubical expansion of 0·0012/°C. Consequently wooden balls (density 0·88 gm./c.c.) float in it at 0° C. If the wood has a coefficient of expansion of 4×10^{-6}/°C. along the grain and 4×10^{-5}/°C. across the grain, calculate at what temperature the balls will just sink. (B.)

8. Describe and explain a method of determining directly the coefficient of real expansion of mercury.

A mercury thermometer is to be made with glass tubing of internal bore 0·5 mm. diameter and the distance between the fixed points is to be 20 cm. Estimate the internal volume of the bulb and stem below the lower fixed point. The coefficient of expansion of mercury is 0·000180 and the coefficient of linear expansion of glass is 0·000009, both in centigrade units. (J.M.B.)

9. Describe in detail one method of determining the mean coefficient of absolute expansion of mercury between 0° and 100° C. Give the theory of the method. (C.)

10. Describe, in detail, a balancing column method of determining the mean coefficient of absolute expansion of a liquid, giving the theory of your method and pointing out the experimental difficulties.

If the value of the coefficient for mercury is 0·00018 per degree C., obtain a value for the difference of level of the hot and cold columns in the apparatus you describe, making any reasonable assumptions for the dimensions of your apparatus. (O.)

11. Distinguish between the *real* and the *apparent* coefficient of thermal expansion of a liquid.

Describe the method by which you could determine the real coefficient of expansion of turpentine.

On a centigrade thermometer the distance between the readings 0° C. and 100° C. is 30 cm., and the area of cross-section of the narrow tube containing the mercury is 0·0015 sq. cm. Find the total volume of mercury in the thermometer at 0° C. Coefficient of *linear* expansion of glass is 0·000009, and the real coefficient of *cubical* expansion of mercury is 0·00018. (Scot. Leav. Cert.)

12. Distinguish between the coefficients of real and of apparent expansion of a liquid.

Deduce an expression relating the density of a liquid, at different temperatures, with a coefficient of expansion.

A glass bottle, volume 50 c.c. at 0° C., is filled with paraffin at 15° C. What is the mass of the paraffin? The density of paraffin at 0° C. is 0·82 gm. per c.c., the coefficient of real expansion of paraffin for the range 0° to 15° C. is 0·0009 and the coefficient of linear expansion of glass is 0·000009, both per deg. C. (J.M.B.)

13. Describe a direct method of measuring the absolute coefficient of expansion of a liquid.

Show that the absolute coefficient of expansion of a liquid is very nearly equal to the sum of the apparent coefficient of expansion of the liquid and the coefficient of cubical expansion of the material of the containing vessel. (O. & C.)

14. A sinker of weight W_0 has an apparent weight W_1 when weighed in a liquid at a temperature t_1 and W_2 when weighed in the same liquid at a temperature t_2. The coefficient of cubical expansion of the material of the sinker is β. What is that of the liquid? (O. & C.)

15. Describe, giving the theory, a method of determining the coefficient of real expansion of a liquid, if a solid which has a known coefficient of expansion and will sink in the liquid is provided.

A loaded glass bulb weighs 156·25 gm. in air, 57·50 gm. when immersed in a liquid at 15° C., and 58·57 gm. when immersed at 52° C. Calculate the mean coefficient of real expansion of the liquid between 15° and 52° C. (Coefficient of linear expansion of glass = 0·000009 per deg. C.) (C.W.B.)

16. Describe a method for determining directly the absolute coefficient of expansion of a liquid.

A compensated pendulum consists of an iron rod, of negligible mass, to which, at a distance of one metre from the knife edge, is fastened a hollow iron cylinder of length 16 cm., internal diameter 5 cm., and mass 800 grams. This cylinder contains 3,200 grams of mercury. Find the change in distance of the centre of mass of the pendulum from the knife edge for a 1° C. rise in temperature. (Coefficient of linear expansion of iron = 10^{-5} per degree centigrade, coefficient of volume expansion of mercury = 2×10^{-4} per degree centigrade, and the density of mercury = 13·6 grams per c.c.) (O. & C.)

17. A thread of liquid, whose coefficient of real expansion is α per deg. C., occupies a length of l_0 cm. in a capillary tube when the temperature is 0° C. What is the true length of the thread at $t°$ C. (a) if the expansion of the tube is negligible, (b) if the coefficient of linear expansion of the material of the tube is λ per deg. C.?

What, in case (b), is the apparent length of the thread at $t°$ C. if it is read from a scale etched on the tube and correct at 0° C.?

(J.M.B., *part question*.)

18. Describe a method of measuring the coefficient of apparent expansion of a liquid.

A glass bulb contains air and mercury. What fraction of the bulb must be occupied by mercury if the volume of the air in the bulb is to remain constant when the temperature changes? The coefficient of linear expansion of glass may be taken as $7\cdot5 \times 10^{-6}$ per °C.; the coefficient of expansion of mercury as $1\cdot8 \times 10^{-4}$ per °C.   (O. & C.)

19. Define the terms " apparent " and " absolute " coefficients of expansion of a liquid, and show how the former is found by means of a weight thermometer.

A litre flask, which is correctly calibrated at 4° C., is filled to the mark with water at 80° C. What is the weight of water in the flask? (Coefficient of linear expansion of the glass of the flask, $8\cdot5 \times 10^{-6}$; mean coefficient of cubical expansion of water $5\cdot0 \times 10^{-4}$).   (O. & C.)

20. Explain what is meant by saying that the coefficient of linear expansion of brass is $0\cdot000019$ per deg. C.

How would you determine this coefficient over the range 0°–100° C.?

The barometric height, as read at 12° C. by a brass scale correct at 0° C. is $76\cdot52$ cm. What is the actual height of the mercury column at 12° C.?   (J.M.B.)

21. If l is the coefficient of linear expansion of a solid, explain carefully why $3l$ may be used as the coefficient of cubical expansion.

The height of a mercury barometer read with a steel scale is 754 millimetres at 20° C. What will it read at 0° C.?

(Coefficient of linear expansion of steel $0\cdot000012$ per °C. Coefficient of cubical expansion of mercury $0\cdot000182$ per °C.)   (O. & C.)

22. Describe an accurate form of barometer.

When the height of such a barometer has been read, what further steps have to be taken in order to obtain an accurate value of the pressure in absolute units?

Evaluate the correction for the expansion of the mercury and of the brass scale for an observed reading of $760\cdot0$ mm. at 20° C. The coefficient of expansion of mercury is $0\cdot000181$ and the coefficient of linear expansion of brass is $0\cdot000019$.   (O.)

23. How can you show that the density of water does not fall steadily as the temperature is raised from 0° C. to 100° C.? What does your experiment indicate about the expansion of water?

What importance has this result in nature?   (C.)

CHAPTER IV

THE EXPANSION OF GASES AND THE GAS LAWS

Two points should be clearly understood before proceeding to consider the behaviour of gases. The first is, that in every case a *fixed mass* of gaseous substance is dealt with; if this point is realised now, later work on saturated and unsaturated vapours (when the mass of gaseous substance may or may not be fixed) may cause less difficulty. We shall not distinguish here between the terms " gas " and " vapour ", deferring this until p. 162. The second point is, that in all ordinary experiments we are working with gases at pressures of the order of one atmosphere and at temperatures between 0° C. and 100° C. ; and we must be prepared to find that experiments performed over wider ranges of pressure and temperature require that the conclusions based upon such limited observations be very considerably revised.

Boyle's Law. The volume of a fixed mass of gas maintained at a constant temperature depends on the pressure to which it is subjected. Boyle, in 1660, showed by means of experiments similar to that described below, that for a fixed mass of gas at constant temperature the product pressure × volume is constant. This is known as Boyle's Law. It is not strictly true for any gas except at extremely low pressures, when all gases obey it ; but all the common gases follow it closely enough under ordinary conditions for the law to be applied in elementary calculations. It is thus of much greater importance than an extremely accurate result applicable to only a few substances, for it is a law *nearly* followed by *all gases*, and thus can be regarded as stating an ideal relationship to which the behaviour of actual gases approaches. For many purposes it is convenient to picture an imaginary substance which does obey Boyle's Law under all conditions. Such a substance (which is supposed to fulfil at least one other ideal condition as well, p. 250) is called an **ideal gas**, or a **perfect gas**.

In symbols, if p stand for the pressure, and v for the volume occupied by the fixed mass of gas at that pressure,

$$p \times v = k,$$

where k is a constant for that sample of gas at the temperature concerned. The actual value of k must be proportional to the mass of gas selected, and depends on the temperature and the molecular weight of the gas in ways to be discussed later.

Verification of Boyle's Law. The usual experiment to test Boyle's Law uses the apparatus shown in Fig. 55. A fixed mass of *dry* air is trapped by mercury in a graduated tube T, which communicates with a reservoir R through a length of rubber pressure tubing ; R is held on a sliding stand which allows a vertical travel of about a metre. The vertical height of the level B above the level A gives the " head " of mercury h, which is the excess of the gas pressure on A above the atmospheric pressure H on B. The total pressure of the gas is thus $(H+h)$ cm. of mercury. If B is below A, h is negative ; or, the total pressure is then obtained by subtracting the numerical value of h from H.

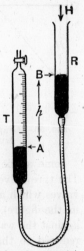

Starting with R as low as possible, and raising it by steps of, say, 10 cm. at a time, readings of the head h and the volume of enclosed gas v are taken, the results being tabulated as below. Compressing a gas causes an appreciable rise in temperature, so

FIG. 55.—Boyle's Law apparatus.

it is necessary to allow a little time to elapse between adjusting R and taking the readings.

Readings :

Barometric pressure H		... cm. mercury.			
Reading A	Reading B	Head h $=(B-A)$	Pressure $p=(H+h)$	Volume v	Product pv

The figures in the last column should be approximately constant.

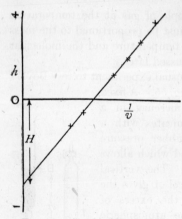

FIG. 56.—Graph of head against 1/volume.

The experiment can be performed without reading the barometer. For, if $pv = k$, as $p = H + h$,

$$(H + h)v = k.$$

$$\therefore h = k\frac{1}{v} - H.$$

Thus the relation between the head h and $1/v$ is linear, and if the law is true the graph of h against $1/v$ should be a straight line. When $1/v = 0$, $h = -H$, so the intercept on the axis of h represents the height of the barometer. The graph is as shown in Fig. 56.

Some applications of Boyle's Law. (a) **Bicycle pump** (Fig. 57). The tyre valve A and the cup washer B on the piston both act as valves which allow air to pass only into the tyre (from right to left in the figure). On the forward stroke of the piston, B presses against the wall of the barrel, and the volume of air in the pump is reduced so that the pressure in the barrel increases. When the pressure in the barrel sufficiently exceeds that in the tyre, air is forced through A, and most of the original barrel-full of air enters the tyre.

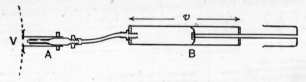

FIG. 57.—Bicycle pump.

Let the volume of the tyre (supposed constant) be V, and the volume of the pump barrel be v, so that each stroke of the pump introduces into the tyre a mass of air which occupies v at atmospheric pressure. Suppose that the initial pressure in the tyre is one atmosphere, and let the final pressure after n strokes be p_n. Then, at the end of the n strokes, a fixed mass of air which occupied

$V + nv$ units of volume at 1 atmosphere pressure occupies V units of volume at pressure p_n atmospheres. So, using Boyle's Law,

$$p_n \times V = 1 \times (V + nv),$$

$$\therefore \quad p_n = 1 + \frac{nv}{V} \text{ atmospheres.}$$

The increase in pressure is thus directly proportional to the number of strokes.

As the pressure in the tyre increases, so does the pressure in the pump barrel required to open the valve A, which thus opens at a later stage in each successive stroke. A cycle pump is only required to produce pressures of (at most) about 2 atmospheres, but if this type of pump is used for other purposes there is a limit to the pressure obtainable, quite apart from that set by the strength of the barrel. Suppose that the space beyond the piston when this is thrust fully forward is $1/20$ of the whole volume of the barrel, the minimum volume to which a pumpful of air can be reduced is $1/20$ of its original volume, and the maximum pressure attainable will be 20 atmospheres.

(b) **Exhaust pumps.** The valves of the simple piston exhaust pump are arranged to allow air to pass only outwards from the vessel to be evacuated (that is, upwards in Fig. 58).

Let the volumes of vessel and pump be V and v respectively, and let the initial pressure in the vessel be p_0 units. Starting with the piston at the bottom of its stroke, on the first upstroke the volume of the space in the pump increases, the pressure decreases, and the valve B is opened by the excess pressure of the air in the vessel over the now diminished pressure in the barrel. At the top of the stroke, V units of volume at pressure p_0 have become $V + v$ units at a lower pressure p_1, whence, applying Boyle's Law to this fixed mass of air,

$$p_1(V + v) = p_0 V,$$

$$\therefore \quad p_1 = p_0 \frac{V}{V + v} \text{ units of pressure.}$$

On the downstroke of the piston, B closes at once since the pressure in the barrel immediately increases, while A opens as soon as the

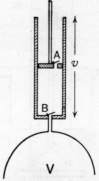

Fig. 58.—Principle of exhaust pump.

pressure in the pump barrel exceeds that of the atmosphere, after which the barrel-full of air escapes to the outside. On the second cycle of operations, the process is repeated, and the pressure p_2 after two strokes is given by

$$p_2 = p_1 \frac{V}{V+v} = p_0 \left(\frac{V}{V+v}\right)\left(\frac{V}{V+v}\right).$$

$$\therefore \ p_2 = p_0 \left(\frac{V}{V+v}\right)^2 \text{ units of pressure.}$$

The calculation can be carried on for each successive stroke, each time applying Boyle's Law to a different fixed mass of air—the mass in the vessel at the beginning of the stroke. After three strokes the pressure p_3 is $p_3 = p_0 \left(\dfrac{V}{V+v}\right)^3$, and after n strokes the pressure p_n is $p_n = p_0 \left(\dfrac{V}{V+v}\right)^n$ units of pressure.

The pressure thus decreases by " compound interest ", and even

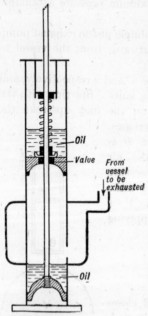

with a perfect pump operating for an indefinitely long time it would be impossible to reduce the pressure in the vessel to zero. Apart from obvious mechanical difficulties, such as leakage past the valves, the chief factor limiting the vacuum attainable is that the valve A can only be opened by superior pressure from below. If the " dead space " above B is, say, one thousandth of the total volume of the pump, and the pressure has been brought down to one thousandth of an atmosphere, when the piston next moves down the barrel-full of air at 1/1000 atmosphere pressure will be compressed to 1/1000 its volume, and will just be at one atmosphere pressure, but this will not give the excess required to open the valve. Fig. 59 shows a modern type of piston pump in which this difficulty is overcome. There is no " dead space " above the piston, as this

Fig. 59.—Modern piston exhaust pump.

is covered with a layer of oil which sweeps out the last traces of air at the top of each stroke. Direct communication by a side tube with the vessel to be evacuated obviates the need for the lower valve B of the simple pump, and it is clear that the air in the vessel expands into the vacuum produced in the cylinder by the *downward*

motion of the piston, instead of having to force open any obstruction. In the figure the piston is shown about to start its upward stroke.

Fig. 60 shows the scheme of one form of modern rotary pump, in which an eccentrically mounted cylinder rotates at high speed inside an outer case fitted with inlet tube and outlet

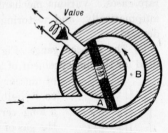

FIG. 60.—Rotary pump.

valve. A vane fitted to the cylinder, and arranged so that it always presses against the wall of the casing, draws in air at A and then sweeps it round to the outlet valve. The theory of the action is the same as that of the piston pump, and it can be seen that for each half revolution the volume v swept out is the volume of the space between the cylinder and the case, while each rotation counts as two "strokes".

The **Toepler** (or **Antropoff**) **pump**, while employing Boyle's Law in just the same way as the simple piston pump, overcomes the valve opening difficulty by using a mercury surface as a piston. Communication between the pump chamber v and the vessel to be exhausted is broken at B by raising the mercury reservoir R (Fig. 61). The mercury is then raised until the air in v has been swept down a long capillary tube A. When R is lowered, a Torricellian vacuum is formed in v, as A is longer than 76 cm., and when the mercury level falls past the junction B, v again communicates with the vessel V. Although cumbersome,

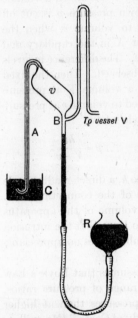

FIG. 61.—Toepler pump.

fatiguing to operate, and requiring large quantities of mercury, this pump is widely used where it is required to evacuate small vessels and to collect the gas pumped off (which can be done by placing the collecting vessel over the end of A). It was used, for example, in the classic work of Ramsay and Travers on the separation of the rare gases. Various mechanical means of raising and lowering R automatically, and restoring mercury from C to R, have been devised.

(c) **The McLeod gauge** (Fig. 62). This pressure gauge is widely used for the measurement of low pressures down to about 1/100 mm.

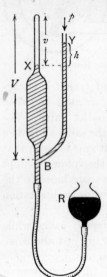

of mercury. A narrow capillary tube is attached to a bulb which communicates at B, through a long vertical tube, with the vessel containing the gas of which the pressure p is to be measured. The volume of the bulb and capillary together, V, and the volume v of the capillary down to a fixed mark X, are known.

By raising the mercury reservoir R, a volume V of gas at the unknown pressure p is cut off at B and compressed to volume v, when the mercury levels stand at X in the capillary and Y in the connecting tube. The difference in levels h between X and Y is observed. Then the fixed mass of gas cut off as a volume V at pressure p cm. has been compressed to volume v at pressure $p + h$ cm. So, using Boyle's Law,

$$pV = (p+h)v, \quad \therefore \quad p = \frac{hv}{V-v}.$$

Fig. 62.
McLeod gauge.

As p is proportional to h, a direct-reading scale is attached to the side of the connecting tube. It is assumed in this calculation that the volume of the apparatus containing the gas under measurement is so large that the intrusion of the mercury column up the connecting tube causes no appreciable increase of the pressure within it.

The above theory of the McLeod gauge assumes that Boyle's Law is accurately obeyed over a considerable range of pressure ratios, a condition more nearly fulfilled at low pressures than at higher ones. Travers, in " The Experimental Study of Gases " (Macmillan,

1901) records the conclusions of Ramsay that the McLeod gauge is untrustworthy as a means of measuring low pressures in the case of air and carbon dioxide, and that no two of the gauges tested ever gave comparable results with these gases. On the other hand, with pure hydrogen it was found that consistent readings were obtained down to about 0·0001 mm. pressure, and it was considered that the gauge could be relied on for measurements on hydrogen and the inert gases.

EXPANSION OF A GAS AT CONSTANT PRESSURE

Charles' Law states that for a fixed mass of gas heated at constant pressure, the volume increases by a constant fraction of the volume at 0° C. for each centigrade degree rise in temperature.

The volume coefficient α for any gas is defined as the increase in volume of *unit volume at* 0° C. for each centigrade degree rise in temperature, when a fixed mass of that gas is heated at constant pressure.

Let V_0 denote the volume occupied by the chosen mass at 0° C., and let V be the volume at $t°$ C. (Note here that V_0 stands specifically for *the volume at* 0° C., and not just the original volume at any selected initial temperature; and that t stands for the actual temperature $t°$ C., and not for any selected temperature rise.)

Then
$$\alpha = \frac{V - V_0}{V_0 t},$$

and
$$V = V_0(1 + \alpha t).$$

In the calculus notation, since $(V - V_0)/t$ is the increase in volume for 1° rise, or the rate of increase of volume with temperature, it can be written $\frac{dV}{dt}$, whence $\alpha = \frac{1}{V_0}\frac{dV}{dt}$.

The value of α is approximately equal to $\frac{1}{273}$ for most gases, and this is the figure employed in all elementary calculations.

The apparatus of Fig. 63, a modification of that originally used by Regnault, can be used to study the variation of volume with temperature for a fixed mass of air enclosed at constant pressure.

Dry air is enclosed in the bulb B of known volume. The lower part of B is a graduated tube to which is connected a branch C open to the atmosphere. When the mercury levels X and Y, which may be adjusted by raising and lowering the reservoir R, are the same,

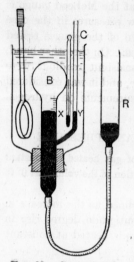

FIG. 63.—Constant-pressure apparatus.

the pressure of the gas in B is the same as that of the atmosphere. Both B and C are surrounded by a water bath containing an electric immersion heater which also serves as a stirrer. The temperature of the bath is observed by a mercury thermometer. The tube C, which at a casual glance seems superfluous, is needed because equality of height of two levels such as at X and Y only denotes equal pressure if the two columns are at the same temperature.

After the first levelling of X and Y, and the recording of the volume of the enclosed air at the cold temperature, the experiment proceeds as follows. Switch on the heater until a temperature rise of, say, 20 centigrade degrees is obtained. Switch off, stir thoroughly, level X and Y, leave for a short time, adjust the levels again if necessary, and read the volume of the air and the temperature of the bath. Repeat this procedure several times, obtaining five or six sets of readings between room temperature and 100° C.

The best way of treating the readings is to plot a graph (Fig. 64) of volume against temperature. It is found that the points all lie on a straight line, showing that equal changes in temperature lead

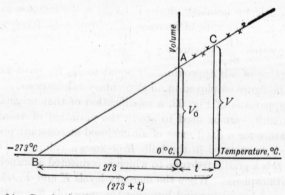

FIG. 64.—Graph of volume against temperature at constant pressure.

to equal changes in volume at constant pressure, as Charles' Law states.

By extrapolating (that is, extending the line beyond the plotted points), the volume V_0 at 0° C. is found. Extrapolating further, by producing the line back until it meets the temperature axis, the point at which this axis is cut represents a temperature of about $-273°$ C. Now, producing the line back in this way gives a complete graph which shows, not what actually does happen, but *what would happen if the behaviour between the extreme observed temperatures were continued at all temperatures.* It is known that air liquefies under ordinary pressure at about $-190°$ C., but that does not invalidate the use of the extrapolated graph to discuss the observations actually taken.

The volume coefficient α, which is $\dfrac{1}{V_0}\dfrac{dV}{dt}$ is found at once from the graph ; for

$$\frac{dV}{dt} = \frac{AO}{BO} \quad \text{and} \quad V_0 = AO,$$

so

$$\frac{1}{V_0}\frac{dV}{dt} = \frac{1}{BO} = \frac{1}{273}.$$

The volume V at any temperature $t°$ C. is represented by CD ; and from the similar triangles AOB, CDB,

$$\frac{CD}{BD} = \frac{AO}{BO},$$

so

$$\frac{V}{273 + t} = \frac{V_0}{273},$$

whence the volume of a fixed mass of air at constant pressure is directly proportional to the absolute temperature, obtained (p. 26) by adding 273 to the centigrade temperature. In other symbols, writing T for $273 + t$, and T_0 for 273, the capital letters standing as usual for the temperatures on the scale which starts at absolute zero and calls this $-273°$ C., we have :

$$\frac{V}{T} = \frac{V_0}{T_0}.$$

All gases give similar results, with values of $\dfrac{1}{V_0}\dfrac{dV}{dT}$ fairly close to $\frac{1}{273}$; this was established by Regnault after a series of careful experiments. Hence Charles' Law can be restated as :

For a fixed mass of *any gas* heated at constant pressure, the volume increases by 1/273 of *the volume at* 0° C. for each centigrade degree rise in temperature.

It must be remembered, however, that this generalisation, which is used in all ordinary gas calculations, holds only when the constant pressure is not greatly above one atmosphere, that the *exact* value of the fraction is not precisely 1/273, and that this figure is not *exactly* the same for all gases.

In this experiment, the expansion of the glass bulb, which can be determined and allowed for, is a little less than 1 per cent. of the observed change in volume of the gas. It is important to read the barometer at the beginning of the experiment, and also at intervals during its progress, to be sure that the atmospheric pressure has remained steady.

Determination of the volume coefficient from two sets of readings only. The purpose of the experiment described on p. 130 was to find out whether or not the expansion of air at constant pressure is uniform ; hence several readings were taken. Once we are assured that the expansion is uniform, only two sets of volume and temperature readings are really required in order to find α. As $V = V_0(1 + \alpha t)$ (p. 129), where V_0 is the volume at 0° C., and V the volume at $t°$ C., then if this formula is to be used, one of the observations must be that of the volume V_0 at 0° C. But if the measurements made are the volume V_1 at $t_1°$ C., and the volume V_2 at $t_2°$ C., we have

$$V_1 = V_0(1 + \alpha t_1) \quad \text{and} \quad V_2 = V_0(1 + \alpha t_2),$$

$$\therefore \frac{V_2}{V_1} = \frac{1 + \alpha t_2}{1 + \alpha t_1},$$

whence, cross-multiplying and simplifying,

$$\alpha = \frac{V_2 - V_1}{V_1 t_2 - V_2 t_1}.$$

The " dry flask " experiment to determine the volume coefficient for air. A dry round-bottomed flask of about 300 c.c. capacity, fitted with a rubber bung, outlet tube, and clip, is weighed. It is then held in a large can of boiling water with the outlet clip open, and left in the boiling water for at least 15 minutes, so that the enclosed air shall attain the temperature $t_2°$ C. of the water, which for the purpose of this experiment may usually be taken as 100° C. The clip is then closed, and the flask removed and submerged, mouth downwards, in a large deep trough or bucket of cold water at a temperature $t_1°$ C. which is observed. The flask should be held entirely below the water for some minutes ; it is then raised until the water levels both inside and outside are the same, so that the pressure of the enclosed air is atmospheric, as it was during the heating, and the clip is closed. The flask is dried on the outside and weighed. Finally, the flask is filled completely up to the clip with cold water and weighed again.

Call the weights successively W_1, W_2, and W_3 gm., and suppose that 1 c.c. of water weighs 1 gm. The mass of water filling the flask completely is $(W_3 - W_1)$ gm., and the volume of the fixed mass of air which fills the flask at the high temperature $t_2°$ C. is $(W_3 - W_1)$ c.c. Call this volume V_2. Similarly the volume of the flask not occupied by water at the temperature $t_1°$ C., which is the volume of the same fixed mass of air at $t_1°$ C., is $(W_3 - W_2)$ c.c. Call this V_1. Calculate the values of V_1 and V_2, and find α by substituting in the formula $\alpha = \dfrac{V_2 - V_1}{V_1 t_2 - V_2 t_1}$.

The chief error in the *principle* of this experiment occurs when levelling in the trough before closing the clip, for though the total pressure inside the flask equals that of the atmosphere, this is made up of the pressure due to the enclosed air and the pressure of the water vapour with which the space is saturated. The water vapour pressure may amount to 15 mm. of mercury, or say 20 cm. of water, which is a greater error than could possibly occur if the flask were just clipped and removed at random. This error can be reduced by using colder water in the trough, when the pressure of the saturated water vapour will be lower, and in any case can be corrected for properly, as described on p. 191. If the student is aiming at an *accurate* result, the true temperature of boiling water should be found by reading the barometer and making the appropriate correction, and the expansion of the flask should be calculated and allowed for. There remains some uncertainty about the actual temperature of the air in the flask when the clip is closed after immersion in the trough, since the temperature of the *water* has been recorded, whereas the flask is in the *air* at that instant ; but if the cold water is only a little below air temperature there should be very little error here if the levelling and closing is done quickly.

This experiment, which is an excellent exercise in manipulation, is really not so crude as it appears, since the accuracy of the result depends entirely on the trouble taken by the student. It should be added that the assumption that 1 c.c. of water weighs 1 gm., even if appreciably inaccurate (which it is not) would introduce no error, as volumes calculated on this assumption are factors of both numerator and denominator of the expression for α.

PRESSURE INCREASE AT CONSTANT VOLUME

Consider a fixed mass of gas of volume V_1 at temperature $t_1°$ C. and pressure p_1, and suppose it to be heated to some temperature $t_2°$ C at which the volume is nV_1, the pressure remaining constant at p_1. Next, let the volume be reduced again to V_1 at the high temperature, by increasing the pressure to p_2. If the gas obeys Boyle's Law, $p_2V_1 = p_1 . nV_1$, or $p_2 = np_1$.

Thus the volume can be maintained at V_1 when the temperature is raised by suitably increasing the pressure, and **the law of increase of pressure at constant volume will be the same as the law of increase of volume at constant pressure, if Boyle's Law is obeyed.**

That is, the rise in temperature which causes an increase from V_1 to nV_1 if the pressure is constant at p_1, causes an increase from p_1 to np_1 if the volume is kept constant at V_1. If Boyle's Law is not obeyed perfectly, then the *theoretical* basis of this argument fails. Nevertheless, *experiments* show that when a fixed mass of gas is heated at constant volume, the pressure increases by a constant fraction of the pressure at 0° C. for each degree centigrade rise in temperature, at least to a considerable degree of accuracy.

The **pressure coefficient** β for any gas is the increase in pressure, expressed as a fraction of the pressure at 0° C., for one centigrade degree rise in temperature, when a fixed mass of that gas is heated at constant volume. If p_0 be the pressure at 0° C., and p the pressure at $t°$ C., then

$$\beta = \frac{1}{p_0} . \frac{p - p_0}{t};$$

or, in calculus symbols, $\quad \beta = \frac{1}{p_0} \frac{dp}{dt}.$

Constant volume experiment. The apparatus usually used is Jolly's constant volume air thermometer (Fig. 65). A bulb V of about 100 c.c. capacity is filled with dry air; V is connected by a glass capillary tube T and rubber pressure tubing to a movable reservoir R. A fixed reference mark X is made on the tube A. The mercury in the tube A is always brought to this mark, which limits the constant volume maintained, before taking a reading. The bulb V is heated in a water bath which is well stirred, and temperatures are read with a mercury thermometer.

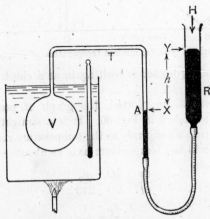

FIG. 65.—Constant volume air thermometer.

The height of the barometer, H, is first read. Then, starting with the water in the heating bath cold, the temperature of the bath is taken and the mercury in A is brought to the fixed mark X. The reading Y of the upper surface of the mercury in R is taken; the difference $(Y - X)$ gives the "head" of mercury h (h is reckoned negative if Y is below X), and the total pressure is then $p = (H + h)$ cm. of mercury. The water bath is then heated through about twenty degrees, heating stopped, and the bath well stirred. The mercury is brought to X and the level watched carefully; a slow downward creep of the mercury indicates that the air in the bulb V is still rising to the temperature of the bath, and re-levelling is necessary when the mercury is steady. The temperature of the bath is then taken, and the level Y observed as before. Heating is then resumed, and further sets of readings

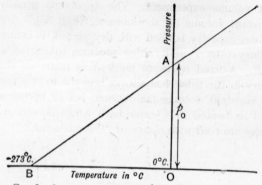

FIG. 66.—Graph of pressure against temperature at constant volume.

are taken. The barometer is read again as a check at the end of the experiment.

When the results are plotted, the graph of pressure against temperature is as shown in Fig. 66. It is a straight line (whence the pressure increases uniformly as the temperature rises), and when extrapolated meets the temperature axis at about $-273°$ C. The slope of the graph,

$$\frac{dp}{dt} = \frac{AO}{BO} = \frac{p_0}{273};$$

so

$$\frac{1}{p_0}\frac{dp}{dt} = \frac{1}{273},$$

and the value of β is $1/273$.

The " dead space " of the capillary tube T causes an error which is difficult to estimate, since the exact temperature of this part of the apparatus is not known. The expansion of the bulb introduces an error in β of the order of 1 per cent.; this can be corrected satisfactorily enough by adding the value of g, the coefficient of cubical expansion of the glass, to the observed value of β. It seems curious to be mixing ordinary coefficients of expansion with the pressure coefficient, but if we suppose the bulb to expand to $(1 + gt)$ of its original volume, and the gas inside then to be brought back to the original volume again by increasing the pressure, Boyle's Law shows that a pressure $(1 + gt)$ times that actually recorded would be needed. Thus, correction for the volume expansion of the glass does give the required correction to the pressure coefficient.

The pressure coefficient can be calculated from two readings, neither of which is made at 0° C., as follows.   Let p_1 be the pressure at t_1° C., p_2 the pressure at t_2° C., and p_0 the pressure at 0° C.

As $\beta = \dfrac{1}{p_0} \dfrac{p - p_0}{t}$, the equation giving the pressure p for any temperature t° C. is $p = p_0(1 + \beta t)$;

$$\therefore \ p_1 = p_0(1 + \beta t_1),$$
$$p_2 = p_0(1 + \beta t_2).$$

So
$$\frac{p_2}{p_1} = \frac{1 + \beta t_2}{1 + \beta t_1},$$

giving
$$\beta = \frac{p_2 - p_1}{p_1 t_2 - p_2 t_1}.$$

Accurate experiments have shown that β is fairly close to $1/273$ for all the permanent gases, and the law of increase with pressure at constant volume can be stated as : **For a fixed mass of any gas heated at constant volume, the pressure increases by 1/273 of the pressure at 0° C., for each centigrade degree rise in temperature.** With the symbols of p. 131, we can write $\dfrac{p}{T} = \dfrac{p_0}{T_0}$.

REAL GASES AND THE IDEAL GAS

Values of α and β for the gases helium, hydrogen, and nitrogen are tabulated below.   These figures are taken from Roberts' "Heat and Thermodynamics", and are results obtained by Heuse and Otto from observations at the ice point and the steam point. (The student who has read Chapter I thoroughly must surely have wondered about the scale of temperature employed in discussing the behaviour of gases ; since, if the constant volume hydrogen scale is used, we are *bound* to obtain results similar to those of the last sections, whereas if we are employing the mercury-in-glass scale the worth of the results may be queried.   The answer that the present author always makes to this comment is, we must suppose that for these exercises and arguments we possess a mercury thermometer which has been graduated so as to record faithfully temperatures on the true thermodynamic scale.)   It can be seen that results taken with the ice point and the steam point as the two temperatures between which the expansions occur must give the mean values of the volume coefficient and the pressure coefficient over this interval *without reference to any particular thermometric scale.*

Initial pressure (cm. of mercury)	Helium		Hydrogen		Nitrogen	
	α	β	α	β	α	β
39·02	0·0036595	0·0036611	0·0036604	0·0036617	0·0036664	0·0036673
63·31	36594	36602	36604	36613	36668	36671
72·71	36587	36611	36593	36620	36699	36709
99·45	36579	36604	36589	36621	36734	36740

The above table shows (a) the value of α is slightly different for different gases, (b) for each individual gas α differs slightly from β, and (c) both α and β depend on the pressure.

Now, at extremely low pressures Boyle's Law is closely obeyed; and if Boyle's Law is obeyed, the values of α and β for the same gas should have exactly the same value, as was stated on p. 134. For, starting with a fixed mass of gas at 0° C., at pressure p_0 and volume V_0, and heating it to $t°$ C. in two ways, first at constant pressure, then cooling it down again and repeating at constant volume,

(a) at constant pressure p_0, volume becomes $V_0(1 + \alpha t)$, product pV becomes $p_0 V_0(1 + \alpha t)$.

(b) at constant volume V_0, pressure becomes $p_0(1 + \beta t)$, product pV becomes $p_0 V_0(1 + \beta t)$.

But if Boyle's Law s obeyed, all values of the product pV at the same temperature must be the same, so $p_0 V_0(1 + \alpha t) = p_0 V_0(1 + \beta t)$, and therefore $\alpha = \beta$.

By plotting a graph of α or β against the pressure, and extrapolating to zero pressure, values of these coefficients at the limiting conditions when Boyle's Law is obeyed are found. These are :

	α	β
Helium -	0·0036607	0·0036609
Hydrogen -	0·0036611	0·0036610
Nitrogen -	0·0036609	0·0036606

Not only are the pressure coefficient and the volume coefficient for each individual gas very closely equal to one another ; but also the values for different gases are all close to the mean value 0·0036608. Hence we can conclude that in the limiting case, at extremely low density and pressure when Boyle's Law is obeyed closely, all gases have the same volume coefficient 0·0036608, and the same pressure coefficient 0·0036608. Real gases, however, behave in this way only at extremely low pressures, and this behaviour is an ideal which is only approached as a limiting case. But we can imagine a gas which would behave in this way at all pressures ; such a substance is the ideal or perfect gas.

Fixing attention now on the product *pressure × volume* instead of merely pressure or volume singly, the value of this product at $t°$ C. can be written as either $p_0 V_0 (1 + \alpha t)$ or $p_0 V_0 (1 + \beta t)$. For the ideal gas $\alpha = \beta = 0·0036608$; this constant can be denoted by the symbol a, when both expressions can be written $p_0 V_0 (1 + at)$.

Hence,
$$pV = p_0 V_0 (1 + at),$$
$$= p_0 V_0 a \left(\frac{1}{a} + t\right),$$

and since $p_0 V_0 a$ is a constant, which we will here call C, for the fixed mass of gas chosen,

$$pV = C\left(\frac{1}{a} + t\right).$$

Absolute zero and absolute temperatures. It is now possible to clear up some ideas about absolute zero and absolute temperatures, and explain the convenience of these in gas calculations.

From the equation $pV = C\left(\frac{1}{a} + t\right)$, the graph of pV against t can be plotted for a perfect gas. The product pV is zero when

$$t = -\frac{1}{a} = -\frac{1}{0·0036608} = -273·2° \text{ C.}$$

At this temperature, therefore, the product pV for a perfect gas would vanish completely. This temperature, denoted by Z on the graph (Fig. 67), is the absolute zero of temperature.

If the origin be transferred back to Z, and temperatures, denoted by the capital letter T, be measured from the absolute zero, the temperature $T°$ on this notation is related to the temperature $t°$ on the centigrade notation by the formula $T = t + 273·2$. Also, as $\left(\frac{1}{a} + t\right) = (273·2 + t) = T$, the equation for the product pV can be rewritten as
$$pV = CT.$$

The addition of 273·2 or any other number to a centigrade

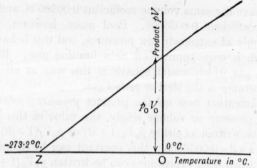

Fig. 67.—Graph of product pV against temperature.

reading is simply a matter of nomenclature or notation ; the term "scale", however, is applied to something much more fundamental than this. What is meant by "the absolute scale of temperature"?

In this argument, the behaviour of an ideal gas between the ice point and the steam point (for example, as found by Heuse and Otto) was used as the starting point ; and the number obtained for the centigrade reading of the absolute zero of temperature is the value of the absolute zero on the ideal gas scale, which is identical with the Kelvin Absolute Thermodynamic Scale, as is proved on p. 281. When this scale is employed for the measurement of all temperatures, whatever the zero of the scale may be named, they are temperatures measured on the absolute thermodynamic scale. The temperature $-273\cdot2°$ C. is the absolute zero on this scale, and temperatures *on this scale* measured from absolute zero are called absolute temperatures, and denoted by the symbol °K. The temperature of the ice point is then $273\cdot2°$ K.

The very searching question "How would you find experimentally the value of the absolute zero of temperature?" is occasionally asked. It is not a straightforward task to obtain a value which is *sound in principle* with simple apparatus. The mercury thermometer must be discarded, and use made of the constant volume air thermometer alone. Using this as on p. 135, values of the pressure at 0° C. and 100° C. are obtained. The two points are plotted on a graph and joined by a straight line ; this then states that equal changes in pressure correspond to equal changes in temperature, so that temperatures on the *constant volume air thermometer scale* are being employed.   Producing the line back to cut the temperature axis, it is found as before to cut the axis somewhere in the neighbourhood of $-273°$ C. ;   the exact point gives the temperature of the absolute zero *on the constant-volume air thermometer scale.* (The reading of the pressure at $100°$ C. should, of course, be corrected for the expansion of the glass bulb.)   Alternatively, the constant pressure apparatus of page 130 could be used, taking readings at the ice point and the steam point, and proceeding as outlined above. This would give the value of the absolute zero *on the scale of the constant-pressure air thermometer.*   It is clear that a mercury thermometer, even if graduated to read perfect gas scale temperatures accurately, must not be used in either of these experiments, for the simple reason that the substance used (air) is not a perfect gas.

The values of the absolute zero obtained with accurate standard constant-volume gas thermometers, using the gases hydrogen, helium, and nitrogen, differ only slightly from the value on the ideal gas scale.   But the differences, though small, are appreciable for accurate work, and are particularly important when a gas thermometer is used for the measurement of very low temperatures.   There are two ways of allowing for the differences.   The first is to determine the values of the " second virial coefficient ", B_v (p. 157), for the gas concerned at $0°$ C. and $100°$ C., and from this calculate the deviation of the gas from ideal gas behaviour. The second is to use the Joule-Kelvin effect (p. 252) to calculate the temperature of the ice point on the absolute thermodynamic scale, which shows for certain *how far the absolute zero of temperature is below* $0°$ C.

Correction of the gas thermometer to the ideal gas scale or absolute thermodynamic scale.   This section involves a certain amount of repetition of what has gone before, but it is essential, in order to be as clear as possible, to collect a number of matters together under one heading here.

If we could obtain an ideal gas and use it in a gas thermometer, its readings would give absolute scale temperatures.   We have, from the observed behaviour of an actual gas used in a thermometer, to make corrections for its departure from the behaviour of an ideal gas.

With an actual gas (say hydrogen) we have the constant-pressure scale (here distinguished by suffix α), which defines $t_\alpha°$ C. as

$$t_\alpha = 100 \frac{V_t - V_0}{V_{100} - V_0},$$

on which

$$V_t = V_0(1 + \alpha t_\alpha) ; \quad ....(1)$$

and also the constant-volume scale (suffix β), which defines $t_\beta°$ C. as

$$t_\beta = 100 \frac{p_t - p_0}{p_{100} - p_0},$$

on which

$$p_t = p_0(1 + \beta t_\beta). \quad ....(2)$$

The values of α and β are different from one another for the same gas, and also have different values for different gases.

For an ideal gas, the equation of p. 139 can be written

$$(pV)_t = (pV)_0(1 + at), \quad ....(3)$$

where t (without any suffix) is the centigrade temperature on the ideal gas scale. The value of the absolute zero is $-1/a$, which is $-273.2°$ C.

Writing A for the product pV for an ideal gas, equation (3) becomes

$$A_t = A_0(1 + at),$$

and the equation defining $t°$ C. on the ideal gas scale is

$$t = 100 \frac{A_t - A_0}{A_{100} - A_0}.$$

Summing up, the three equations defining $t°$ C. on the three gas scales are :

Ideal gas scale.	Constant pressure gas scale, depending on α for the chosen gas.	Constant volume gas scale, depending on β for the chosen gas.
$t = 100 \dfrac{A_t - A_0}{A_{100} - A_0}$	$t_\alpha = 100 \dfrac{V_t - V_0}{V_{100} - V_0}$	$t_\beta = 100 \dfrac{p_t - p_0}{p_{100} - p_0}$

The following method is that developed at Leyden by Kamerlingh Onnes for the correction of the helium gas thermometer.

For an ideal gas, $pV = A$, where A depends only on the temperature. For a real gas, the behaviour is represented by a " virial expansion " of the form

$$pV = A\left(1 + \frac{B_v}{V} + \frac{C_v}{V^2} + \frac{D_v}{V^3} \dots\dots\right),$$

where A is the same constant as in the expression for a perfect gas, and where B_v, C_v, etc., are empirically determined coefficients called " virial coefficients ", which are functions of the temperature only. This is only one of several alternative ways of writing down the expression for pV as a series. This method of expressing the behaviour of a gas in terms of empirical constants, together with certain limitations as to its usefulness in general, is discussed later (p. 169). For helium, the " second virial coefficient " B_v is of the order 0·0005, and C_v and the succeeding coefficients are very small indeed. The values of B_v determined at 0° C. and 100° C. are written B_0 and B_{100}.

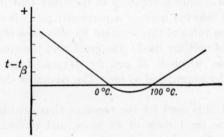

FIG. 68.

Then
$$\beta = \frac{p_{100} - p_0}{100\,p_0} = \frac{(pV)_{100} - (pV)_0}{100(pV)_0},$$

V being constant.

Taking the virial expansion to the first two terms, substituting the values $(pV)_0 = A_0\left(1 + \frac{B_0}{V}\right)$ and $(pV)_{100} = A_{100}\left(1 + \frac{B_{100}}{V}\right)$. and simplifying,

$$\beta = \frac{A_{100} - A_0}{100\,A_0} + \frac{A_{100}}{100\,A_0}\left(\frac{B_{100} - B_0}{V}\right).$$

As $A_{100} = A_0(1 + 100a)$ this simplifies to

$$\beta = a + \frac{1 + 100a}{100\,V}(B_{100} - B_0).$$

Thus, from the observed value of β and the virial coefficients B_0 and B_{100}, a, which would be the value of the pressure coefficient of an ideal gas, is found. A correction graph giving the ideal gas scale temperatures from the constant volume thermometer readings can be drawn. The form of the graph will be roughly as in Fig. 68.

THE IDEAL GAS EQUATION

We shall here assume (as is approximately true) that actual gases behave as ideal gases.

In the equation $pv = CT$, the value of C is

$$p_0 v_0 a, \text{ or } \frac{p_0 v_0}{273 \cdot 2}.$$

Now the pressure p_0 and the temperature $273 \cdot 2°$ K. fix the density of the gas, whence the volume v_0 is proportional to the mass considered for that particular gas. The value of C is proportional to this mass, and is only a constant in the sense that it has a fixed value for each selected mass of a particular gas. It is convenient to work out the value of this constant for unit mass of gas.

Two kinds of unit are used : the gram, and the gram-molecular-weight or mole, which is 32 gm. for oxygen, 4 gm. for helium, 2·016 gm. for hydrogen, and so on. The second is the more usual unit.

The symbol R is used for the constant thus calculated ; R has the same value for 1 mole of all gases, and this value, denoted throughout this book by the letter R without suffix, is called the gas constant.

The value of C for 1 gm. of any given gas is of course different for different gases, and may be denoted by the symbol R_{unit} or R_1, or with a distinguishing suffix referring to the gas concerned.

The ideal gas equation, referring to one mole of any gas (since we are supposing that all gases obey the equation) is

$$pV = RT,$$

the capital V denoting volume from now on when this equation is used.

At first sight, the mole appears a curious unit, and its choice needs some explanation. Avogadro's Hypothesis states that equal volumes of all gases under the same conditions of temperature and pressure contain equal numbers of molecules. Further, it is found experimentally that one mole of any gas under standard temperature and pressure occupies approximately 22·4 litres ; and the number of molecules in one mole of any gas, denoted by the symbol N, has been determined by several independent methods, the value accepted in 1941 being, according to Birge, $6·03 \times 10^{23}$ molecules, to three significant figures. Hence, in dealing with one mole of any gas we have something much more fundamental than a fixed mass of gas, for whatever the chosen gas may be, we have always *the same number of molecules*.

So important is this method of reckoning that nowadays it is usual to express any mass of gas as its molar fraction n. For example, 1 gm. of oxygen is $1/32$ of 1 mole of oxygen, whence n is $1/32$. The ideal gas equation for a molar fraction n is then

$$pV_n = nRT.$$

Alternatively, if m is the mass in grams, and M the molecular weight,

$$n = \frac{m}{M} \quad \text{and} \quad pV_n = \frac{m}{M}RT \quad \text{for this mass.}$$

It is clear that this avoids all the confusion and ambiguity which surrounds the use of the symbol R to denote several different things.

Calculation of R for one mole of any gas (supposed ideal). We know that when

$$p = 76 \text{ cm. of mercury} = 76 \times 13·6 \times 981 \text{ dynes per sq. cm.,}$$

and $T = 273·2° \text{ K.,}$

then $V = 22·4 \text{ litres} = 22400 \text{ c.c. } \textit{for all gases.}$

$$\therefore R = \frac{pV}{T} = \frac{76 \times 13·6 \times 981 \times 22400}{273·2}$$

$$= 8·3 \times 10^7 \text{ units.}$$

The units are usually given as *ergs per mole per centigrade degree*, for reasons which will be evident later.

Calculation of R_{unit} for a given gas. Here, and in all calculations involving actual gases, we shall take $0° \text{ C.}$ to be $273°$ absolute, using the relation $T = t + 273$. There is a good reason for this. It is not that there is any extra hardship in multiplying or dividing by $273·2$ instead of 273, nor yet because it is usual. The point is, that actual gases are not perfect gases ; $273·2$ is $1/a$ for a perfect gas, but 273 is nearer to $1/\alpha$ for air and hydrogen and helium, and it thus appears more accurate to use the latter figure. In this calculation, if we use the figure 273·2, we calculate R_{unit} for an ideal gas of the same molecular weight as hydrogen ; with 273 we calculate a value of R_{unit} which is a little closer to the value for hydrogen itself. There is no inconsistency here with what has been said on p. 144 ; for the perfect gas equation is being used, and at the same time also a figure which corrects in the right direction for the fact that the gases used are not quite perfect gases.

The data supplied are usually corresponding figures of density, temperature, and pressure. For example, given that the density of hydrogen at 0° C. and 76 cm. pressure is 0·00009 gm. per c.c.,

$$p = 76 \times 13·6 \times 981 \text{ dynes per sq. cm.,}$$

$$V = \frac{1}{0·00009} \text{ c.c., } T = 273° \text{ absolute,}$$

and
$$R_{unit} = \frac{pV}{T} = \frac{76 \times 13·6 \times 981}{273 \times 0·00009} = 4·12 \times 10^7 \text{ erg/gm./°C.}$$

If the density (or the volume occupied by a stated mass) at some other temperature and pressure is given, there is no need to reduce to standard temperature and pressure, for always $R_{unit} = pV/T$, where V is the volume in c.c. of 1 gm. at the pressure p dynes per square centimetre and temperature $T°$ absolute stated.

Reduction of gas volumes to standard (or normal) temperature and pressure. A temperature of 0° C. or 273° absolute, and a pressure of 76 cm. of mercury under specified conditions are called standard temperature and pressure (S.T.P.), or normal temperature and pressure (N.T.P.)

Let V be the volume measured at pressure p cm. and temperature $t°$ C., and V_0 the required volume occupied by the same sample of gas at 0° C. and 76 cm. pressure.

First, express the temperatures in degrees absolute :

$$0° \text{ C.} = 273° \text{ absolute, } t° \text{ C.} = (273 + t)° \text{ absolute.}$$

Then as pV/T is constant for the fixed mass of gas,

$$\frac{pV}{t + 273} = \frac{76 \times V_0}{273},$$

or
$$V_0 = V \cdot \frac{p}{76} \cdot \frac{273}{t + 273} \text{ c.c.}$$

Conversion of densities from one set of conditions to another. As density is inversely proportional to volume, and we are considering a fixed mass, say m gm., the density $\rho = m/V$, so $V = m/\rho$; and the equation $pV/T = $ constant, becomes

$$\frac{pm}{\rho T} = \text{constant, so } \frac{p}{\rho T} = \text{constant.}$$

The mass of a given volume of pure gas under given conditions can be found by multiplying the density calculated as above for these conditions by the given volume; or else by reducing the volume to N.T.P., and multiplying by the density at N.T.P.

Calculation of the mass of a given volume of mixed gases. Dalton's Law of Partial Pressures states that the pressure due to a mixture of gaseous substances which do not interact in any way equals the sum of their partial pressures. A gas introduced into a closed container expands so as to fill the whole of the container as if it alone were present. For example, when a closed vessel contains air at a pressure of 40 cm. of mercury, this air entirely fills the vessel; when a quantity of hydrogen, such that if it were the only substance present in the vessel it would exert a pressure of 30 cm. of mercury, is introduced, the total pressure is 70 cm.; if in addition a quantity of carbon dioxide which, if filling the vessel alone would exert a pressure of 10 cm. is added, the total pressure is 80 cm. of mercury. Each gas, in fact, fills the vessel and exerts its own pressure just as if the other gases were absent.

To calculate the mass of any volume of such a mixture, the density of each gas at the given temperature and under its own partial pressure is first calculated; the density of the mixture is the sum of the densities thus calculated; and the total mass is the product *volume × total density*.

THE KINETIC THEORY

A molecule of any substance is defined as the smallest portion of that substance capable of independent existence, and there is abundant evidence that for any given substance the molecules are all alike in their chief properties. It was considered, before the discovery that many of the elements have several isotopes, that all the molecules of a given substance have exactly the same mass; here we shall neglect the existence of isotopes. The molecules of all bodies are continually moving, and thus possess mechanical energy; and it is believed that the energy of the moving molecules themselves is in fact the form of energy known as heat.

The difference between solids, liquids, and gases can briefly be summarised as follows.

In a solid, the molecules are anchored in position under strong mutual attractions, the nature of which need not here be discussed. Each molecule oscillates about its mean position, the amplitude of the oscillations increasing as the temperature rises ; this gives a qualitative explanation of expansion. When the melting point is reached, the oscillations are sufficiently violent to overcome the attractive forces, and the " rigid " structure breaks down, giving a liquid. The latent heat of fusion absorbed in melting represents the supply of energy needed to break down this structure.

In a liquid, the molecules are free to move about at random, though they are still held together in a body of fixed volume by the attractions between them. The energies of the molecules are distributed about a certain average value at any temperature, and at any instant some have energies much less than, and others energies much greater than, this value. The faster molecules in the neighbourhood of the surface escape, and are free to move about as individuals in the space above. If the most energetic molecules escape, the average energy of those remaining is reduced, so that evaporation cools the liquid (or it may be that latent heat is supplied from outside to make good the deficiency).

Now consider what happens when 1 gm. of water at 100° C., occupying approximately 1 c.c., is converted into steam at 100° C. and one atmosphere pressure. The volume of the steam is 1600 c.c., so that the molecules which would formerly have occupied a cube of 1 cm. side now occupy a cube of $\sqrt[3]{1600}$, or 11·7 cm., side. It is clear that the actual bulk of the molecules themselves cannot be more than 1/1600 of the volume occupied by the steam, the rest of the space (although " occupied " in the sense that other matter is excluded from it) being empty. Also, the molecules must be, on the average, nearly twelve times as far apart in the gaseous state as they were in the liquid state.

No satisfactory " law of force " for molecular attractions has been completely worked out, though variations inversely as different powers of the distance have been suggested from time to time.

But it is certain that the attractions diminish greatly as the average distances between the molecules increase. Let us suppose the steam to be maintained at 100° C. when, as an unsaturated vapour (p. 162) we can apply Boyle's Law if we expand it. If the volume of the steam is increased ten times, the pressure is reduced to about 1/10 atmosphere, the molecules now fill only 1/16,000 of the total volume occupied, and the average distance apart is increased to 25·2 times the original distance in the liquid state.

Reducing the pressure thus (1) reduces the fraction of the occupied volume which is actually filled by the molecules themselves, and (2) by increasing the average separation of the molecules reduces the effect of their attractions for one another. At extremely low pressures, the fraction of the total volume filled by the molecules themselves is vanishingly small, and so is the effect of attractions. But at extremely low pressures the physical behaviour of an actual gas approaches that of the ideal gas ; hence, *low-pressure conditions with an actual gas are the conditions always obtaining with an ideal gas at all pressures.*

The difference between a real gas and the ideal gas, therefore, is the same in kind as the difference between a real gas at high pressure and a real gas at low pressure. In one case, the molecules occupy an appreciable fraction of the total volume and attract one another appreciably ; in the other case, the molecules fill only an infinitesimally small fraction of the total volume, and attractions between them are entirely negligible. In applying the kinetic theory to an ideal gas, then, we shall neglect the volume of the molecules themselves, and also neglect the effect of their attractions. When the discrepancies between the behaviour of a real gas and an ideal gas come to be discussed, these two points will be the first to be considered.

Pressure of an ideal gas. The suppositions made for the purposes of this calculation are :

(1) The molecules *behave* as if they were hard, smooth, perfectly elastic spheres. (What is now known about atomic and molecular structure does not refute this supposition, but rather explains why it is helpful.)

(2) The molecules are continually in random motion, colliding with one another and with the walls of the containing vessel.

(3) The average kinetic energy of the molecules is proportional to the absolute temperature.

(4) The molecules do not exert any appreciable attractions on one another.

(5) The space actually filled by the molecules themselves is only an infinitesimal fraction of the total volume occupied.

A perfectly elastic sphere of mass m and velocity u impinging perpendicularly on a fixed rigid wall has its momentum reversed, from mu to $-mu$, and the wall receives an impulse equal to the change of momentum of the sphere, $2mu$. If, during one second, a large number of such impacts occur, the average force on the wall, by Newton's Second Law of Motion, is equal in absolute units to the total change of momentum in that second. The pressure is then obtained by taking the force on unit area of the wall. This is an outline of the principles of the calculation which will be used.

Suppose that a closed vessel of volume v c.c. contains a fixed mass of gas at pressure p dynes per sq. cm., the total number of molecules being n. The number of molecules per c.c., ν, is then given by $\nu = n/v$. Let m gm. be the mass of each molecule.

Imagine for the moment that all the molecules are moving in a direction perpendicular to one wall of the container with velocity u cm./sec., and consider 1 sq. cm. of this wall (Fig. 69). All the molecules contained in a prism of length u cm. and base 1 sq. cm. strike the selected area in one second. The volume of this prism is u c.c., and the number of molecules contained in it is νu. Each molecule undergoes a momentum change $2mu$ at right angles to the wall when it strikes it, giving the wall a corresponding impulse $2mu$.

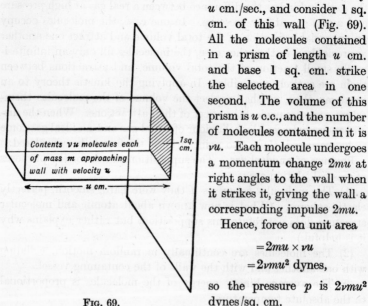

Contents νu molecules each
of mass m approaching
wall with velocity u
— u cm. —
1 sq. cm.

FIG. 69.

Hence, force on unit area

$$= 2mu \times \nu u$$
$$= 2\nu mu^2 \text{ dynes},$$

so the pressure p is $2\nu mu^2$ dynes/sq. cm.

Apart from demanding a somewhat extensive space in which to construct the prism (though this does not invalidate the argument, because a suitably short time interval could easily be chosen instead of one second), two extremely unlikely assumptions have been made.

If the molecules are moving at random in all directions, it is highly improbable that at a given instant they will all be simultaneously moving in the same direction. It is more reasonable to suppose that they will, on the average, be distributed equally in six directions along any set of rectangular co-ordinate axes we like to choose, as shown in Fig. 70. On the average, then, only one sixth of the vu molecules considered in the prism will be moving towards the wall in a direction at right angles to it. So it would be more accurate to write

$$p = \tfrac{1}{6} \cdot 2vmu^2 = \tfrac{1}{3}vmu^2 \text{ dyne/sq. cm.}$$

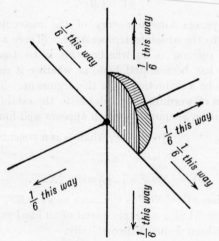

Fig. 70.—Average resolved distribution of molecular velocities.

The second false assumption must now be shed. All the molecules do not have the same value of u^2, and we should by rights consider the average value of u^2 for all the molecules. This is called the *mean square velocity*, and is given the symbol $\bar{c}^2$. Hence, the expression arrived at for the pressure is

$$p = \tfrac{1}{3}vm\bar{c}^2 \text{ dyne/sq. cm.}$$

Now,
$$v = n/v,$$
$$\therefore \quad p = \tfrac{1}{3}nm\bar{c}^2/v,$$

or
$$pv = \tfrac{1}{3}nm\bar{c}^2.$$

We shall not stress here the unsatisfactory features of the above deduction (which lie entirely in the mathematics, and not in the physical principles employed). It justifies itself as a method of presentation first on account of its relative simplicity, and secondly because the most rigid statistical treatment of the two averaging processes leads to exactly the same equation as that obtained here.

Now consider 1 mole, and write V for the volume occupied and N for the number of molecules.

Then
$$pV = \tfrac{1}{3}Nm\bar{c}^2.$$

Or, as Nm equals the molecular weight in grams, M,

$$pV = \tfrac{1}{3}M\bar{c}^2.$$

Let the average kinetic energy of the molecules be directly proportional to the absolute temperature. (There appears to be a difference of opinion as to whether this is an assumption made originally, as has been stated here, or whether it can properly be considered to be a deduction from the argument. This is perhaps all a question of wording ; as it leads to the established equation $pV = RT$, it is an assumption which appears well-founded.)

Then
$$\tfrac{1}{2}m\bar{c}^2 = \alpha T, \text{ where } \alpha \text{ is a constant ;}$$

$$\therefore \quad \tfrac{1}{2}Nm\bar{c}^2 = N\alpha T,$$

and
$$pV = \tfrac{1}{3}Nm\bar{c}^2 = \tfrac{2}{3} . \tfrac{1}{2}Nm\bar{c}^2 = \tfrac{2}{3}N\alpha T.$$

The equation $pV = \tfrac{2}{3}N\alpha T$ is the same as $pV = RT$, if $\tfrac{2}{3}N\alpha = R$.

Thus, by considering a simple model of an ideal gas, the equation $pV = RT$ has been deduced theoretically.

As $\tfrac{2}{3}N\alpha$ is the same as R, $R = \dfrac{2}{3}\alpha N$ or $\alpha = \dfrac{3}{2}\dfrac{R}{N}$.

The ratio R/N (which is the value of R for one molecule) is called Boltzmann's Constant, and is usually given the symbol k. Thus

$$\alpha = \tfrac{3}{2}k \quad \text{and} \quad \tfrac{1}{2}m\bar{c}^2 = \tfrac{3}{2}kT.$$

DEDUCTIONS FROM THE IDEAL GAS EQUATION

1. Determination of the value of $\sqrt{\bar{c}^2}$.

As
$$pV = \tfrac{1}{3}Nm\bar{c}^2,$$
$$p = \tfrac{1}{3}\frac{Nm}{V}\bar{c}^2.$$

But Nm/V is the total mass of gas divided by its volume, and thus equals the density ρ.

Hence
$$p = \tfrac{1}{3}\rho\bar{c}^2 \quad \text{or} \quad \sqrt{\bar{c}^2} = \sqrt{\frac{3p}{\rho}}.$$

This gives the square root of the mean square velocity, which is not quite the same thing as the average velocity ; the difference depends on the distribution of the velocities of the individual molecules, and can be calculated, but we will here suppose that it is small.

For hydrogen at N.T.P. assuming the figures $\rho = 0.00009$ gm./c.c., $p = 76 \times 13.6 \times 981$ dynes/sq. cm.,

$$\sqrt{\bar{c}^2} = \sqrt{\frac{3 \times 76 \times 13.6 \times 981}{0.00009}}$$

$$= 1.86 \times 10^5 \text{ cm./sec.}$$

The following table, taken from Kaye and Laby's "Tables", gives the values of $\sqrt{\bar{c}^2}$ at $0°$ C. for the common gases.

Gas.	$\sqrt{\bar{c}^2}$.
Hydrogen - - -	18.39×10^4 cm./sec.
Helium - - -	$13.1 \ \times 10^4$,,
Nitrogen - - -	4.93×10^4 ,,
Oxygen - - -	4.61×10^4 ,,
Carbon dioxide -	3.92×10^4 ,,

It is interesting to compare the value of $\sqrt{\bar{c}^2}$ with the velocity of sound in the same gas. The formula for the velocity of sound, in terms of the pressure and the density, is velocity $= \sqrt{\dfrac{\gamma p}{\rho}}$, where γ is the ratio between the two specific heats (p. 259) and has the value 1.40 for a diatomic gas. Thus, for air or hydrogen, at a given pressure,

$$\sqrt{\bar{c}^2} : \text{velocity of sound} = \sqrt{\frac{3p}{\rho}} : \sqrt{\frac{\gamma p}{\rho}} = \sqrt{3} : \sqrt{1.40}.$$

2. Graham's Law of Diffusion. When a gas flows through a wide tube under a pressure gradient, it behaves as if it were a continuous fluid. But when a gas passes through a fine hole or tube, or a porous solid which is composed of numerous very fine tubes, it travels through molecule by molecule. This process is called diffusion, and was investigated thoroughly by Graham. The rate of diffusion depends on the density of the gas, other things being equal ; the lighter the gas, the greater the rate of diffusion. There are several well-known simple experiments to demonstrate this. For example, a closed tube of unglazed earthenware is fitted with a manometer and filled with hydrogen ; the pressure inside the tube falls rapidly, as hydrogen escapes faster than air enters through the pores. If the same vessel is filled with carbon dioxide, the pressure rises, as air enters faster than carbon dioxide escapes.

Graham's Law of Diffusion states that the rates of efflux of different gases through a porous septum under given conditions are inversely proportional to the square roots of their densities. For two gases, 1 and 2, at the same pressure, if the rate of efflux is taken as proportional to $\sqrt{\bar{c}^2}$ for each gas,

as
$$\sqrt{\bar{c_1}^2} = \sqrt{\frac{3p}{\rho_1}} \quad \text{and} \quad \sqrt{\bar{c_2}^2} = \sqrt{\frac{3p}{\rho_2}},$$

$$\frac{\sqrt{\bar{c_1}^2}}{\sqrt{\bar{c_2}^2}} = \sqrt{\frac{\rho_2}{\rho_1}}.$$

whence Graham's Law should theoretically be true.

3. Avogadro's Hypothesis. This states that equal volumes of all gases under the same conditions of temperature and pressure contain equal numbers of molecules.

Consider two equal volumes V at the same pressure and the same temperature (which means that $\frac{1}{2}m\bar{c}^2$, the average molecular kinetic energy, is the same in both cases).

Let there be n_1 molecules of mass m_1 in one gas and n_2 molecules of mass m_2 in the other, and let the mean square velocities be $\bar{c_1}^2$ and $\bar{c_2}^2$.

Then $pV = \frac{1}{3}n_1 m_1 \bar{c_1}^2$, and also $pV = \frac{1}{3}n_2 m_2 \bar{c_2}^2$,

whence $n_1 m_1 \bar{c_1}^2 = n_2 m_2 \bar{c_2}^2$.

But as the temperatures are the same, $\frac{1}{2}m_1\bar{c_1}^2 = \frac{1}{2}m_2\bar{c_2}^2$, hence $n_1 = n_2$, and the two volumes contain the same number of molecules.

4. Dalton's Law of Partial Pressures. Consider a volume V containing n_1 molecules each of mass m_1 and mean square velocity $\bar{c}_1^2$ exerting a pressure p_1, n_2 molecules each of mass m_2 and mean square velocity $\bar{c}_2^2$, exerting a pressure p_2, and n_3 molecules each of mass m_3, and mean square velocity $\bar{c}_3^2$, exerting a pressure p_3, the whole mass of course being at the same temperature.

As each gas expands to fill the whole of the container and occupies volume V at its own pressure,

$$p_1 V = \tfrac{1}{3} n_1 m_1 \bar{c}_1^2, \qquad p_2 V = \tfrac{1}{3} n_2 m_2 \bar{c}_2^2, \qquad p_3 V = \tfrac{1}{3} n_3 m_3 \bar{c}_3^2.$$

But as the whole is at the same temperature, the average kinetic energy of the molecules of each kind is the same,

$$m_1 \bar{c}_1^2 = m_2 \bar{c}_2^2 = m_3 \bar{c}_3^2 = m \bar{c}^2 \text{ say };$$

whence $\qquad\qquad (p_1 + p_2 + p_3) V = \tfrac{1}{3} (n_1 + n_2 + n_3) m \bar{c}^2.$

But $(n_1 + n_2 + n_3)$ is the total number of molecules n, and the total pressure p should be represented by $p V = \tfrac{1}{3} n m \bar{c}^2$.

Thus the total pressure p is the same as $p_1 + p_2 + p_3$; or, the pressure due to a mixture of gases or vapours which do not interact in any way is equal to the sum of their partial pressures.

Thus the simple kinetic theory, which leads to the equation $p V = RT$ for an ideal gas, goes much beyond this, and appears to be able to explain nearly all the general rules about gaseous behaviour which are obeyed approximately by real gases. Unfortunately, these rules are not strictly obeyed by any real gases, but the theory is clearly working in the right direction. The lines along which the theory must be modified to deal with real gases have already been indicated ; these modifications will now be discussed in detail.

PROPERTIES OF REAL GASES

Air, oxygen, nitrogen, hydrogen, and the other " permanent gases " obey Boyle's Law to within less than one part in a thousand (that is, the products $p V$ agree to well within this limit) at ordinary pressures and temperatures. At higher pressures and lower temperatures, the deviations are more pronounced.

Many investigators have tested the validity of Boyle's Law at high pressures. Regnault performed a series of experiments to test whether doubling the pressure reduced the volume to exactly one half, and Amagat conducted experiments in which pressures up to about

3,000 atmospheres were reached. Amagat's earlier experiments, up to about 300 atmospheres, were done with apparatus similar in principle to that of Fig. 55 (p. 123), the chief difference being that the reservoir R was not movable, but was fixed to the face of a high cliff in one set of experiments and to the side of a mine shaft in another set, the pressure being increased by pumping mercury in at the bottom of the tube corresponding to R.

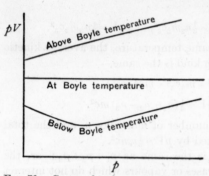

FIG. 71.—Curves showing general variation of pV with p.

All the experiments show that the product pV for a fixed mass of gas at constant temperature is not constant, but is a function of the pressure. The variation of pV with p is as shown in Fig. 71, which in its general form applies for all gases. For each gas there is a certain temperature called the Boyle temperature, at which pV is approximately independent of p and Boyle's Law is obeyed closely. For higher temperatures, pV increases as p increases, while for temperatures below the Boyle temperature pV at first decreases, reaches a minimum, and then begins to increase.

The Boyle temperature for helium is 23° K., for hydrogen 109° K., and for nitrogen 323° K. In experiments done at ordinary temperatures, then, the first two gases follow the highest of the three curves of Fig. 71, while nitrogen follows the lowest line.

The variation of pV with p (or with $1/V$) at any temperature can be expressed analytically as a virial expansion, or virial equation. One form of this was used on p. 143, namely :

$$pV = A\left(1 + \frac{B_v}{V} + \frac{C_v}{V^2} + \frac{D_v}{V^3} \ldots\ldots\right).$$

Another form is :

$$pV = A\left(1 + \frac{B_v}{V} + \frac{C_v}{V^2} + \frac{E_v}{V^4} \ldots\ldots\right),$$

in which odd powers of $1/V$, except the first, are omitted.
A third form is : $pV = A(1 + B_p p + C_p p^2 + D_p p^3 \ldots)$,

the A term in each case being the "ideal gas" term, and A and all the B's, C's, etc., being functions of the temperature alone. A, B, C, ... called the first, second, third ... virial coefficients, are characteristic of the individual gas.

The first virial coefficient, A, is the value of the product pV when p is exceedingly small, and it should be the same for all gases. The second virial coefficient B_v is of great importance in discussing the behaviour of individual gases, while C_v, D_v, and the succeeding coefficients are progressively smaller and are usually neglected. The values of the second and succeeding virial coefficients may be either positive or negative, depending on the temperature. The Boyle temperature is the temperature at which the second virial coefficient B_v is zero ; and Boyle's law is obeyed closely at this temperature provided that p is not so great that the higher terms in the expansion containing the very small coefficients C_v, D_v, ... become appreciable. Below the Boyle temperature B_v is negative, while above the Boyle temperature B_v is positive.

These expansions are empirical equations, the "constants" of which are adjusted to fit the observed results, and are simply the algebraic equivalents of the plotted curves.

In looking for a simple physical explanation of this behaviour of real gases, it is necessary to recall that the kinetic theory suggests that Boyle's Law should be obeyed *if the molecules are themselves infinitesimally small*, and *if they do not attract one another at all*, assumptions which were shown on p. 149 to be extremely improbable.

At low temperatures, the value of pV decreases as the applied pressure increases ; that is, the applied pressure required for a given volume decrease is smaller than Boyle's Law suggests. If the molecules do attract one another, and the attraction increases as the average distance between them decreases, this attraction helps to pull them together, and is equivalent to an extra applied pressure from without, so that the pressure actually needed is less than it would be if there were no attraction. The subsequent rise in the graph at higher pressures may be explained if we suppose that the molecules themselves occupy a finite volume, so that the observed volume V is greater than that actually available for the molecules to move about in, and the product pV is really over-estimated. These two tendencies, effectively adding to the applied pressure and reducing the observed volume, act in opposite directions on the product pV, and both will be affected by the temperature. **At** higher temperatures, the molecules will, on the average, be moving more rapidly. The effect of attractions will be less, since each molecule spends less time close to other attracting molecules ; also, the volume effectively occupied by the molecules might be expected to be greater when they are moving faster, just as the area of a cricket field defended by, say, cover-point, depends on how fast he can run.

At the Boyle temperature, the second tendency just counteracts the first, whereas above the Boyle temperature the second tendency is the greater ; so the product pV increases from the start.

Continuity of state. Another question now arises. Sulphur dioxide, carbon dioxide, and many other gases do not at ordinary temperatures behave like air or hydrogen. If a sufficiently great pressure is applied they liquefy. The change of state is evidenced by a sudden considerable reduction in volume, the evolution of latent heat, and the appearance of a visible surface ; if none of these is observed in an experiment it may reasonably be concluded that the substance remains gaseous. Increasing the pressure and reducing the volume should, if the earlier deductions be sound, favour liquefaction, since molecular attraction should be strongest at close quarters. But, if some gases liquefy under pressure, why not all?

The first experiment leading to a solution of this question is that of Cagniard de la Tour (1822). A liquid such as water or ether, trapped by mercury, was heated in the short limb of a closed tube, the longer end of which served as a closed air manometer. As the temperature increased, a stage was reached at which the liquid meniscus had disappeared, the whole of the contents appearing homogeneous. The temperature at which this occurred was called by de la Tour the **critical temperature** for the substance. On cooling again, the boundary reappeared. Fig. 72 illustrates a Science Museum apparatus for demonstrating this effect.

These observations can be described in several ways. It is known that the surface tension of a liquid diminishes as the temperature rises, and it may be that the surface tension has become vanishingly small, so that the visible surface disappears, though liquid substance remains in the bottom of the tube, and gaseous substance at the top. Or, as the temperature rises the liquid becomes less dense and the saturated vapour (p. 162) denser ; it may be that at the critical

FIG. 72.—The glass tube contains carbon dioxide at about 60 atmospheres pressure, the liquid meniscus at air temperature being about half-way up the tube. The meniscus disappears when the hot air current raises the temperature above the critical temperature, to reappear on cooling.

Reproduced from the Science Museum Handbook, on Very Low Temperatures, by permission of the Controller of H. M. Stationery Office.

temperature both liquid and vapour have the same density (and this is actually the case). But the ability to form a homogeneous mixture depends on molecular attraction rather than merely on density, so that the molecular attractions must be the same for liquid and vapour molecules at this stage.

These different descriptions really all amount to the same thing. What can be said of a liquid which has no surface, which has the same density as the vapour above it, and in which the molecular attractions are the same as in the vapour, so that it mixes with the vapour and is indistinguishable from it? We can only say that *at the critical temperature* there is no visible distinction between a liquid and its vapour, and that *above the critical temperature the liquid state no longer persists*, and the substance is all in the gaseous state.

Andrews' experiments on carbon dioxide. Andrews, in 1863, obtained a series of values of pressure and volume at constant temperature, and plotted a series of isothermal curves—that is,

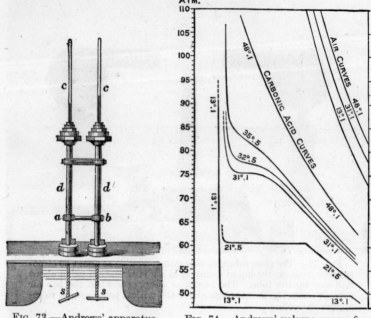

FIG. 73.—Andrews' apparatus.　　FIG. 74.—Andrews' volume curves for carbon dioxide.

curves showing how V depends on p when the temperature is constant.

Carbon dioxide was contained in a calibrated glass tube by a pellet of mercury, the open end of the tube being in a liquid chamber to which pressure was applied by screwing in a plunger. The pressure was measured by observing the diminution in volume of air or nitrogen (the behaviour of which was known) in a similar tube (Fig. 73). The resulting curves are shown in Fig. 74, and these curves can be divided into two classes.

(1) *For* 31·1° C. *and above*, continuous curves similar to, though not so steep as, the air curves shown in the upper right-hand corner of the figure.

(2) *Below* 30° C., each curve showed three distinct portions (Fig. 75, p. 162); a smooth curve AB somewhat similar in general trend to those at higher temperatures, a horizontal part BC, along which, for one value of the pressure, the volume may have any value lying

between B and C, and a very steep part CD along which a very small change in volume is caused by a large increase in pressure, and the substance is practically incompressible. Between A and B the substance is gaseous ; between B and C the substance is liquefying, both liquid and vapour being present together in equilibrium, and the gaseous portion is a saturated vapour. At B the substance is entirely gaseous, at C entirely liquid ; the length of BC denotes the difference between the volumes of the fixed mass of vapour and the same mass of liquid. Along CD the substance is entirely liquefied. Fig. 75 refers to one of the lowest isothermals obtained. For higher temperatures, the length of the horizontal part decreases, showing that the difference between the volume of the liquid and that of the vapour is less. Just below $31 \cdot 1°$ C., the horizontal part is reduced to a point, while at $32 \cdot 5°$ C. there is no horizontal part at all, though there is a kink in the curve, showing abnormally high compressibility. At $35 \cdot 5°$ C. the kink is less pronounced, while at $48 \cdot 1°$ C. the curve is smooth and very similar to the air curves.

The critical temperature of carbon dioxide, as determined by observing the temperature at which the meniscus of liquid carbon dioxide disappeared, was found by Andrews to be $30 \cdot 9°$ C. The $31 \cdot 1°$ C. isothermal is then practically that for the critical temperature, and really represents a dividing stage between the two types of curve. At this temperature it is just possible to liquefy the gas by pressure, and at the point when this occurs the volumes of liquid and gas are the same. Above this temperature it is not possible to obtain the substance in the liquid state.

The critical temperature ($\theta_c°$ C. or $T_c°$ K.) of a substance is thus defined as that temperature above which the substance cannot be liquefied, however great the pressure.

The critical point is that point on the isothermal for the critical temperature at which the substance passes from the gaseous to the liquid state.

The critical pressure p_c is the pressure at the critical point.

The critical volume V_c will in this book denote the volume occupied by unit mass at the critical temperature and the critical pressure. (The name is also sometimes used for the same volume expressed as a fraction of the volume occupied by the same mass under standard conditions.)

Gases and vapours. We can now distinguish properly between the terms " vapour " and " gas ".

The term " gas " denotes a substance in the gaseous state at a temperature above its critical temperature.

The term " vapour " implies the possibility of liquefaction, which can only happen below the critical temperature, and a vapour is defined as a substance in the gaseous state at a temperature below its critical temperature.

Considering again the carbon dioxide isothermal for a low temperature ; gaseous substance, or vapour, is present over the whole of the region from A to C (Fig. 75). From A to B the whole of the material present is gaseous. There is a fixed mass of gaseous substance present, and a fixed number of gaseous molecules. Hence Boyle's Law, which applies to a fixed mass of gaseous substance at constant temperature, is more or less obeyed. The vapour is said to be an unsaturated vapour.

From B to C the substance is a mixture of gas and vapour in equilibrium (p. 178). At B the substance is all vapour, and at C all liquid, and all possible proportions between these limits occur. The mass of gaseous substance is not constant, so there is no question of Boyle's Law or any other gas law being obeyed. The pressure is constant all the way from B to C, and this is the greatest pressure at which the vapour can exist at that temperature. An infinitesimal change in pressure brings the substance from BC on to CD, where all is liquid, or on to the portion AB where all is unsaturated vapour.

Hence, a saturated vapour at any temperature is a vapour in equilibrium with its liquid at that temperature. The pressure it exerts at this temperature is constant, and is the maximum pressure the vapour can exert at that temperature. This pressure is independent of the volume, providing this is not increased beyond the point B (when the liquid would all evaporate), or reduced beyond C (when all the vapour would condense).

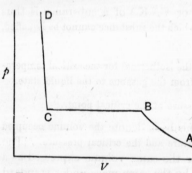

Fig. 75.—Isothermal below critical temperature.

Decreasing the volume occupied by a saturated vapour *changes the mass of gaseous substance present*, so once again it is emphasised that we cannot expect Boyle's Law, or anything approaching it, to be obeyed.

The pressure of a saturated vapour at any temperature is called the **maximum vapour pressure**, or **saturated vapour pressure** of the substance at that temperature. At all pressures in excess of this the substance is completely liquefied at that temperature, while at all pressures below this the substance is completely gaseous at that temperature.

Andrews believed that the whole of the process from *A* to *D* was continuous—that is, the difference in the molecular forces operating in the liquid, saturated vapour, and unsaturated vapour was one of *degree* rather than of *kind*. Gas and liquid are only distant stages in a long series of continuous physical changes. What is the importance of this idea of " continuity of state "? Surely it suggests that *all gases can be liquefied*, if only the proper means to do this can be found.

James Thomson's Hypothesis. James Thomson suggested that the curves of Andrews might be represented by a family of cubic equations with different parameters, and that the parts *AB* and *CD* of the isothermals below the critical temperature were really part of a continuous curve typical of a *cubic* equation with three real roots, going below *CB* at *C*, above *BC* at *B*, and crossing *BC* (Fig. 76). A short portion of the part below *C* is actually realised in practice with superheated liquid, and part above *B* by supersaturated vapour; but the rest of the dotted part is not obtainable in practice.

The idea that the whole family of isothermals for a real gas can be represented by a family of similar equations, or a single *equation of state*, in just the same way as the isothermals for a perfect gas are all embraced in the equation of state $pV = RT$, is very attractive. Many attempts have been made on theoretical grounds to modify the equation $pV = RT$ to fit the observed results for a real gas.

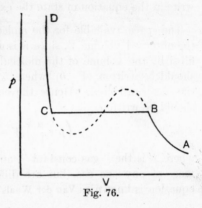

Fig. 76.

Van der Waals' Equation. To account for the difference between the compressibility of a real gas and that of an ideal gas, the obvious method of attack is to allow for *molecular attractions* and for the *finite volume occupied by the molecules*.

Considering unit mass of gas, the equation of state for an ideal gas is $pV = RT$. If the molecules attract one another, the pressure p observed at the walls of the container is less than the true pressure within the body of the gas, since a molecule within the gas is attracted symmetrically from all sides (and so *unaffected by any resultant force*), while a molecule impinging on a wall is retarded by an attractive pull acting towards the body of the gas only. The effect of the attraction on any one individual molecule is assumed to be proportional to the number of molecules per unit volume or, since we are considering a fixed number N of molecules in volume V, to N/V. But (p. 150) the number of impacts thus affected in any interval is also proportional to the density, that is, to N/V. The resulting pressure diminution is thus proportional to

$$\frac{N}{V} \times \frac{N}{V}, \quad \text{or} \quad \frac{N^2}{V^2}.$$

This argument is not strictly accurate ; though the general idea is sound, and we can say that the true pressure inside the gas exceeds the observed pressure at the walls by an amount proportional to $\frac{1}{V^2}$, say $\frac{a}{V^2}$, where a is a constant for unit mass of the particular gas under examination. Hence, instead of p we should write in the equation of state the expression $\left(p + \frac{a}{V^2}\right)$

The space available for the molecules to move about is less than the observed volume V, since it is diminished by the space actually filled by the volume of the molecules themselves ; and the volume should be written $(V - b)$, where b is a constant for unit mass of the gas considered. Hence the equation of state for a real gas should be written

$$\left(p + \frac{a}{V^2}\right)(V - b) = RT,$$

where R is the " gas constant ", and a and b are constants for unit mass of any one gas, but are different for different gases. This equation is known as **Van der Waals' Equation.**

The constant b is called the " co-volume " ; simple considerations suggest that b should be four times the actual volume of the molecules. For, if we consider two molecules A and B colliding, the centre of A cannot get nearer to the centre of B than a distance equal to its diameter away. We can imagine B to be surrounded by a " sphere of influence ", of radius equal to the diameter of the molecule, which is forbidden to the centre of A. The volume of this sphere is *eight times* the volume of a *single molecule*, or *four times* the volume of *the pair of molecules* involved in the collision. Taking all the molecules in pairs like this, it can be seen that the sum of the " forbidden volumes " is four times the volume of all the molecules. The same result is given by Jeans in " The Dynamical Theory of Gases ", as the conclusion of a probability calculation ; other calculations have suggested that b should be $4\sqrt{2}$ times the actual volume of the molecules instead of 4 times.

Van der Waals' equation is the simplest of the many attempts that have been made to derive an equation of state for real gases, and on the whole it fits the facts fairly well provided that conditions are such that the deviations from Boyle's Law are small. Partington and Shilling, in " The Specific Heats of Gases ", pp. 29–34, list fifty-six different equations of state, some extremely complicated, and some closely accurate for particular gases over fairly narrow limits. The importance of Van der Waals' equation lies in its *general application as an approximate equation over wide ranges for a wide range of substances*, rather than the accuracy with which it fits any particular case.

The isothermals obtained by using Van der Waals' equation to plot p against V do not agree closely in form with those obtained experimentally by Andrews, though they certainly give a better approximation than do the isothermals of an ideal gas (which are a family of rectangular hyperbolas). In the neighbourhood of the critical point, just where the equation affords some extremely interesting results, it is certainly inaccurate. We shall, however, proceed for the present on the assumption that Van der Waals' equation is closely obeyed.

The critical constants. Consider the isothermal ACB (Fig. 77) for the critical temperature T_c. Going from A to the critical point C, the gradient of the curve, dp/dV, gets (numerically) less and less until at C the tangent is horizontal, and $dp/dV = 0$.

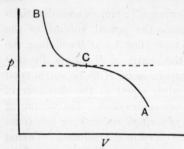

FIG. 77.—Critical-temperature isothermal.

Proceeding from C to B, the gradient steadily increases, so that dp/dV has a turning value at C, whence

$$\frac{d}{dV}\left(\frac{dp}{dV}\right)=0, \quad \text{or} \quad \frac{d^2p}{dV^2}=0.$$

The tangent at C is horizontal, and *the point C is a point of inflexion.* Hence, using these two statements, whatever the equation of state may be, at the critical point,

$$\frac{dp}{dV}=0 \ \text{ and } \ \frac{d^2p}{dV^2}=0.$$

Now, writing Van der Waals' equation in the form,

$$p=\frac{RT}{V-b}-\frac{a}{V^2},$$

we have

$$\frac{dp}{dV}=\frac{-RT}{(V-b)^2}+\frac{2a}{V^3},$$

and

$$\frac{d^2p}{dV^2}=\frac{2RT}{(V-b)^3}-\frac{6a}{V^4}.$$

For the critical point, substituting in all these equations $p=p_c$, $V=V_c$, and $T=T_c$, and putting $\dfrac{dp}{dV}$ and $\dfrac{d^2p}{dV^2}$ equal to 0,

$$p_c=\frac{RT_c}{V_c-b}-\frac{a}{V_c{}^2}, \quad\quad\quad\dotfill(1)$$

$$-\frac{RT_c}{(V_c-b)^2}+\frac{2a}{V_c{}^3}=0, \quad\quad\dotfill(2)$$

$$\frac{2RT_c}{(V_c-b)^3}-\frac{6a}{V_c{}^4}=0, \quad\quad\dotfill(3)$$

giving three equations which should enable p_c, V_c, and T_c to be calculated in terms of a, b, and R.

From (2) and (3),

$$\frac{2a}{V_c{}^3}=\frac{RT_c}{(V_c-b)^2} \ \text{ and } \ \frac{6a}{V_c{}^4}=\frac{2RT_c}{(V_c-b)^3},$$

whence, dividing the left-hand side of the former by the left-hand side of the latter, and similarly the two right-hand sides,

$$\frac{V_c}{3} = \frac{V_c - b}{2}, \text{ whence } V_c = 3b.$$

Substituting for V_c in (2),

$$T_c = \frac{2a}{V_c{}^3} \cdot \frac{(V_c - b)^2}{R} = \frac{2a \times 4b^2}{27b^3 \cdot R} = \frac{8a}{27Rb};$$

and finally, substituting for both V_c and T_c in (1),

$$p_c = \frac{8a}{27Rb} \cdot \frac{R}{2b} - \frac{a}{9b^2} = \frac{4a}{27b^2} - \frac{3a}{27b^2} = \frac{a}{27b^2}.$$

Hence $\qquad p_c = \dfrac{a}{27b^2}, \quad V_c = 3b, \quad T_c = \dfrac{8a}{27Rb}.$

Now, the values of a and b can be obtained by substituting observations of p and V in the original equation, and the critical pressure, volume, and temperature can be observed independently, so that the validity of the calculation can be tested.

If the equation is accurate, V_c/b should be 3 for all gases ; actual values vary between 2·80 for hydrogen and 1·41 for argon.

Also the expression $\dfrac{RT_c}{p_c V_c} = \dfrac{R \cdot 8a}{27Rb} \cdot \dfrac{1}{3b} \cdot \dfrac{27b^2}{a} = \dfrac{8}{3} = 2\cdot 67$; observed values of $\dfrac{RT_c}{p_c V_c}$ are all in the neighbourhood of 3·5.

Thus Van der Waals' equation is not *closely* obeyed by any gas *in the neighbourhood of its critical point.*

It may be mentioned here that *any* equation of state should enable the critical constants to be computed, since three equations solvable for the three unknowns p_c, V_c, and T_c should be obtained by writing down the equations for p, $\dfrac{dp}{dV}$, and $\dfrac{d^2p}{dV^2}$ at the critical point.

Corresponding States. The Reduced Equation of State. If the pressure, volume, and temperature of a fixed mass of gas, denoted by p, V, and T respectively, be divided by the critical values of these quantities, p_c, V_c, and T_c, the resulting *numbers* are called the reduced pressure p_r, reduced volume V_r, and reduced temperature T_r.

Thus $\qquad p_r = \dfrac{p}{p_c}, \quad V_r = \dfrac{V}{V_c}, \quad$ and $\quad T_r = \dfrac{T}{T_c}.$

Whence $\qquad p = p_r\, p_c = p_r \dfrac{a}{27b^2}$ (using p. 167),

$$V = V_r\, V_c = V_r \cdot 3b,$$

and $\qquad T = T_r\, T_c = T_r \dfrac{8a}{27Rb}.$

Substituting these values for p, V, and T in Van der Waals' equation,

$$\left(\frac{p_r a}{27b^2} + \frac{a}{9V_r^2 b^2}\right)(V_r 3b - b) = RT_r \frac{8a}{27Rb},$$

which simplifies to

$$\left(p_r + \frac{3}{V_r^2}\right)(3V_r - 1) = 8T_r.$$

This equation does not contain the constants a and b characteristic of a particular gas, and should be true for *all* gases. This is called the reduced form of Van der Waals' equation. Different gases with the same p_r, V_r, and T_r are said to be in corresponding states. The reduced equation is only followed approximately—that is, as closely as Van der Waals' equation itself is followed by a given gas.

To obtain the reduced equation we have had to eliminate three constants a, b, and R, by substituting values of p_c, V_c, and T_c. This elimination is possible with any equation of state which involves only two characteristic constants such as a and b. The so-called " law of corresponding states " which states that all gases should follow the reduced equation, is thus not a consequence peculiar to Van der Waals' equation. In recent years many authors have used the reduced quantities, and a reduced equation of state, in discussing properties common to all real gases and certain problems for which this method of expression is most convenient.

Other equations of state. Clausius, considering that the chief defect in Van der Waals' equation lay in assuming that the effect of molecular attractions is independent of the temperature, gave the equation $\left(p + \dfrac{a'}{T(V + C)^2}\right)(V - b) = RT$, where a', C, and b are constants characteristic of the gas. But this equation agrees little better than does that of Van der Waals with the experimental facts.

Dieterici's equation, $pe^{\frac{a}{RTV}}(V - b) = RT$, which differs from that of Van der Waals only in the first factor, agrees more closely with experiment, giving values of V_c/b approximately equal to 2, and of RT_c/p_cV_c in the neighbourhood of the observed value 3·6. Also, as the expansion of e^x is $1+x+x^2/1\,.\,2+\ldots$, it leads to Van der Waals' equation as a first approximation, for

$$pe^{\frac{a}{RTV}} = p\left(1 + \frac{a}{RTV}\right),\ \text{expanding and taking the first term only ;}$$

and substituting the approximate value pV for RT in this,

$$p\left(1 + \frac{a}{RTV}\right) = p\left(1 + \frac{a}{pV^2}\right) = \left(p + \frac{a}{V^2}\right),$$

the first factor of Van der Waals' equation. As Dieterici's equation, like Van der Waals' equation, contains two characteristic constants, a reduced equation of state can be found, and this is

$$p_r(2V_r - 1) = T_r\,e^{2\left(1 - \frac{1}{V_r}\right)}.$$

Dieterici's equation agrees very closely with experiment for pressures up to about twelve atmospheres, and fairly well far beyond this range.

Empirical equations can, of course, be made to fit observations to any degree of accuracy by introducing a sufficient number of arbitrary constants. Such equations are of value in particular investigations. Berthelot, in 1907, when engaged on the problem of the correction of the gas thermometer, suggested the equation

$$\left(p + \frac{a}{TV^2}\right)(V - b) = RT\,;$$

and also a second similar equation, purely empirical, which fitted the observations made fairly closely. The above equation of Berthelot, like the equations of Van der Waals and Dieterici, gives values of the critical constants in terms of a, b, and R, and also a reduced equation of state.

Kamerlingh Onnes resorted to the empirical form, or " virial expansion " discussed on p. 156, using equations involving a large number of adjustable constants, in which the odd powers of $1/V$ or p after the first are omitted ; for example :

$$pV = A\left(1 + \frac{B_v}{V} + \frac{C_v}{V^2} + \frac{E_v}{V^4} + \frac{G_v}{V^6}\ldots\right).$$

It is not proposed to work steadily through the fifty-six equations of state listed by Partington and Shilling. The three most important ones are Van der Waals' equation, which is a satisfactory second

M

approximation to the behaviour of an actual gas, and is used almost universally in calculations for which the first approximation of the ideal gas equation is not permissible ; Dieterici's equation, of which Van der Waals' equation can be considered an approximate form ; and Berthelot's equation. These are compared below :

Equation	b	a	$\dfrac{RT_c}{p_c V_c}$.
Van der Waals -	$V_c/3$	$3p_c V_c^2$	$8/3 = 2\cdot67$
Dieterici - -	$V_c/2$	$e^2 p_c V_c^2$	$e^2/2 = 3\cdot69$
Berthelot -	$V_c/3$	$3p_c V_c^2 T_c$	$8/3 = 2\cdot67$

All three equations predict a critical point, and a continuous isothermal of the type suggested by James Thomson during condensation. All of them give a satisfactory representation of the facts over quite considerable ranges, provided that the values of a and b are *determined experimentally and not deduced from the critical constants*.

Much interest centres around the second virial coefficient B_v, and a great deal of theoretical work has recently been done to compute its value using modern knowledge of atomic and molecular structure and the methods of quantum mechanics. It is interesting to see the values for B_v which these three equations give when rearranged and expanded. Van der Waals' equation may be written,

$$p = \frac{RT}{V-b} - \frac{a}{V^2},$$

$$\therefore\ pV = \frac{RTV}{V-b} - \frac{a}{V} = \frac{RT}{1-\dfrac{b}{V}} - \frac{a}{V} = RT\left(1 - \frac{b}{V}\right)^{-1} - \frac{a}{V},$$

$$= RT\left(1 + \frac{b}{V} - \frac{b^2}{V^2} \cdots \frac{-a}{RTV}\right) = RT\left(1 + \left(b - \frac{a}{RT}\right)\cdot\frac{1}{V}\cdots\right),$$

$$= A\left(1 + \left(b - \frac{a}{RT}\right)\frac{1}{V}\cdots\right),$$

whence $B_v = b - \dfrac{a}{RT}$ and $B_v = 0$ at the Boyle temperature (when $T = T_b$).

$$\therefore\ T_b = \frac{a}{Rb}.$$

Dieterici's equation gives the same value for B_v, while Berthelot's equation treated similarly gives $B_v = b - \dfrac{a}{RT^2}$ and $T_b = \sqrt{\dfrac{a}{Rb}}$.

Thus the first two equations predict that a graph of B_v against $1/T$ will be a straight line, while Berthelot's equation predicts that a graph of B_v against $1/T^2$ should be a straight line. For many substances the graph of B_v against $1/T$ is *almost* linear over a considerable temperature region, dropping below the straight line at low temperatures, and at high temperatures reaching a maximum, and finally dropping so that B_v approaches zero at very high temperatures, as $1/T$ approaches zero. Thus none of the three equations predicts fully the way in which B_v varies with the temperature.

Recent work on equations of state. There are two chief reasons for wanting to find an expression for the equation of state of a real gas. The first is entirely practical, in order that calculations on the compressibility of a given gas, and the calculations involved in the liquefaction of the gas or its use as a thermometric substance, may be made as accurately as possible. For this purpose an empirical equation suffices. The second is to derive information about molecular forces and molecular attractions, by probing with different assumptions as to the nature of these forces until a set of assumptions giving a satisfactory theoretical equation is obtained. This second reason has led to a great body of recent work on equations of state.[*] One of the most famous is that of Beattie and Bridgman (1927):

$$pV = RT \left(1 - \epsilon\right)\left(1 + \frac{B}{V}\right) - \frac{A}{V} ;$$

where $\qquad B = B_0 \left(1 - \dfrac{b}{V}\right), \quad A = A_0 \left(1 - \dfrac{a}{V}\right), \quad \epsilon = \dfrac{c}{VT^3},$

and A_0, B_0, a, b, and c are constants.

A completely satisfactory theory of the equation of state requires (a) the correct application of kinetic theory or statistical mechanics and (b) a detailed knowledge of intermolecular forces. The investigations of the era of Van der Waals were handicapped by the absence of any real data about intermolecular forces. Recent workers, following slightly different lines of approach, have been

---

[*]See the article "Equations of State", by J. A. Beattie and W. H. Stockmayer, in vol. 7 of the Physical Society's Reports on Progress in Physics (1940).

able to calculate an expression for the second virial coefficient B_v, and different methods appear to lead to the same result. It thus appears that a satisfactory equation of state, at least as far as the first two terms of the virial expansion, has been devised.

QUESTIONS ON CHAPTER IV

1. State Boyle's Law and give a diagram of a form of apparatus used to test the truth of the law.

A Boyle's Law tube had a piece of chalk floating on the mercury in the space containing the enclosed air. The pressure on this air was varied and readings were taken as follows :

Volume of enclosed space
above the mercury in c.c. 11·5 10·7 10·0 9·5 8·8 8·0
Pressure, in excess of
atmospheric pressure,
in cm. of mercury - 4·0 14·0 24·0 34·0 49·0 74·0

Atmospheric pressure being taken as 76·0 cm. of mercury, tabulate the total pressure, *P*, and the value of $1/P$ corresponding to each of the above volumes, *V*, and plot a graph of $1/P$ against *V*. From this graph determine the volume of the chalk above the mercury, indicating how you make your deduction. (J.M.B.)

2. Describe an experiment in which Boyle's Law is used to determine the atmospheric pressure in the laboratory.

A column of air in a uniform tube, closed at one end, occupies 26·4 cm. at atmospheric pressure. When subjected to the pressure of the water supply the column of air occupies 20·4 cm. Calculate the pressure of the water supply, the atmospheric pressure being 76·5 cm. of mercury. (The density of mercury = 13·6 gm. per c.c.)

How could you confirm the result with an open mercury manometer?
(J.M.B.)

3. Explain, with the aid of suitable diagrams, the construction and principle of action of a bicycle pump and a tyre valve.

The bottom of a bicycle pump was closed and the pump was lowered into deep water. The pump handle moved in so that, at the deepest point reached, the length of the enclosed air column was reduced to ⅔ of its former value. To what depth was the pump lowered into the water? Assume that the barometric pressure was 29·7 in. of mercury, and that the specific gravity of mercury is 13·6. (J.M.B.)

4. Describe a simple form of piston pump for reducing the pressure of the air in a closed vessel. If the volume of the pump cylinder is *v*, and that of the vessel and connecting tubes is *V*, what reduction in pressure is theoretically obtainable after *n* complete strokes? What, in practice, limits the vacuum obtainable?

Give a brief account of some method of producing a good vacuum.
(O. & C.)

5. Describe, with diagrams, the construction and mode of action of a pump that will reduce the pressure of the air in a vessel to 0·001 mm. of mercury. How are pressures of this order of magnitude measured?

A piston pump of effective volume 200 c.c. is used to exhaust a vessel of volume 1 litre. How many complete strokes will be required to reduce the pressure of the air in the vessel to one-hundredth of its initial value? (Neglect the volume of the connecting tubes, etc., and assume that the temperature remains constant.) (O. & C.)

6. Explain the corrections which have to be made to the readings of the Fortin barometer to obtain the absolute pressure of the atmosphere.

A little air has leaked into a barometer tube 100 cms. long. The mercury stands at the 70 cms. mark when the tube is vertical, and at the 78 cms. mark when the tube is inclined at 30° to the vertical. What is the atmospheric pressure in mms. of mercury? (O.S.)

7. Explain what is meant by a *coefficient of expansion*.

Describe an experiment to determine the coefficient of volume expansion of a fixed mass of air kept at constant pressure.

The density of argon is 1·60 gm. per litre at 27° C. and at a pressure of 75 cm. of mercury. What is the mass of argon in an argon-filled electric lamp bulb of volume 100 c.c. if the pressure inside is 75 cm. of mercury when the average temperature of the gas is 120° C.? (J.M.B.)

8. How does the density of a gas vary with its pressure and temperature?

Calculate the volume occupied at 27° C. and 720 mm. pressure by 1 gm. of dry oxygen ; the density of oxygen at N.T.P. being 1·36 gm. per litre. What would be the volume if the oxygen were saturated with water vapour, assuming the saturation vapour pressure at 27° C. to be 30 mm. of mercury? (C.)

9. If a gas rigorously obeys Boyle's Law, and if temperature is measured by assuming that the gas obeys Charles's Law, prove that the coefficient of expansion of the gas at constant pressure is equal to its coefficient of increase of pressure at constant volume.

Describe the constant volume gas thermometer, and explain how it may be applied to determine the steady temperature of an oil-bath. What difficulties are encountered if an accurate value of this temperature is required? (C.W.B.)

10. Describe a constant volume gas thermometer. How would you calibrate such an instrument for use over a range of about − 20° C. to 150° C.?

The bulb of a constant volume gas thermometer contains air and sufficient alcohol to keep the air saturated. The pressure in the bulb is 1,168 mm. at 60° C. when the saturated vapour pressure of alcohol is 350 mm. What will be the pressure in the bulb at 20° C. when the saturated vapour pressure of alcohol is 44 mm.? (C.)

11. Describe a constant volume air thermometer. Describe in detail how you would use it to determine the boiling-point of a salt solution.

How would the result compare with that for pure water? How would the boiling-point be affected if the solution were allowed to boil for some time?

A balloon is partially inflated to a volume of 5,000 cubic metres at ground level where the pressure is 76 cm. of mercury and the temperature 15° C. What will be its volume at a height where the pressure is 62 cm. and the temperature 6° C., assuming that the fabric is not stretched?

(J.M.B.)

12. State the general laws connecting the pressure, volume, and temperature of a gas, and explain how you would verify one of them.

Two equal glass bulbs are joined by a narrow tube and the whole is initially filled with gas at N.T.P. and sealed. What will the pressure of the gas become when one of the bulbs is immersed in boiling water and the other in ice?

(O. & C.)

13. Explain the difference between the centigrade and the absolute scales of temperature.

It is found that the volume of a certain gas increases in the ratio of 1·035 : 1 between 15° C. and 25° C. Calculate the absolute zero on the centigrade scale for this gas.

(O. & C.)

14. How would you determine the value of the gas constant, R? What errors would be involved in using air at atmospheric pressure in making the determination? Which gas would be the most suitable one to use for the experiment?

(C.S.)

15. Explain how the coefficient of increase of pressure of air at constant volume may be determined experimentally.

A thin-walled vessel made of quartz, whose expansion is negligible, is sealed when it contains dry air at a pressure and temperature of 75·3 cm. of mercury and – 22° C. respectively. Calculate the temperature to which the vessel can be safely heated, if the maximum internal pressure it can be depended upon to withstand without breaking is 114·0 cm. of mercury.

(C.W.B.)

16. State the law of thermal expansion of a gas, explaining under what conditions it holds, and how you would verify it.

A vertical tube, a metre long, open at the top, is surrounded by a steam jacket. The lower end is connected to a differential pressure gauge. Calculate the pressure this will indicate, if the atmospheric pressure is 760 mm. of mercury, and the atmospheric temperature is 15° C. (Density of air at N.T.P. = 0·00129 gm. per c.c.)

(O. & C.)

17. State the laws connecting the pressure, volume, and temperature of gases.

A barometer tube 90 cm. long contains some air above the mercury. The reading is 74·5 cm. when the true pressure is 76 cm. and the temperature 15° C. If the reading is observed to be 75·8 cm. on a day when the temperature is 5° C., what is the true pressure?

(O. & C.)

18. Draw pressure-volume diagrams and pressure-temperature diagrams to illustrate how the behaviour of a gas differs from that of a saturated vapour.

A bottle full of water is sealed and placed in a strong container full of air at 15 lb. per square inch and 10° C. The temperature is raised to 100° C. (a) Calculate the pressure inside the container if the bottle of water has remained sealed. (b) What happens if the water escapes from the bottle and saturates the air? What will then be the pressure within the container? (Normal atmospheric pressure should be taken as 14·7 lb. per square inch.) (O.)

19. Explain very briefly what is meant by the absolute scale of temperature and describe an experiment by which the zero of absolute temperature may be determined.

The height of the mercury column in a uniform barometer tube containing some air is 54 cm. when the temperature is 22° C. When the temperature is raised to 63° C. the height of the column is 52 cm. If the distance of the top of the tube from the level in the cistern is 100 cm. in each case and the atmospheric pressure is 76 cm. of mercury, calculate the temperature of melting ice on the absolute scale. Neglect any effects due to the change in temperature of the mercury. (J.M.B.)

20. Discuss the departures from Boyle's and Charles's law in the case of the so-called permanent gases ; how are these departures explained by the kinetic theory of gases? (C.S.)

21. Discuss the relation $pv = RT$ for a gas, and describe experiments to verify it. To what causes may the departures found be attributed? (C.S.)

22. State exactly the meaning of the equation $pv = RT$ and give the evidence for supposing that R is the same for all gases. Give an account of an equation which represents more accurately the equation of state of a gas. (C.S.)

23. What essential conditions must be fulfilled by an absolute scale of temperature? Outline the steps by which a practical thermometer can be calibrated in terms of the Kelvin Thermodynamic scale. (O.S.)

24. Explain what is meant by a difference in temperature of one degree C. as shown by (a) a constant-volume hydrogen thermometer, (b) a mercury in glass thermometer. Why do observations of the same temperature made with these two thermometers differ at different parts of the scale? Explain carefully why temperature measurement by the gas thermometer is regarded as the more fundamental.

Two vessels each of volume 100 c.c., one being at 27° C. and the other at 227° C., contain different mixtures of carbon dioxide and hydrogen at atmospheric pressure. The contents of the two vessels are allowed to mix through a short connecting tube while the temperature throughout becomes uniform at 27° C. The final proportion by volume of carbon dioxide in the mixture in both vessels is found to be 50 per cent. If the initial proportion by volume of carbon dioxide in the vessel at 27° C. was 53 per cent., what was the initial proportion by volume of carbon dioxide in the hotter vessel? Any change in volume of the containing vessel can be neglected. Assume that the gases behave as ideal gases. (J.M.B.)

25. Give an account of the kinetic theory of matter, indicating on broad lines how this theory explains (a) surface tension, (b) the laws of partial pressures of vapours, (c) the absolute zero. (C.S.)

26. How is Boyle's law for gases explained on the kinetic theory? Calculate the mean square molecular velocity of hydrogen at $0°$ C. (1 gm. of hydrogen at $0°$ C. and 760 mm. pressure occupies a volume of 11·2 litres.) (C.S.)

27. Show how the kinetic theory can be used to give information about the velocity of the molecules of a gas if the density and pressure are known. Explain what average velocity is thus obtained. How is the kinetic energy of translation of the molecules, per c.c. of different gases, related to the pressure?

The temperature of (a) argon and (b) nitrogen is raised from $0°$ C. to $1°$ C. at constant volume. Using the following data, find in each case what proportion of the total heat energy given to the gas for this purpose takes the form of energy of translation of the molecules. Comment on your results and indicate their physical significance.

Density of argon at $0°$ C. and a pressure of 10^6 dynes per sq. cm. $= 1·77$ gm. per litre.

Density of nitrogen at $0°$ C. and a pressure 10^6 dynes per sq. cm. $= 1·24$ gm. per litre.

Specific heat of argon at constant volume $= 0·074$ cal. per gm. per degree C.

Specific heat of nitrogen at constant volume $= 0·175$ cal. per gm. per degree C.

Joule's equivalent $= 4·2 \times 10^7$ ergs per calorie. (J.M.B.)

28. How is it possible to account for Boyle's law by means of the kinetic theory of gases?

Draw curves to show how the behaviour of real gases, e.g. hydrogen, nitrogen, carbon dioxide, differs from that indicated by Boyle's law, and show how such deviations may be explained by the kinetic theory. (J.M.B.)

29. Distinguish between the " average velocity " and the " root mean square velocity " of the molecules of a gas.

From considerations of kinetic theory obtain an expression for the pressure of a gas in terms of the root mean square velocity of the molecules.

Determine the root mean square velocity of hydrogen molecules at N.P.T. (Density of hydrogen at N.T.P. is $0·09$ gm. per litre ; density of mercury is $13·6$ gm. per c.c. ; g may be taken as 981 cm./sec.) (C.)

30. Find the root mean square velocity of the oxygen molecules in the atmosphere at $0°$ C., the density of oxygen at standard temperature and pressure being $1·43 \times 10^{-3}$ gm./c.c. (C.S., part question)

31. Discuss the assumptions which form the basis of the simple kinetic theory of gases and explain under what circumstances the simple laws require modification.

Calculate the root mean square velocity of molecules of a gas for which the specific heat at constant pressure is $6·84$ cal. per gm. mol.

per deg. C. ; the velocity of sound in the gas being 1,300 metres per second.

(Gas constant $R = 8 \cdot 31 \times 10^7$ ergs per gm. mol. per deg. C.) (J.M.B.)

32. Without deriving any formulae, use the kinetic theory of gases to explain (a) how a gas exerts a pressure, (b) why the temperature of a gas rises when the gas is compressed, (c) what happens when a quantity of liquid is introduced into a closed vessel.

How are the differences in the behaviour of real and ideal gases explained by the kinetic theory?

If there are $2 \cdot 7 \times 10^{19}$ molecules in a cubic centimetre of gas at $0°$ C. and 76 cm. of mercury pressure, what is the number per cubic centimetre (i) at $0°$ C. and 10^{-6} mm. pressure, (ii) at $39°$ C. and 10^{-6} mm. pressure?

(J.M.B.)

CHAPTER V

VAPOURS AND VAPOUR PRESSURE

IN Chapter IV a vapour was defined as a substance in the gaseous state below its critical temperature, and a distinction was made between saturated and unsaturated vapours. Saturated vapours will now be considered in greater detail.

Saturated vapours. Evaporation is the passage of a substance from the liquid to the gaseous state, taking place at the surface of the liquid. The rate at which evaporation takes place depends on the area of surface, the temperature, and several other factors to be discussed later.

Consider first the evaporation of a liquid into a closed space, initially evacuated. The energy of the faster-moving of the molecules near the surface of the liquid will enable them to get beyond the attraction of the neighbouring molecules, and they will pass out into the surrounding space. As more and more molecules enter the space, the pressure they exert by their collisions with the walls of the enclosure increases. But the molecules moving in the space above the liquid collide with the liquid surface as well as with the walls of the enclosure and with one another, and those striking the liquid surface may be supposed to return to the liquid. As the number of molecules in the space increases, so does the number returning to the liquid per second. Eventually a state of affairs will be reached at which as many molecules return to the surface per second as leave it per second ; when this happens, the number of molecules present in the vapour state remains steady, and the pressure of the vapour has reached a maximum steady value. The space is said to be *saturated with vapour*, and the vapour itself is called a *saturated vapour*.

Evaporation has not ceased when saturation occurs ; it continues all the while, but is balanced by condensation taking place at exactly the same rate. A state of affairs such as this, in which no change is apparent because two continually opposing tendencies are operating at exactly the same rate, is called *dynamic equilibrium*.

178

Thus a saturated vapour at any temperature is a vapour which is in dynamic equilibrium with its liquid at that temperature.

Since the pressure exerted by a gaseous substance is proportional to the number of molecules per unit volume, it is clear that the pressure of the saturated vapour at any temperature must be the greatest pressure that the vapour can exert at that temperature, under the conditions considered.

The effect of altering the volume, the external pressure, or the temperature of a saturated vapour can be forecast by continuing the foregoing ideas. *The fundamental action is the rate of evaporation from the surface,* for this precedes the return of the molecules which establishes equilibrium. Increasing the temperature of the space increases the average kinetic energy of the liquid molecules, increases the rate of evaporation, and so increases the pressure of the saturated vapour. The rate of evaporation from the liquid surface is unaffected by either increasing or decreasing the volume of the enclosure containing the vapour, and so *the pressure of the saturated vapour is independent of the volume.* If the pressure of the vapour in the chamber could be kept at a value very slightly above the saturated vapour pressure, more molecules would return to the liquid per second than leave it per second, and the whole of the vapour would condense ; if the pressure of the vapour in the space is maintained at a value very slightly below the saturated vapour pressure, fewer molecules return to the liquid per second than leave it per second and the whole evaporates.

To sum up : The pressure exerted by a saturated vapour at any temperature is the greatest pressure that the vapour can normally exert at that temperature. This pressure is called the saturated vapour pressure (s.v.p.), maximum vapour pressure, or often simply the vapour pressure of the liquid at that temperature. The value of the saturated vapour pressure depends *only* on the temperature, and increases with rise in temperature. It is not affected by changes in volume, provided these are not so extreme as to cause all the vapour to condense or all the liquid to evaporate. This pressure is the only pressure at which liquid and vapour can exist together in equilibrium for that particular temperature ; for all greater pressures, the whole of the substance is in the liquid state, while for all smaller pressures the whole of the substance is in the gaseous state as an unsaturated vapour.

Dalton's Law of Partial Pressures. Throughout this argument it has been supposed that the enclosure into which evaporation occurs is a vacuum to begin with. But it is found experimentally that the presence of air or any other gas which does not react with the vapour in any way makes no appreciable difference to the final state of affairs as between liquid and vapour, though it retards the rate at which the final state is reached. If the closed space contained air, it might be spoken of as " air saturated with vapour ", meaning a mixture of air and saturated vapour.

For example, at 20° C. the s.v.p. of water is 17·5 mm. mercury ; when equilibrium is reached at 20° C. between water and water vapour in a space which contains no other material, the pressure in the space is 17·5 mm. mercury. But if the space, previous to the introduction of the water, contained air at a pressure of 760 mm. mercury, the pressure exerted by the saturated vapour would still be 17·5 mm. mercury, and the total pressure $760 + 17\cdot5 = 777\cdot5$ mm. mercury.

This is one of the most important applications of Dalton's Law of Partial Pressures (p. 155), which states that the pressure of a mixture of gaseous substances which do not interact in any way is equal to the sum of their partial (that is, individual) pressures. The law, like most other simple generalisations about gases, is only approximately true, but is a satisfactory working rule.

Evaporation and boiling. Both evaporation and boiling are the change of state from liquid to vapour, and both require that latent heat should be supplied. Evaporation is invisible, takes place from the surface only, takes place at all temperatures, and can be accelerated by raising the temperature, by increasing the surface area, and by promoting the removal of saturated vapour from the neighbourhood of the surface, by pumping it off or driving it away by a draught of air.

Boiling is visible, takes place in the body of the liquid from the points at which heat is supplied, takes place at one fixed temperature only for a given pressure (this temperature is called the **boiling point**) and is accelerated only by increasing the rate at which heat is supplied. The bubbles which form in the boiling liquid and rise to the top are, of course, bubbles of saturated vapour, and as these do not collapse the pressure inside them (which is the s.v.p. of the liquid at that temperature) must equal the external pressure.

Hence, the saturated vapour pressure at the boiling point equals the external pressure on the liquid; or, a liquid boils at the temperature at which the saturated vapour pressure is exactly equal to the external pressure.

In a vessel heated at the bottom, the pressure at the point where the bubbles of vapour originate exceeds the atmospheric pressure (or the applied surface pressure) by the pressure due to the head of liquid in the vessel. Thus when a liquid is boiling steadily, the temperature at the bottom of the vessel may be a little in excess of the true boiling point. When water is heated in a beaker, the earliest visible sign of bubbling occurs well below the boiling-point ; trains of small bubbles of dissolved air rise to the surface. Next, the " singing " which precedes boiling is due to the collapse in the upper part of the liquid of bubbles of vapour, probably formed round air bubbles as nuclei, which were self-supporting when they originated in the slightly hotter liquid in the neighbourhood of the source of heat. Nuclei of some sort appear to be necessary for the continuous steady boiling of a liquid at its true boiling point under a given pressure ; without them, " bumping " or delayed boiling occurs. This is due to local superheating at the base of the liquid ; bubbles of vapour do not form until the temperature of the base is well above the true boiling point, so that when they are at length formed, the pressure in the bubbles is considerably greater than the outside pressure, and the bubbles rise with miniature explosions.

MEASUREMENT OF SATURATED VAPOUR PRESSURE

There are three general methods for the absolute measurement of saturated vapour pressures over a range of temperatures.

1. *The statical method*, in which the depression of a barometer column by saturated vapour in the " Torricellian " space is observed directly. This method is satisfactory for vapour pressures of between about 2 cm. and 40 cm. of mercury.

2. *The dynamical method*, which depends on the fact that a liquid boils at the temperature at which its saturated vapour pressure is equal to the outside pressure. This is applicable over a very wide range of pressures.

3. *The evaporation method*, in which the rate of loss of the material by free evaporation is observed, and the vapour pressure calculated

from this by means of the kinetic theory. This has been used chiefly for such substances as metals at high temperatures.

Statical method. A barometer tube A (Fig. 78) is surrounded by a water jacket B provided with a heater C, stirrer D, and thermometer. A little of the liquid under investigation is introduced up the mercury column by means of a special small pipette, sufficient

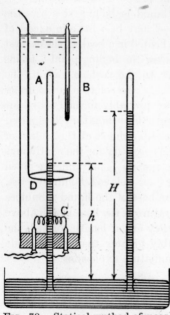

to form a thin layer over the surface of the mercury. The heating bath is well stirred and the temperature taken ; the height of the mercury column h is measured. This is subtracted from the height H of a good barometer recording the atmospheric pressure, and the difference $H - h$ measures the depression of the mercury column due to the pressure of the saturated vapour. It would, of course, be better to have the good barometer also inside B, and measure $H - h$ directly.

There are many sources of error in this simple experiment. It is difficult to measure the height of the mercury column accurately through the water jacket. The mercury inside the jacket is heated, and its density is less than that of cold mercury. Allowance should

FIG. 78.—Statical method of measuring saturated vapour pressure.

be made for the pressure of the layer of liquid over the mercury, and also for the effect this liquid exerts on the surface tension of the mercury. Also, the whole column must be at a uniform temperature. It is not sufficient to take the temperatures at different levels and take the average in the hope of correcting for non-uniformity thereby. The reason is, that if the temperature of the vapour column is not exactly uniform, the pressure inside the tube is the s.v.p. for the coldest part of the tube, since condensation will occur there from the hotter portions.

Most of these sources of error in the statical method were considered and corrected for in Regnault's careful experiments. The apparatus is really unsuitable for the measurement of very small vapour pressures, and for pressures much greater than 30 or 40 cm. of mercury. In one case, the pressure to be measured is going to be of the same order as the corrections to be applied, and in the other there is the difficulty of keeping a long column satisfactorily at a uniform temperature.

Dynamical method. As a liquid boils when its saturated vapour pressure equals the external pressure, the external pressure at the boiling point must equal the saturated vapour pressure at the boiling point. Hence, observations of the temperatures at which boiling occurs under different pressures give corresponding readings of temperature and saturated vapour pressure. Suitable simple apparatus is shown in Fig. 79. The liquid boils in the flask A, which is fitted with a thermometer in the vapour. The reflux condenser B condenses the vapour and returns it to the flask. The difference between the levels X and Y of the mercury manometer, subtracted from the atmospheric pressure if X is above Y, and added to the atmospheric pressure if Y is above X, gives the pressure throughout the apparatus. The total volume of the apparatus is increased by the flask C, so that gradual and controlled changes in pressure can

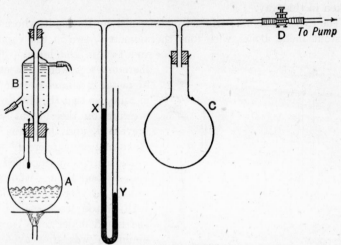

FIG. 79.—Dynamical method of measuring saturated vapour pressure.

be produced. The screw clip D separates the apparatus from the pump, which may be a water filter pump for pressures between about 2 cm. and 76 cm. of mercury, or a football pump for pressures above atmospheric.

It is sometimes difficult to grasp exactly how the apparatus works. The flask is filled above the liquid with the saturated vapour the pressure of which is required, but what happens when most of the vapour is condensed in the condenser? The condenser itself contains vapour and air, and the space beyond the condenser is full of air saturated with vapour at the temperature of the surroundings, but as all parts of the apparatus are in communication they must be at the same pressure as the inside of the flask. The pressure of the air recorded on the manometer is thus the pressure of the saturated vapour in the flask. This point has been stressed, because there is a tendency to think that " the vapour condenses leaving a partial vacuum ", as happens in some elementary experiments of a different type, and to forget that the colder portion of the apparatus contains air.

In the course of an experiment, the barometer is first read. The pressure in the flask is adjusted to a suitable value, and the clip closed. The steady temperature is read from the thermometer, and both the levels of the manometer are read. A series of readings is taken in this way.

The experiment was originally performed by Regnault, who used a stout metal boiler with four thermometers, two in the vapour

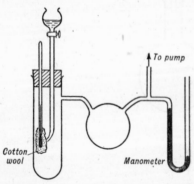

and two in the liquid. The thermometers were protected by metal tubulures containing mercury, so that the change in pressure on their bulbs was prevented, and there was no " external pressure error ".

The method was modified by Ramsay and Young, who surrounded a thermometer bulb with cotton wool soaked in the liquid under test. Actual ebullition was thus avoided, but the steady thermometer

FIG. 80.—Vapour pressure apparatus of Ramsay and Young.

reading gave the temperature at which liquid and vapour were in equilibrium under the observed pressure. Fig. 80 shows the apparatus used.

Evaporation method. Kinetic theory calculations of a type too advanced to give here enable the number of molecules striking and leaving unit area of a surface per second in the equilibrium state to be calculated for any temperature. This must equal the number of molecules *leaving* unit area per second *whether equilibrium is preserved or not* at that same temperature, and so gives the number of molecules of the substance which are removed permanently from unit area per second if the evaporation takes place into a high vacuum. The formula for the mass lost per square centimetre per second is

$$m = \alpha p \sqrt{\frac{M}{2\pi RT}},$$

where m is the mass evaporated, p is the saturated vapour pressure, T is the absolute temperature, R the gas constant, and α a constant for the material. The experiment thus consists of exposing the substance in a vessel of known surface area, in a highly evacuated enclosure maintained at the desired temperature, and weighing at the beginning and end of a measured interval of time.

Results. The vapour pressure curve for water. Fig. 81 shows how the S.V.P. of water varies with the temperature. At 0° C., the S.V.P. is not zero, being about 4·7 mm. of mercury. As the temperature increases, the curve rises, gradually at first and then more steeply. At 100° C., the pressure is 760 mm. mercury. The curve continues to rise and become steeper until the critical temperature is reached. Above this temperature there can, of course, be no such thing as saturated water vapour.

The vapour pressure curves of all other pure liquids are of the same general shape. Several empirical formulae for the vapour pressure curve have been suggested, but no theoretical equation seems to have been established. The Clausius-Clapeyron equation

$$\frac{dp}{dT} = \frac{LJ}{T(v_2 - v_1)},$$

where dp is the small change in vapour pressure corresponding to a small change dT in the absolute temperature T, L is the latent heat of evaporation, and v_1 and v_2 the volumes of unit mass of liquid and

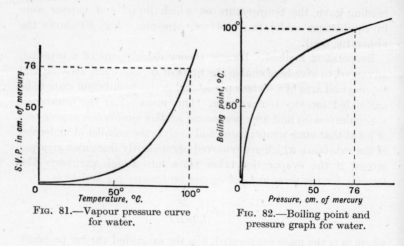

FIG. 81.—Vapour pressure curve for water.

FIG. 82.—Boiling point and pressure graph for water.

of vapour respectively, enables dp to be calculated if dT and the other quantities are provided. But as L, v_1, and v_2 are all functions of the temperature, it is obviously impossible to obtain the equation for the curve from this equation as it stands.

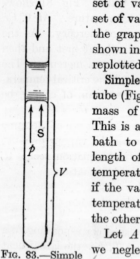

FIG. 83.—Simple tube experiment.

Variation of boiling point with pressure. As a set of values of temperature and s.v.p. are also a set of values of boiling point and external pressure, the graph of boiling point against pressure is as shown in Fig. 82. This is, of course, simply Fig. 81 replotted with the axes interchanged.

Simple tube experiment. Consider a wide capillary tube (Fig. 83) sealed at one end, containing a fixed mass of air imprisoned by a thread of water. This is attached to a scale, and heated in a water bath to different known temperatures. If the length of the air column is measured at different temperatures between about 20° C. and 70° C., and if the value of the s.v.p. of water at one of these temperatures is known, the values of the s.v.p. at the other temperatures can be calculated.

Let A be the pressure of the atmosphere. If we neglect the pressure of the small column of water, this is also the pressure of the enclosed mixture of air and saturated water vapour. At any temperature $T°$ absolute, let p be the pressure of the air, S the s.v.p. of water, and V the volume of the mixture, which may conveniently be measured in centimetres length of tube.

By Dalton's Law of partial pressures,

$$A = p + S.$$

Now, the air in the tube obeys the gas laws, so we can imagine this isolated and calculate its behaviour; while no calculations can be done with the saturated vapour.

Considering the air pressure alone,

$$p = (A - S).$$

Now, for the fixed mass of air in the tube, $pV/T = $ constant.

$$\therefore \frac{(A - S)V}{T} = \text{constant.}$$

At temperature $T_1°$ absolute, let V_1 be the observed volume and S_1 the known s.v.p.

At temperature $T_2°$ absolute, let V_2 be the observed volume and S_2 the unknown saturated vapour pressure.

Then
$$\frac{(A - S_1)V_1}{T_1} = \frac{(A - S_2)V_2}{T_2};$$

whence
$$S_2 = A - (A - S_1)\frac{V_1}{V_2} \cdot \frac{T_2}{T_1}.$$

The " Wet Flask " experiment. The object of this exercise is to find the value of the saturated vapour pressure of water at a temperature in the neighbourhood of 60° C., its value at air temperature being supplied. The operations are almost the same as those of the dry flask experiment (p. 132) except that at the beginning of the experiment the inside of the flask is wet, and the heating of the flask only goes up to about 60° C.

The empty wet flask, with fittings, is weighed, and heated up to about 60° C. (no higher) with the clip open. The clip is then closed, the flask removed and the clip opened under cold water at the temperature of the air, which is known. The high temperature will be called $T_2°$ abs., and the air temperature $T_1°$ abs. After levelling, the clip is closed, the outside of the flask dried, and the flask weighed.

Finally, the whole flask is filled with water and weighed. The barometer is read, and tables are used to give the s.v.p. of water at air temperature, S_1.

From the first and third weighings the weight of water filling the whole flask is found, while from the second and third weighings the weight of water to fill up the space occupied by the cold air is given. Assuming the density of water to be unity, we have the volume V_2 occupied by a fixed mass of air saturated with water vapour at the high temperature T_2—this is the total volume of the flask—and also the volume V_1 occupied by the same mass of air saturated with water vapour at T_1.

Let S_1 be the known s.v.p. at the low temperature, S_2 the unknown s.v.p. at the high temperature, and A the pressure of the atmosphere.

Then, as on p. 187, the pressure of the air at the low temperature is $(A - S_1)$, and at the high temperature $(A - S_2)$. Hence, using the relation

$$\frac{(A - S)V}{T} = constant \text{ for the air,}$$

$$\frac{(A - S_1)V_1}{T_1} = \frac{(A - S_2)V_2}{T_2};$$

whence $\qquad S_2 = A - (A - S_1)\dfrac{V_1}{V_2} \cdot \dfrac{T_2}{T_1}.$

Determination of vapour density. The term vapour density as used in Chemistry usually refers to the ratio

$$\frac{density \ of \ vapour \ under \ given \ conditions \ of \ temp. \ and \ pressure}{density \ of \ hydrogen \ under \ same \ conditions \ of \ temp. \ and \ pressure}.$$

The determination of the absolute density in gm./c.c. is first made, and from this the density relative to hydrogen is calculated.

Several methods are available. Dumas' method is to weigh a large bulb of thin glass (Fig. 84) the volume of which is known, insert a quantity of the substance in the liquid state, heat the bulb in a bath at a known steady temperature above the normal boiling point of the liquid until all the liquid has evaporated and the bulb is filled with vapour, and seal the tip of the bulb, which is then removed and weighed when cool. The mass of vapour occupying a known volume at known temperature and pressure is thus found ; hence its density under these conditions is calculated and can be compared with the density of hydrogen at the same temperature and pressure.

FIG. 84.—Dumas' method for vapour density.

In Victor Meyer's apparatus (Fig. 85), a weighed quantity of the liquid in a small stoppered bottle is held at the top of a long tube, the bulb B at the lower end of which is maintained at a steady known temperature by means of a liquid of suitable boiling point. The apparatus is firmly sealed, and the small bottle A is then dropped into the lower bulb. The liquid vaporises, and air (less dense than the vapour) is displaced and collected over water or mercury at D, the temperature and pressure of the collected air being observed. From this, the mass of air which is displaced by the vapour is calculated, and the density of the vapour relative to air is simply *mass of liquid taken/mass of air displaced*. This must be so, since if the lower bulb is at, say, 120° C., and the contents of the bottle on volatilising occupy 7 c.c., 7 c.c. of air at 120° C. is displaced from the lower bulb (though it fills a much smaller volume in the collecting vessel).

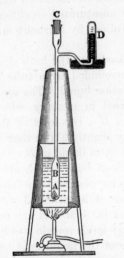

The mass of liquid taken vaporises to occupy 7 c.c. at 120° C., and the mass of air collected occupies the same volume at the same temperature ; thus the ratio of the two masses gives the ratio of the densities.

The density relative to hydrogen is easily worked out from the density relative to air. Alternatively, the volume of air collected can be imagined to be hydrogen for the purpose of the calculation.

The value of the vapour density is required so that the molecular weight of the substance can be calculated, using Avogadro's Hypothesis, which states that equal volumes of all gases under the same conditions of temperature and pressure contain equal numbers of molecules. Hydrogen is known to be

FIG. 85.—Victor Meyer's method for vapour density.

diatomic. If the number of molecules in 1 c.c. be n, then vapour density

$$= \frac{\text{mass of 1 c.c. substance}}{\text{mass of 1 c.c. hydrogen}}$$

$$= \frac{\text{mass of } n \text{ molecules of substance}}{\text{mass of } n \text{ molecules of hydrogen}}$$

$$= \frac{\text{mass of 1 molecule of substance}}{\text{mass of 2 atoms of hydrogen}}$$

$$= \frac{\frac{1}{2} \text{ mass of 1 molecule of substance}}{\text{mass of 1 atom of hydrogen}}$$

$$= \tfrac{1}{2} \text{ molecular weight of substance.}$$

Or, *molecular weight* $= 2 \times$ *vapour density.*

Avogadro's hypothesis should apply strictly for an ideal gas only; for actual gases it holds best as low densities are attained. It is therefore best to measure the vapour density at as low a density as possible, certainly as far as possible from saturation.

Density of a saturated vapour. The density of a saturated vapour must be determined directly. Since the gas laws do not hold closely up to the point of saturation, the density cannot be calculated from observations of the vapour density in the unsaturated condition. The density of a saturated vapour was determined by Fairbairn and Tate by the following method.

A weighed amount of liquid was introduced into the bulb A of known volume (Fig. 86), and this was surrounded by a tube B containing a much larger quantity of the same liquid. The open

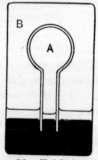

end of A is immersed in mercury which fills the lower end of B. The level of the mercury in A is very slightly above that in B, on account of the extra liquid in B. The whole is immersed in a bath and heated, the mercury levels being observed carefully. As long as the space A is saturated with vapour, the pressures in A and B are the same, and the mercury levels remain steady. As soon as the whole of the liquid in A has evaporated, and the space begins to be unsaturated, the mercury rises in A, since the

Fig. 86.—Fairbairn and Tate's experiment.

pressure of the still saturated space B increases more rapidly with the temperature than the pressure of the now unsaturated vapour in A. The temperature at which the mercury levels begin to alter is noted ; the mass of liquid originally in A just fills it and just saturates it at this temperature, so the density of the saturated vapour at this temperature is known.

Collection of a gas over water. When a gas is collected over water, the pressure of the gas itself is less than the observed external pressure by the pressure of the saturated water vapour with which it is necessarily mixed. The following example shows the method of correction.

EXAMPLE. 197 c.c. of hydrogen are collected over water at 20° C. and 756 mm. pressure. Find the volume occupied by the hydrogen at N.T.P. The S.V.P. of water at 20° C. $= 17\cdot5$ mm.

Using Dalton's Law of partial pressures,

pressure of hydrogen $= 756 - 17\cdot5 = 738\cdot5$ mm.

$$\text{volume at N.T.P.} = 197 \times \frac{273}{293} \times \frac{738\cdot5}{760} = 178\cdot4 \text{ c.c.}$$

If the water vapour pressure is not allowed for, the figure obtained is $182\cdot6$ c.c., an error of about 2 per cent being involved. In very elementary work in Chemistry the water-vapour correction is often neglected on account of its difficulty, yet great care is taken to ensure that the water levels inside and outside the measuring tube are the same. As it would require a difference in levels of nearly 24 cm. of water to cause an error as great as that made in neglecting the vapour pressure in this case, this precaution seems rather trivial if the water vapour pressure is not considered. But as the column of water standing in a eudiometer or other vessel reduces the pressure of the enclosed gas below the outside pressure, and thus causes a further error in the same direction as the vapour pressure, levelling is at least a step in the right direction.

Mass of a mixture of air and saturated water vapour.

EXAMPLE. Find the mass of a litre of air at 750 mm. pressure and 20° C., saturated with water vapour, given that the density of water vapour is $0\cdot625$ that of air under the same conditions, and that the density of air at N.T.P. is $1\cdot29$ gm. per litre. The S.V.P. of water at 20° C. is $17\cdot5$ mm. mercury.

The first step is to apply Dalton's Law of partial pressures.

The mixture comprises

    (1) 1 litre of air at 20° C. and $750 - 17.5 = 732.5$ mm. pressure,

    (2) 1 litre of water vapour at 20° C. and 17·5 mm. pressure.

Now the mass of (1) could be found by reducing the volume to N.T.P. and multiplying by the given density. But (although it would give the right answer) we cannot apply this treatment to (2), for the very good physical reason that, however the arithmetic may work out to hide such a mistake, we cannot possibly have water vapour at N.T.P. (At 0° C. the S.V.P. is 4·7 mm., and water vapour can only exist at Normal Temperature at this or a lower pressure ; at Normal Pressure, water vapour can only exist at temperatures of 100° C. or higher.) It is therefore more sensible to avoid this reduction of the volume to N.T.P., and instead to work the other way round, reducing the density of air (with which we can take any liberties) to that at the given conditions.

The density of air at 20° C. and 732·5 mm. is

$$1.29 \times \frac{732.5}{760} \times \frac{273}{293} \text{ gm. per litre.}$$

$$= 1.158 \text{ gm. per litre.}$$

The density of air at 20° C. and 17·5 mm. pressure is

$$1.29 \times \frac{17.5}{760} \times \frac{273}{293} \text{ gm. per litre}$$

$$= 0.0277 \text{ gm. per litre.}$$

The density of water vapour at 17·5 mm. and 20° C. is

$$0.0277 \times 0.625 = 0.017 \text{ gm. per litre.}$$

Hence the mass of one litre of the mixture is

$$1.158 + 0.017 = 1.175 \text{ gm.}$$

Steam distillation. This is an application of Dalton's Law of partial pressures. Nitrobenzene, aniline, and many organic liquids which do not mix with water can be distilled at temperatures very much below their normal boiling points by passing a current of steam from a generator through the mixture (maintained at about 100° C.) from which it is required to distil the liquid.

The vapour pressure of nitrobenzene at 99° C. is about 27 mm. of mercury, while that of water at the same temperature is 733 mm., the total pressure of a mixture of the saturated vapours of the two liquids at 99° C. being, by Dalton's Law, $733 + 27 = 760$ mm. Hence, under an external pressure of 760 mm., a mixture of nitrobenzene and water should boil at 99° C. So far as the evaporation of the nitrobenzene is concerned, this is simply equivalent to distilling it in a partial vacuum at a pressure of 27 mm.—the pressure of the steam as it were " neutralises " 733 mm. of the external pressure. (A similar principle is used in the Electrolux refrigerator described on page 208 ; in this, the part of the steam is played by hydrogen.) But the composition of the distillate is the important thing here. On the simple kinetic theory assumption that pressure is proportional to the number of molecules per unit volume, for any volume of the vapour distilling over

$$\frac{\text{no. of nitrobenzene molecules}}{\text{no. of water molecules}} = \frac{\text{pressure of nitrobenzene}}{\text{pressure of water vapour}} = \frac{27}{733},$$

and this is the molecular composition of the distillate—27 molecules in every 760, or about one molecule in 28, are nitrobenzene molecules.   But the molecular weight of water is 18, and that of nitrobenzene is 123.   The masses distilling over are thus in the ratio

mass of nitrobenzene : mass of water $= 27 \times 123 : 18 \times 733$,

or nearly 1 : 4.   So one part in five by weight of the distillate is nitrobenzene.   It can be seen that the chief reason for the effectiveness of the method is the low molecular weight of water.

Vapour pressure of a solution.   The vapour pressure of a solution is always less than that of the pure solvent.   The relation is easily worked out for a dilute solution of a non-volatile substance by making certain simple assumptions, and can be deduced properly by thermodynamics.

Evaporation from the surface of the liquid takes place as molecules of sufficient energy reach the surface from below.   For a pure liquid, all such molecules are able to leave the surface.   Suppose that the molecules of the solute behave in the liquid exactly like molecules of the solvent in every way, but are unable to evaporate. Let the solution contain n moles of solute and N moles of solvent. Of the molecules reaching the surface in any given time, a fraction n/N are solute molecules which do not vaporise, hence the number of molecules leaving the surface per second is reduced by a fraction n/N, and the saturated vapour pressure is reduced in the same ratio. Thus, if δp be the reduction in the s.v.p., which has the value p for the pure solvent,

$$\frac{\delta p}{p} = \frac{n}{N}.$$

If m be the mass of solute and M the molecular weight, the number of moles present n, is m/M. It can be seen that, for a given mass of a given solvent, the lowering of the vapour pressure is directly proportional to the mass of solute dissolved, and inversely proportional to the molecular weight of the solute.

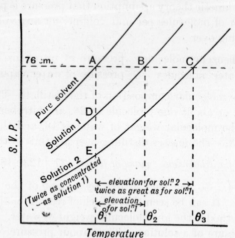

FIG. 87.—Showing effect of concentration on vapour pressure and on boiling point.

It follows that the boiling point of a solution of a non-volatile substance is always higher than that of the pure solvent. Considering the curves of Fig. 87, the s.v.p. of the pure solvent reaches 760 mm. at $\theta_1°$ C., while solution 1 must be raised to $\theta_2°$ C. before the s.v.p. reaches 760 mm. Solution 2, twice as concentrated as solution 1, must be raised to $\theta_3°$ C. before this happens. If the concentrations and the changes in vapour pressure are relatively small, the curves of Fig. 87 can be regarded as being very nearly parallel straight lines. As the lowering of vapour pressure is proportional to the molecular concentration (that is, to n/N), $AE = 2AD$: and as the lines are regarded as parallel, $AC = 2AB$. Hence, the elevation of the boiling point is, for all practical purposes, proportional to the molecular concentration n/N.

In determining the boiling point of a solution, the thermometer must be placed *with its bulb in the liquid*, which is maintained in steady ebullition. As has been pointed out on p. 7, a thermometer with its bulb in the vapour records the temperature at which the vapour of the solvent is in equilibrium with the pure solvent condensed on the thermometer, and thus registers the boiling point of the pure solvent, and not the required boiling point of the solution.

Vapour pressure over a curved surface. Surface tension theory shows that, if p_1 dynes per sq. cm. be the pressure on the concave side, and p_2 dynes per sq. cm. that on the convex side, of a spherical liquid surface of radius r cm. (Fig. 88), then

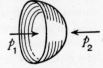

$$p_1 - p_2 = 2T/r,$$

where T is the surface tension of the liquid in dynes per cm.

FIG. 88.

Consider a liquid in an enclosure containing only its saturated vapour, and let a vertical capillary tube of radius r stand upright in the liquid (Fig. 89). Let p_3 be the s.v.p. at the plane surface, p_1 that over the concave surface, and p_2 that just inside the liquid in the tube. Let ρ be the density of the liquid in gm. per c.c., σ the density of the saturated vapour, in the same units, and let h cm. be the vertical height of the column.

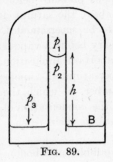

Then
$$p_1 - p_2 = \frac{2T}{r},$$

and, writing down the two expressions for the pressure at B inside and outside the tube, which must be the same,

$$\left.\begin{array}{l} p_1 + g\sigma h = p_3 \\ p_2 + g\rho h = p_3 \end{array}\right\}.$$

Eliminating h and p_2,

FIG. 89.

$$p_3 - p_1 = \frac{2T}{r} \cdot \frac{\sigma}{\rho - \sigma} \text{ dynes per sq. cm.}$$

Thus the vapour pressure over a concave surface of radius r is less than that over a plane surface by an amount $\dfrac{2T}{r} \cdot \dfrac{\sigma}{\rho - \sigma}$; similarly, the vapour pressure over a convex surface of radius r exceeds that over a plane surface by $\dfrac{2T}{r} \cdot \dfrac{\sigma}{\rho - \sigma}$. Some idea of the size of this difference may be gained by substituting rough values and making an approximate calculation.

For a water drop of radius 0·0001 cm. at 20° C., $\rho = 1$ gm. per c.c., $\sigma = 0·000017$ gm. per c.c., $T = 73$ dynes per cm. The pressure excess is $\dfrac{2 \times 73}{0·0001} \times \dfrac{0·000017}{1}$ dynes per sq. cm., $\backsimeq 25$ dynes per sq. cm., or about 2×10^{-2} mm. mercury.

The effect thus does not seem to be very large for a reasonably small drop, but it must be remembered that it increases as the radius of the drop decreases. It means that drops of liquid always tend to evaporate, and the smaller the drop the greater the vapour pressure excess, and the faster it evaporates. In a cloud consisting of a mixture of drops of different sizes suspended in a space saturated with water vapour, the smaller drops (with the greatest vapour pressure excess) evaporate, and the larger drops (with the smallest vapour pressure excess) grow. It is hard to imagine how a vapour can ever condense at all if it has to start with droplets of extremely small dimensions. In practice, in the absence of small dust particles, which offer a nucleus of appreciable radius to begin with, or charged ions the electric field of which tends to increase the radius of a drop condensing on them, the vapour pressure can be increased considerably beyond the normal saturated vapour pressure before condensation occurs. A vapour at a pressure above the saturated vapour pressure for that temperature is said to be supersaturated. Some degree of supersaturation is usually necessary before a vapour will condense at all, even on nuclei. A very important application of the condensation of droplets from a supersaturated vapour upon charged ions is the Wilson Cloud Chamber, in which the tracks of ionising particles are made visible by the condensation of small drops of water on the ions they produce in their passage through air supersaturated with water vapour.

Surface tension also affects the formation of bubbles in a boiling liquid. In order to blow a bubble of radius r, there must be a pressure excess of $2T/r$ inside it, so that the s.v.p. must exceed the outside pressure by $2T/r$ before ebullition can occur. (The additional $\dfrac{2T}{r} \cdot \dfrac{\sigma}{\rho - \sigma}$ term is very small and is neglected in this argument.)

At 140° C. for water, $T = 50$ dynes per cm. approximately, and the s.v.p. of water is about 5×10^6 dynes per sq. cm.; so, as the atmospheric pressure is about 10^6 dynes per sq. cm. the excess is

4×10^6 dynes per sq. cm. The radius of bubbles which would just be supported from within by their own vapour pressure is given by substituting in the equation

$$\text{pressure excess} = \frac{2T}{r},$$

whence

$$4 \times 10^6 = \frac{2 \times 50}{r},$$

and

$$r = 2 \cdot 5 \times 10^{-5} \text{ cm.}$$

Hence, in order to initiate steam bubbles of this radius, the temperature of the water would have to be about 140° C. Once the bubble is formed, the pressure excess required decreases as the radius increases and the bubble grows ; so such a bubble would swell rapidly and burst explosively. This is the cause of " boiling by bumping " (p. 181). Ordinary water boils steadily at first, as bubbles of dissolved air act as nuclei of appreciable radius into which the water vapour can evaporate. But after water has been boiled for some time so that most of the dissolved air has been removed, bumping can only be prevented by the addition of small pieces of porous pot or other substance, which serve the double purpose of providing nuclei and also help to break up large bubbles as they rise.

COOLING DUE TO EVAPORATION

Whenever a substance changes from the liquid to the vapour state, latent heat of evaporation must be supplied. The lower the temperature, the greater is the value of the latent heat. This is easily seen, since we can turn one gram of water at 20° C. into steam at 100° C. either (a) by heating the water first to 100° C., and then supplying 540 calories, or (b) by evaporating it at 20° C. and then heating the vapour up to 100° C. As the initial state and final result are the same in both cases, the same quantity of heat must have been used in both cases. As the specific heat of water vapour is considerably less than that of water, the latent heat at 20° C. must be considerably greater than that at 100° C.

If evaporation is promoted and no other source of heat is available, the latent heat is drawn from the liquid itself and from its surroundings, which are thus cooled. This is the principle of most commercial refrigerators, in which a volatile liquid is made to evaporate rapidly, the vapour then being condensed and returned by the use of a compressor or some other means. It is also the basis of many simple everyday devices, such as the use of unglazed earthenware for butter coolers ; the earthenware is kept moistened with water, and evaporation from the porous surface keeps the temperature of the vessel and its contents cool.

The temperature of the human body is maintained at about 98·4° F., whatever the temperature of the surroundings and the nature of the thermal insulation with which it is clad. Heat is continually generated by the chemical actions which occur in the body, and this must be dissipated as fast as it is produced if the temperature is to remain steady. This dissipation is achieved largely by the evaporation from moist internal surfaces of water which is exhaled, and by the evaporation of perspiration from the skin. If the evaporation is too rapid, as when one sits in a draught, a sense of chill and discomfort is felt. If the evaporation is not rapid enough, as in a small inadequately ventilated room, the even more acute discomfort of " stuffiness " is produced ; this has little to do with the actual temperature or with the accumulation of carbon dioxide or " bad air ", for it is experienced in the open at all temperatures in moist climates. It is because the air is so near saturation that necessary evaporation from the body is reduced below the comfort level. The factor which determines personal comfort is not how much water vapour the air contains, but *how much more there is room for at that temperature*—in other words, how far the air is from being saturated with water vapour.

The moisture content relative to that of saturated air, called the relative humidity, is thus the really important quantity which controls the evaporation of water from a surface.

Relative Humidity. Definition I. The relative humidity of the atmosphere is the ratio

$$\frac{\text{mass of water vapour present in a certain volume of the air}}{\text{mass of water vapour required to saturate the same volume at the same temperature.}}$$

Assuming that water vapour obeys Boyle's Law closely right up to the point of saturation, the density of the vapour, and hence the mass present in a given volume, is proportional to the pressure it exerts. This assumption is not quite correct, but the inaccuracy is not really important for this purpose. It leads to a second and not quite identical definition.

Definition II. The relative humidity of the atmosphere is the ratio

actual pressure of water vapour present in the atmosphere
———————————————————————————————————
saturated vapour pressure of water at the temperature of the
atmosphere.

Instruments for determining relative humidity are called **hygrometers.** These may be classified broadly as :

(*a*) *absorption hygrometers*, which employ definition I, and have to be used with tables stating the mass of water vapour to saturate a given volume, say 1 cubic metre, of air at different temperatures. A set of such tables was compiled by Regnault. The chemical hygrometer is the standard example of this type.

(*b*) *dew point hygrometers*, which employ definition II, and have to be used with tables giving the S.V.P. of water at different temperatures.

(*c*) *empirical hygrometers*, for which no complete theory has yet been worked out. These are by far the most important instruments. The two chief types are the wet-and-dry bulb hygrometer and the hair hygrometer.

A brief account only of the more important instruments will be given here.*

Chemical hygrometer. In this instrument, a stream of air is aspirated slowly over drying tubes, and the gain in weight of the tubes and the volume of air passed over are recorded. The mass of water vapour actually present in a given volume of air is thus calculated, and this is compared with the mass required to saturate the same volume of air at the same temperature, as given in tables. The apparatus is large and not readily portable, the experiment takes a considerable time, rather laborious corrections must be applied, and by the time the result has eventually been worked out conditions will probably have changed. Its chief use is in the laboratory for standardising the simpler types of instrument.

Dew point hygrometers. The dew point is the temperature to which the air must be cooled in order to deposit dew on a surface in contact with it. As the cooling takes place at constant pressure, the pressures of both air and water vapour are unaffected by it.

The usual method of determining the dew point is to cool the

* For further information the reader should consult " A Discussion on Hygrometry " (The Physical Society, 1921).

surface on which dew is to be deposited, observe the temperature of the surface at which a film of dew first appears on it and the temperature at which the film disappears as the surface is allowed to warm up again ; the mean of the two temperatures is taken as the dew point.

At the dew point, *the water vapour actually present in the air is sufficient to saturate it.* Thus the *actual pressure* of the water vapour in the air is the *saturated water vapour pressure* at the dew point. Hence the relative humidity

$$= \frac{\text{actual water vapour pressure in the air}}{\text{s.v.p. of water at air temperature}}$$

$$= \frac{\text{s.v.p. of water at the dew point}}{\text{s.v.p. of water at air temperature}}.$$

All that is needed then is to observe the air temperature and the dew point, and to have available tables of saturated vapour pressures. For example, if the air temperature is 18·0° C., and dew is first deposited at 11·0° C. and disappears at 11·8° C., the dew point is 11·4° C. From tables,

s.v.p. of water at 11·4° C. = 10·11 mm.

s.v.p. of water at 18·0° C. = 15·46 mm.

$$\text{Relative humidity} = \frac{10·11}{15·46} = 0·655 = 65·5 \text{ per cent.}$$

The most convenient form of dew-point hygrometer is that due to Regnault (Fig. 90). Two glass tubes are mounted side by side, the lower end of each tube being closed by a thin highly polished silver thimble. One tube contains a quantity of ether, through which air entering by the tube shown is bubbled by connecting the outlet tube to an aspirator or filter pump. This stream of air both provides a large surface from which the ether can evaporate (the interior surface of the bubbles) and also removes air saturated with ether vapour, so that the ether evaporates rapidly, with consequent cooling of the silver thimble. The observer, standing some distance away, takes the reading of the thermometer at the instant when the dew is first noticed on the thimble. Comparison with the appearance of the thimble on the second tube enables this to be judged with considerable accuracy, and the thermometer in this gives the air temperature. The flow of air is then stopped, and the thimble is allowed to warm up again, the temperature of the thermometer being read when the last trace of dew has disappeared. As the thermometer is close to the thimble, and as during the cooling part of the experiment the current of air stirs the ether well, it can be taken that the reading of the thermometer does give the temperature of the thimble surface fairly accurately. Ezer Griffiths found, by connecting one junction of a thermocouple to the outside of the thimble and the other junction to the thermometer bulb, that with this type of thimble the difference between the thermometer reading

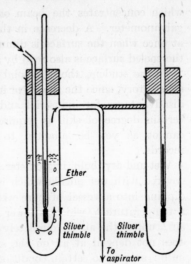

FIG. 90.—Regnault's dew-point hygrometer.

and the true thimble temperature at the instant of deposition and vanishing of the dew film was about 0·3° C.

The chief experimental difficulties with the dew-point method are in observing the instant at which dew appears, and in the uncertainty as to how far the temperature of the thermometer represents that of the surface. Many of the earlier forms of dew-point hygrometer failed in one or both of these respects. Also, the instrument should be used in still air, since the temperature at which dew is deposited from a current of air streaming past the surface is lower than the true dew point. The observer himself is a source of water vapour, and should stand as far from the apparatus as possible.

In a modern form of Regnault's hygrometer, due to Griffiths, a sample of air is trapped in a cubical box containing the silver thimble, which is observed through a window ; it is then certain that the air is still and that the observer cannot affect the result. A distant-reading form of dew-point hygrometer has also been devised by Griffiths. This uses the fact that the formation of a fine film of dew on a polished surface causes a huge decrease in its reflecting power for radiant heat. Radiation from an incandescent lamp is reflected from the cooled surface on to a concave mirror which concentrates the beam on a thermocouple connected to a galvanometer. A decrease in the thermocouple reading indicates at once when the surface is dimmed by dew. The temperature of the cooled surface is also read by a thermocouple.

To the student, the dew-point hygrometer probably seems very satisfactory, since the theory of it is so straightforward. The chief disadvantages for industrial and meteorological work are that a certain degree of skill is required for its operation, and that it cannot as yet be adapted to the production of continuous records.

Wet-and-dry bulb hygrometer. When a thermometer bulb is covered with wet muslin which is kept moist by means of a wick dipping into a vessel of pure water, the thermometer will record a temperature t_w which is lower than the true temperature of the air t, unless the air is completely saturated. The difference $(t - t_w)$ does not depend at all on the size or shape of the thermometer bulb; subject to certain conditions to be mentioned later, it varies only with the relative humidity of the atmosphere. An ordinary thermometer is usually mounted by the side of this, to give the air temperature t, and the whole apparatus is called the *wet-and-dry bulb hygrometer*.

The theory can be outlined in a general way. The lower the relative humidity the more rapidly will evaporation take place from the muslin; and the faster the evaporation the more rapidly is the necessary latent heat abstracted from the thermometer bulb, and the lower is the steady temperature to be reached before this is balanced by heat gained from the air. As the problem seems essentially to be that of furnishing latent heat from the surrounding air, it seems reasonable that the intermediate surfaces involved (the muslin and bulb itself) should not affect the steady state of affairs, since they are always at a steady temperature.

The deduction of an explicit formula giving relative humidity in terms of the difference $(t - t_w)$ is a formidable task, as so many factors are involved. Theoretical formulae were derived by Clerk Maxwell for still air, and by G. I. Taylor for moving air. Regnault employed an empirical formula advanced earlier by August and Apjohn,

$$p = p_w - AP(t - t_w),$$

where p is the actual vapour pressure, p_w the S.V.P. at the wet-bulb temperature, P the atmospheric pressure, and A a "constant". Having calculated p, the relative humidity is obtained by dividing p by the s.v.p. at $t°$, thus constructing tables from which the relative humidity for a given t and $(t - t_w)$ can be read. Regnault's formula is the basis of the tables now in use in Great Britain.

The value of the "constant" A depends on the strength of the air-draught past the wet bulb if this is small, though its value is constant for all speeds exceeding about 2·5 metres per sec. Thus the speed of the draught *if low* must be known, so that the appropriate A can be used ; or else an artificial "strong wind" exceeding 2·5 metres/sec. must be maintained.

The standard British instrument, Mason's hygrometer, is intended to be exposed in a Stevenson screen, the ventilating louvres of which are assumed to give a "light air" draught of 1–1·5 metres/sec. The Meteorological Office *Hygrometric Tables* are based on A for a draught of this speed. The value of A varies slightly with t_w because the latent heat of evaporation varies with temperature, but this small effect is neglected in British tables.

Below 0° C. the wet bulb may be found coated with either super-cooled water or ice. The standard practice is then to brush the wet bulb with distilled water at 0° C. This coats the bulb with ice for certain. Now, below 0° C. the s.v.p. of water vapour in equilibrium with ice is less than the s.v.p. of water vapour in equilibrium with liquid water. The depression of the iced bulb depends on how far the air is from saturation *with respect to ice*. In the 1940 edition of the *Hygrometric Tables*, the relative humidity at temperatures below 0° C. is defined as the ratio "actual vapour pressure/s.v.p. *over ice* at the dry-bulb temperature", and the tables for use below the freezing point give this quantity. If the actual vapour pressure lies between the values for the s.v.p. over water and the s.v.p. over ice, the reading of the ice-coated wet bulb is above that of the dry bulb, since the air is supersaturated with respect to ice. The relative humidity with respect to ice then exceeds 100 per cent. !

Aspirated hygrometers, or psychrometers, are used in confined spaces, and are also favoured as standard meteorological instruments in some countries. By whirling the instrument on a sling, or other suitable means, a draught in excess of 2·5 metres sec. is obtained ; tables based on the "strong wind" value of A are employed.

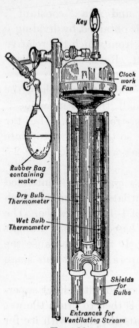

Key

Clock
work
Fan

Rubber Bag
containing
water

Dry Bulb
Thermometer

Wet Bulb
Thermometer

Shields
for
Bulbs

Entrances for
Ventilating Stream

FIG. 91.
Assmann psychrometer.

Fig. 91 shows the **Assmann psychro-meter**, in which the necessary ventilation is provided by a clockwork-driven fan. Before each observation the clockwork is wound up, and the muslin round the wet bulb moistened by distilled water from a rubber bag. The bulbs of the thermometers project through the inverted U portion of the ventilation tube, the open ends of which are highly polished to act as a radiation screen.

The Cambridge Instrument Co. manu-factures recording hygrometers (or **hygro-graphs**) which use the wet-and-dry bulb principle. Mercury-in-steel thermometers, or electrical resistance thermometers, are used. Each thermometer operates its own recording pen, which traces out a line on a chart driven by clockwork. From these traces, the relative humidity at any instant can be found from the usual tables. In other forms of instru-ment, the relative humidity may be recorded directly by a single tracing pen. Such apparatus has been adapted to the control of relative humidity in air-conditioning plants, by causing the recording apparatus at the same time to operate a valve controlling the moisture intake to the chamber concerned.

Hair hygrometer. Human hair increases in length as the relative humidity of the surrounding air increases, the difference between the length in dry air and that in saturated air being of the order of 3 per cent. The hair hygrometer, first invented by de Saussure in 1783, uses this change in length to move a pointer over a dial which is graduated to read the relative humidity of the air directly. It was formerly thought that the instrument was extremely crude, and it was found that the readings were not self-consistent and tended to change with age and exposure. The unreliability is probably due to two causes : permanent elongation of the hair which is always under tension, and fouling of the surface of the hair.

As work has to be done in order to rotate the pointer, a certain tension must be maintained in the fibre (the small spring *b* in Fig. 92 is for this purpose). The smaller this tension, the more reliable the instrument should be. The instrument should be calibrated at intervals under normal working conditions ; it is then satisfactory enough.

The chief advantages of the hair hygrometer are : (1) *It can be used at temperatures below 0° C. without any modification.* For this

FIG. 92.—Hair hygrometer.

reason it is the standard meteorological hygrometer in Norway and elsewhere. (2) It gives direct readings of the relative humidity, requiring no skill whatever to read it. (3) It is rapid and continuous in its readings. (4) It is small and portable.

Most ordinary recording hygrographs use bundles of hairs as the sensitive elements. The following instructions are given by Messrs. Casella and Co. for use with their hygrographs : " The bundle of hairs should be wetted once a week with a camel hair brush. When they are thoroughly wet the pen should read 95 per cent. If it does not, adjustment may be made by means of the screw at one end of the bundle. The reason why this figure is not 100 per cent. is that the weight of water on the hairs depresses them slightly. The hygrograph may be adjusted by comparing its readings with an aspirated hygrometer (i.e. wet and dry bulb type)."

The measurement and control (by " air-conditioning ") of relative humidity is of great importance in many industries, particularly in the manufacturing of textiles, the seasoning of timber, and the storage of various foodstuffs.

Other methods of measuring relative humidity. The following are among the many methods which have been suggested for the measurement of relative humidity in various circumstances.

1. *Heating of cotton.* Perfectly dry cotton is warmed appreciably when brought into a moist atmosphere. The change in temperature, which depends on the relative humidity, is sufficient to be observed with a delicate thermometer; but this is rather a slow process.

2. *Electrical resistance of a ground glass surface.* Glass, particularly ground glass, is hygroscopic, and the amount of moisture collected by the surface depends on the relative humidity; this affects the electrical resistance of the surface. Unfortunately, this does not appear to work very consistently.

3. *Refractive index of glycerin.* Glycerin absorbs moisture until the vapour pressure of the mixture equals the pressure of the water vapour in the atmosphere; the composition of the equilibrium mixture can be ascertained from its refractive index. It is essential that only a thin film of liquid be exposed, for example, a smear of glycerin on a cigarette paper. A refractometer of the type used for finding the refractive index of a small quantity of liquid can be calibrated to give relative humidities directly.

4. *Thermal conductivity.* The " Katharometer ", which is described later (p. 354), is normally used for the measurement of small proportions of hydrogen or carbon dioxide in the air. These gases, on account of the considerable difference in molecular weight, have thermal conductivities which are respectively much greater and much less than that of air. The method should, if water vapour is the only " foreign gas " present in the air, also be applicable to the determination of the percentage of water vapour in the air, by comparing the thermal conductivity of the sample chosen with that of dry air. This method would give the absolute percentage of water vapour, not the relative humidity; consequently at low

temperatures, when the absolute percentage is very small even at high relative humidity, this method is very insensitive.

Further accounts of these and one or two other methods will be found in the " Discussion on Hygrometry " mentioned on p. 199. Lest it should be thought that they have been dismissed summarily here, it must be remembered that " the important matter is the practical utility of the instrument in service conditions, rather than its scientific precision in conditions which are appropriate to a well-equipped laboratory ", as Sir Napier Shaw states in emphasising the great practical importance of the simplest of all such instruments, the hair hygrometer.

In conclusion, mention must be made of an improved type of electric hygrometer described in 1939 by F. W. Dunmore. A small aluminium tube, about $1\frac{1}{2}$ in. long and $\frac{3}{8}$ in. diameter, is coated with an insulating layer of polystyrene resin. Two coils of palladium wire are wound, side by side, over this, as shown in the diagram (Fig. 93). The surface of the insulator is then covered with a thin film of lithium chloride solution mixed with partially hydrolysed polyvinyl acetate. The lithium chloride solution is the hygroscopic material, and the acetate serves as a binder so that a very thin uniform film is obtainable, at the same time being slightly hygroscopic itself. The resistance of the film between the two palladium wires depends on the proportion of absorbed water, and thus on the relative humidity. It is usual to use a battery of several such tubes, each with a lithium chloride solution of different concentration, for different humidity ranges. Such a battery with a resistance of 7 megohms at 10% humidity has a resistance of only 0·15 megohms at 90% relative humidity. The design of the instrument, and the very thin film used, make it very rapid in action. It is used in " radio-sonde " balloons, which are sent up to the upper atmosphere carrying instruments and a small radio transmitter which signals the indications of the instruments ; thus readings of the relative humidity at great heights are obtained.

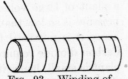

Fig. 93.—Winding of electric hygrometer.

Refrigerators. Fig. 94 illustrates the principle of the usual type of refrigerating machine, in which the evaporation of a suitable liquid abstracts latent heat from the surroundings.

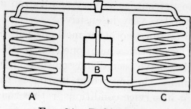

FIG. 94.—Refrigerator.

The vessel A contains a pipe coil which is surrounded by the substance to be chilled, usually calcium chloride brine. The liquid evaporates inside this coil, cooling the brine by the abstraction of heat. The pump B removes the vapour and condenses it in the pipe passing through the vessel C, which contains cold water to remove the latent heat given up. The liquid passes through a valve to the pipe in A, whence the whole cycle of events is repeated.

Sulphur dioxide, carbon dioxide, and ammonia are among the substances commonly used as refrigerants, though several suitable organic liquids are also used. The material chosen depends on the use to which the refrigerator is to be put. Sulphur dioxide requires a plant of large volume, and at very low temperatures its vapour pressure is so low that there is the risk of air leaking into the plant ; hence it is not used for the production of very low temperatures. Carbon dioxide requires very high pressures, but the volume of the plant is small, hence it is chiefly favoured for installations on board ship. Ammonia is probably most generally used in ordinary small installations. Modern organic refrigerants include " Freon " (CCl_2F_2), and several other volatile hydrocarbon derivatives of similar type.

The " Electrolux " refrigerator works on the same thermal principle, but without the use of a mechanical compressor. Ammonia, which is very soluble in water, is used as the refrigerant. The apparatus (Fig. 95) contains four main units—the boiler A, in which ammonia gas is generated from a concentrated aqueous solution by an electric heater H ; the condenser B, surrounded by a cold water jacket or cooled by radiator fins, in which the ammonia gas condenses to ammonia liquid; the evaporator C, inside the space to be cooled, in which the liquid ammonia evaporates ; and the absorber D, cooled by a water jacket, in which ammonia gas is absorbed in a weak aqueous solution of ammonia.

Hydrogen circulates between D and C, entering at the top of C with the liquid ammonia, leaving at the bottom with the ammonia vapour, and passing through D unchanged while the ammonia

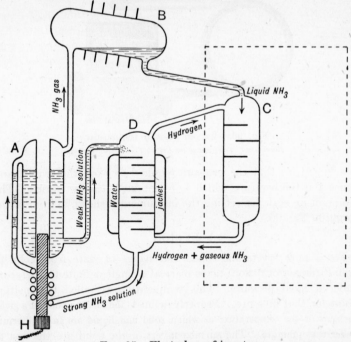

FIG. 95.—Electrolux refrigerator.

dissolves. The strong aqueous solution from the bottom of D is pumped to the top of A by winding the tube round the heater H, so that bubbles of vapour are formed in the tube. The circulation of hydrogen between C and D really performs the evaporating (low pressure) function of the pump in the ordinary refrigerator, while the circulation of water between A and D corresponds to the condensing action (high pressure) in the simple scheme of Fig. 94.

Vapour pressure thermostats. The vapour pressure of a suitable volatile liquid can be used to operate a simple and very ingenious type of thermostat (Fig. 96). The liquid is contained in a metal tube, which communicates by means of a fine capillary tube with a flexible metallic bellows which, when expanded by the vapour pressure of the liquid, closes a switch in the electrical heating circuit it is set to control. Movement of the bellows is opposed by a spring, which is adjusted by the knob shown on the right of the

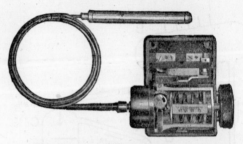

FIG. 96.—Vapour-pressure thermostat.
Reproduced by courtesy of the British Thermostat Co., Ltd.

instrument, so that the pressure required to work the switch, and hence the temperature which is maintained, can be varied. The temperature scale for setting the instrument is shown in front of the spring in Fig. 96.

FUSION

For a pure crystalline solid, the change of state from solid to liquid (the act of fusion) takes place at a single definite temperature under a fixed pressure. This temperature is called the melting point for that pressure. Properly defined, **the melting point at a given pressure is the temperature at which solid and liquid are in equilibrium under that pressure.** The surface layers of the solid are the first to melt. Impure substances, mixtures, and non-crystalline substances do not as a rule have a sharp melting point ; for example, waxes behave in this way, and glass (which is usually regarded as a super-cooled liquid) gradually softens throughout its bulk as the temperature is raised.

Fusion is accompanied by a change in volume, which may be either an increase or a decrease. Ice is less dense than the water it forms, consequently there is a decrease in volume when ice melts ; but solid wax is denser than molten wax, so there is an increase in volume when wax melts.

Determination of the melting point of naphthalene. A thin glass test-tube containing a thermometer is about one third filled with crystals of naphthalene and heated to 100° C. in a water bath. It is then quickly removed, and suspended in an empty beaker to protect it from draughts. Readings of the temperature are taken each minute, until the temperature has fallen to about 40° C., and a graph of temperature against time is plotted. If the liquid be well stirred as long as this is possible, the curve obtained will be as *ABCD* (Fig. 97), the flat horizontal portion indicating that latent heat is being evolved during the change of state. If the liquid is not stirred, a curve such as *ABEFCD* may be obtained. Along the portion *BE* the substance, although below the true melting point, is still liquid ; it is said to be a supercooled liquid. At *E*, solidification begins, and the latent heat evolved raises the temperature to the true melting point, after which matters proceed normally. When the solid melts, it does so invariably and sharply at the melting point ; hence the steady equilibrium temperature is often referred to as " the *melting point* of the *solid* " rather than " the *freezing point* of the *liquid* ".

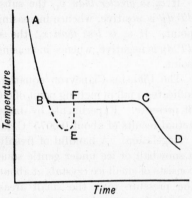

FIG. 97.—Cooling curve for naphthalene.

Effect of pressure on the melting point. The effect of a change of pressure on the melting point depends on whether the substance expands or contracts in volume when the change of state occurs. For a substance which contracts on melting (such as ice), increasing the pressure lowers the melting point, while decreasing the pressure raises the melting point. For a substance which expands on melting (such as wax), increasing the pressure raises the melting point, while decreasing the pressure lowers the melting point.

This might be expected from general considerations. In the case of ice, for example, if the pressure is increased this aids contraction and hence aids melting of the solid, which should thus take place more readily, or at a lower temperature. This line of argument, properly developed by thermodynamics, not only explains the change in melting point, but also enables the size of the change to be calculated. The formula derived (the Clausius-Clapeyron equation rearranged) is

$$\frac{dT}{dp} = \frac{T(v_2 - v_1)}{LJ},$$

where dT is the change in the absolute temperature T of the melting point caused by change in pressure dp, L is the latent heat of fusion in cal. per gram, v_1 the volume of unit mass of the solid, and v_2 the volume of unit mass of the liquid.

If v_2 *is greater than* v_1, the substance expands on melting, and dT/dp is positive, whence increasing the pressure raises the melting point. If v_2 *is less than* v_1, the substance contracts on melting, dT/dp is negative, whence increasing the pressure lowers the melting point.

The Clausius-Clapeyron equation applied to the melting of ice indicates a fall in melting point of $0 \cdot 0072°$ C. per atmosphere increase of pressure. Experiments by James Thomson and by Dewar give actual results of about $0 \cdot 0075°$ C. fall per atmosphere increase.

Regelation. A handful of freshly fallen soft snow " binds " into a snowball of ice under gentle squeezing of the hands. The snow consists of small ice crystals at about $0°$ C. ; when they are squeezed, the pressure over the small areas of contact between adjacent crystals is large, the melting point is lowered below $0°$ C., and the crystals melt at these places. Releasing the pressure enables solidification to take place at $0°$ C. again, with the result that the crystals are now welded together in a solid mass (re-freezing, or regelation). If the snow is at a temperature much below $0°$ C., snowballs cannot readily be made. It may be that, over the very small area of contact between the crystals, a gentle squeeze may give a pressure between the surfaces equivalent to about 100 atmospheres. This should lower the melting point by $100 \times 0 \cdot 0075°$ to $-0 \cdot 75°$ C. But if the temperature of the crystals is initially $-1 \cdot 0°$ C., this will not suffice to produce melting at the edges in contact.

The famous regelation experiment due to Faraday, in which a loaded metal wire hung over a block of ice cuts its way through, leaving the ice intact, depends for its successful operation on the transfer of latent heat through the wire. Beneath the wire the ice is melted under pressure, and receives the necessary latent heat from above. The water thus formed flows over the wire, and gives out latent heat as it freezes again at $0°$ C. Heat must thus be conducted steadily downwards through the wire, across which there must be a small temperature gradient. If this is true, a copper wire should be much more effective than an iron one of the same diameter.

Much of the ineffectiveness of ordinary string in this experiment may be due to its poor conductivity, though any soft substance will obviously offer a large area of contact and hence apply a relatively small pressure.

The slipperiness of ice is due to its melting under pressure, affording a lubricating film of water.

Sublimation. The vaporisation of solids. The process of evaporation is not confined to liquids ; all solids behave in this way as well. Solids with a marked smell, such as naphthalene and camphor, must vaporise appreciably and exert a measurable vapour pressure. Normal solids which are regarded as non-volatile have infinitesimally small vapour pressures at ordinary temperatures.

Iodine, carbon dioxide, and ice are three well-known examples of substances which pass directly from the solid to the vapour state at temperatures below the ordinary melting point ; this process, or the complete operation of vaporisation and then condensation of the vapour to solid again (the counterpart of the distillation of a liquid), is called **sublimation**.

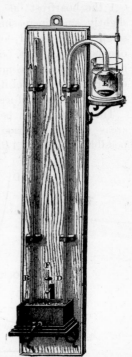

The saturated vapour pressure of ice at different temperatures can be measured by an adaptation of the barometer-tube method (in which the ice is contained in a bulb E at the top of the tube, which is immersed in a suitable freezing mixture, as in Fig. 98), or by the method of Ramsay and Young. The results give a curve of S.V.P. against temperature which is not a continuation of the vapour-pressure curve for water ; the two graphs intersect at an angle.

The triple point. Water-substance is chosen in the following argument as the experimental results are familiar. The conclusions are true for all substances which do not undergo change in composition, if we substitute the words " solid " for " ice ", " liquid " for " water ", and " vapour " for " steam ".

Fig. 98.—Measurement of s.v.p. at low temperatures.

The graph of s.v.p. against temperature for water is the locus of all sets of values of the two variables pressure p and temperature t at which water and its vapour can exist together in equilibrium; this graph is called the **boiling curve** or **steam line**.

The graph of s.v.p. against temperature for ice is the locus of all sets of values of the two variables p and t at which ice and its vapour can exist together in equilibrium; this is the **sublimation curve** or **hoarfrost line**.

The graph of pressure against freezing point is the locus of all sets of values of the two variables p and t at which water and ice can exist together in equilibrium. This is called the **solidification curve**, or **ice line**.

All these curves can be plotted on the same diagram (Fig. 99, which is not drawn to scale). AB represents the steam line, CA the hoarfrost line, and AD the ice line, sloping backwards slightly, since increasing p lowers t (for a substance contracting on solidifying it would slope forwards). All three curves intersect in one point A. This point is called the **triple point.** It should be mentioned that A is not quite at $0°$ C., but a little above it; since, under the pressure of its own saturated vapour at that temperature, the melting point of ice is about $+0.0075°$ C.

These curves can be regarded as lines bounding three different areas of the diagram in which the different states alone are possible. Below CAB, the substance is entirely in the form of

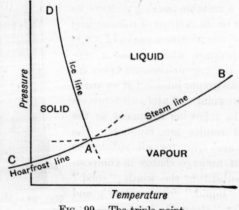

Fig. 99.—The triple point.

vapour ; in the space DAB, it is entirely liquid ; and in the space bounded by CAD, entirely ice.

To prove that the three lines must meet in a point, consider what must happen if this is not the case. Suppose, as in Fig. 100, the hoarfrost and steam

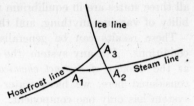

FIG. 100.—Impossible intersections of ice, steam, and hoarfrost lines.

lines intersect at A_1, the ice line and the steam line intersect at A_2, and the ice line and the hoarfrost line at A_3. What would be the state of the substance at points within the triangle $A_1 A_2 A_3$? As it is below the hoarfrost line, the substance is entirely vapour ; as it is above the steam line, the substance is entirely liquid ; and as it is to the left of the ice line, the substance is entirely solid. So the region bounded by $A_1 A_2 A_3$ represents an impossible state of affairs, whence it is inferred that the triangle $A_1 A_2 A_3$ cannot exist, and the three lines must be concurrent.

Degrees of freedom. The phase rule. Providing only that we keep within the conditions of the space DAB of Fig. 99, we can obtain water-substance at any p and t chosen at will. We have two free choices, and the system *water alone* can be said to have two degrees of freedom. Similarly, subject only to the limits of the spaces bounded by the appropriate lines, we can have *ice alone* or *steam alone* at any chosen p and t.

Now, in constructing any one of these lines, say the steam line, experimentally, the procedure is to vary at will one of the variables p or t, and observe the change in the other. That is, we can *choose* a value of p and observe the *resulting* value of t, or we can *choose* a value of t and observe the *resulting* value of p. We cannot vary both p and t at will. The system *water + saturated water vapour* thus has one degree of freedom, or one condition only that can be varied at will. Similarly, the ice line and the hoarfrost line each indicate conditions under which two states can coexist together, but each equilibrium system has only one degree of freedom.

Finally, at the triple point A, both the temperature and the pressure are fixed. Under no other conditions can the three states ice, water, and water vapour exist together in equilibrium. When all three states are in equilibrium there is no choice open, no possibility of varying anything, and thus no degrees of freedom.

These results can be generalised to apply to all equilibrium conditions. For any system, the number of *components* is defined as the *number of distinct chemical species involved*. In the case considered here, we have water-substance throughout, and the system has only one component. The different *states* involved are called the *phases of the system* ; the single component can exist in three phases, solid, liquid, or gaseous. For this one-component system the following table summarises the way in which the number of degrees of freedom depends on the number of phases.

No. of phases, P.	No. of degrees of freedom, F.	$P+F$.
1	2	3
2	1	3
3	0	3

Thus, for all possible conditions of a one-component system the sum $(P+F)$ is 3, which equals (*no. of components* $+2$).

This can be generalised for any system containing any number of components, writing C for the number of components, when

$$P+F=C+2.$$

In words, *the sum of the number of phases and the number of degrees of freedom exceeds the number of components by two.*

This statement is known as the **Phase Rule**. It was first enunciated by Willard Gibbs.

Effect of dissolved substances on the freezing point. When an aqueous solution is cooled, the freezing point is lowered, and the first solid portion to appear is pure ice. The freezing point of a solution is defined as that temperature at which the solution is in equilibrium with the solid solvent. The lowering of the freezing point by the dissolved substance is proportional to the concentration of the solute. This statement is known as **Blagden's Law**.

It has been shown that the vapour pressure of the solution of a non-volatile substance is lowered according to the formula $\dfrac{\delta p}{p} = \dfrac{n}{N}$, and thus the " steam line " is lowered to an extent which is proportional to the molecular concentration.

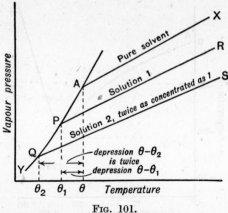

FIG. 101.

In Fig. 101, AX is the vapour-pressure curve of the pure liquid solvent, YA that for the solid solvent, the melting point or freezing point being given by the point of intersection of these two lines. Curves lower than XA intersect the line YA at points such as P and Q, which correspond to temperatures θ_1 and θ_2, lower than the normal freezing point of the pure solvent, θ.

Suppose that the *molecular* concentration of the solute in solution 2 (for which SQ is the " steam line ") is twice that of solution 1 (for which RP is the corresponding line) ; SQ is then twice as far below AX as is RP, and if the curves are all approximately straight lines, $AQ = 2AP$ and $\theta - \theta_2 = 2(\theta - \theta_1)$. That is, the depression of the freezing point is proportional to the concentration in moles of solute per mole of solvent.

Equilibrium diagrams for mixtures. The two curves of Fig. 102 for a solution of common salt in water show how the temperature of equilibrium depends on the concentration. Starting at A with a weak solution of salt at $0°$ C. and cooling it, pure ice separates out, increasing the concentration of salt in the remainder and lowering its freezing point still further. Pure ice continues to separate out until the point indicated by C is reached, at a temperature of $-21°$ C. and a concentration of about 23 per cent. of salt. Similarly, starting with a strong solution containing about 27 per cent. of salt at B and cooling it, salt crystallises out leaving behind a weaker solution which on cooling still further deposits more salt,

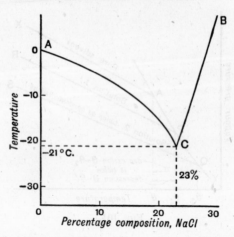

FIG. 102.—Equilibrium diagram for salt solution.

until eventually the point C is reached. To the left of C then, the solid deposited on cooling is pure ice ; to the right of C, the solid is pure salt. At C, both ice and salt are deposited together, or the substance *appears to solidify as a whole*. Hence, a mixture of which the composition is that for the point C has a definite freezing point, behaving in this respect like a pure substance. The point C is called the **cryohydric or eutectic point,** and the mixture the composition of which corresponds to C is called a **cryohydric mixture, or eutectic mixture.**

Ice and salt as a freezing mixture. Two simple points which require some careful thought for their explanation are (*a*) how it is possible to obtain a low temperature by the use of a mixture of ice and salt, and (*b*) why salt placed on an icy pavement will melt the ice. Both depend on the same effect. When salt dissolves in water heat is absorbed, and the resulting solution has a lower freezing point than the pure water. In the freezing mixture, then, progressive solution of the salt, with resulting lowering of temperature, takes place until the proportions of the mixture are those of the eutectic mixture, and the temperature is that of the eutectic point. When salt is used to " thaw " an icy pavement the same thing happens ; the resulting mixture will remain liquid if the temperature is above the eutectic temperature, as is the case except in extremely cold climates.

Alloys. Results very similar to those for a solution of salt in water are obtained with alloys. The simple case of the alloys of lead and tin, which is of great practical importance, will be considered in some detail.

The melting point of lead is 327° C., and that of tin is 232° C. Molten alloys containing known proportions of each constituent can be made by melting a known mass of lead in a crucible, and dissolving the required amount of tin in the liquid lead. Using a 360° mercury thermometer, or a suitable thermocouple, cooling curves for the pure metals and for alloys of different known compositions can be obtained.

Pure lead and pure tin give cooling curves with a single horizontal portion, like the curve for naphthalene, denoting a definite melting point. Alloys, except those with compositions in the neighbourhood of about 60 per cent. tin and about 40 per cent. lead, give curves with two " halt " stages, as shown in Fig. 102 (a). The upper halt X shows that solidification is beginning ; at this temperature one of the pure metals is being deposited, just as salt *or* ice is at first deposited when brine is cooled. At the lower halt Y, the whole mass solidifies, just as does brine at $-21°$ C. Between the temperatures of these two halts, the alloy is in a pasty state, containing crystals of solid in the liquid. At the lower temperature, which is the same whatever the composition of the alloy and is the **eutectic temperature**, the liquid portion of the pasty mass, which has the

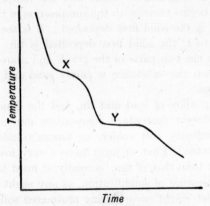

Fig. 102 (a).—Cooling curve for alloy.

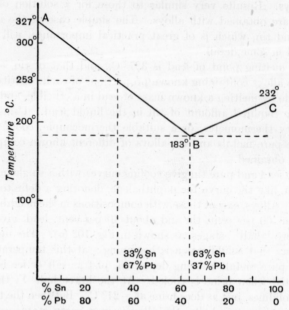

FIG. 102 (b).—Equilibrium diagram for Pb : Sn alloys.

eutectic composition of 63 per cent. tin and 37 per cent. lead, solidifies as a whole. This temperature is 183° C.

The graph of Fig. 102 (b) shows how the temperature at which solidification begins varies with the composition of the alloy. From A to B, lead is the solid first deposited ; B is the eutectic point ; and from B to C the solid first deposited is tin. The triangular areas beneath the two parts of the graph and above B contain the points at which the substance is partly solid and partly liquid, in the pasty stage.

Solder is an alloy of lead and tin, and the diagram shows why solders of different percentage composition are used for different purposes. Ordinary soft solder, or tinman's solder, must satisfy two requirements. First, it must have a very low melting point, at least lower than that of tin ; secondly, it must have a sharp and definite temperature of solidification, as any slight displacement of the parts which might occur during protracted solidification would cause the soldered join to be weak. The ideal composition would thus be that of the eutectic mixture, with 63 per cent. of tin ; as tin is expensive the usual solders contain about 60 per cent. of tin, but the proportion cannot be reduced much below this without losing the sharp setting point. Plumber's solder, on the other hand, need only have a melting point below that of lead ; and a large range of temperature during which it is partially solid is required, to enable the plumber to work the metal and " wipe " the joint. Plumber's solder usually contains about 67 per cent. of lead and 33 per cent. of tin. As the graph shows, an alloy of this composition will begin to solidify at about 253° C., and continues in a pasty state until it has cooled to 183° C., giving a range of 70° during which the plumber can work on it.

FRACTIONAL DISTILLATION

Two completely miscible liquids. Consider a mixture of two liquids A and B which can form a mixture in any proportions. The vapour in equilibrium with the liquid always contains both constituents, and in general the composition of the vapour is different from that of the liquid. Hence, if a graph of boiling point against percentage of one component, say A, is drawn, there will be two possible curves ; one of these curves is the graph of boiling point against *percentage of A in the liquid,* and the other is the graph of boiling point against *percentage of A in the vapour.* Fig. 103 shows such a diagram. The lower line is the liquid curve, the upper the vapour curve. The horizontal line at some temperature $\theta_1°$ cuts the liquid curve at X and the vapour curve at Y, whence it is seen that at $\theta_1°$ the boiling liquid contains 29 per cent. of A and the vapour from it contains 80 per cent. of A. Points within the space bounded by the curves indicate *mixtures* of liquid and vapour ; for example, P in the figure represents a *mixture* of liquid and vapour at $\theta_2°$ containing 50 per cent. of A.

A mixture boils when the total pressure of the mixture of vapours equals the external pressure. The boiling point is the temperature at which the pressure of the mixed vapours is 76 cm. There are three possible cases to consider.

1. The boiling points of all intermediate mixtures lie between the boiling points of the two pure liquids. In this case, the constituents can be separated by fractional distillation. Examples

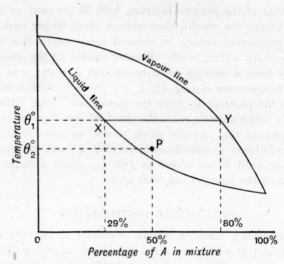

FIG. 103.—Mixture of two liquids.

are mixtures of alcohol and water, and of liquid nitrogen and liquid oxygen.

2. All mixtures boil at temperatures above the boiling points of both the pure liquids.

3. All mixtures boil at temperatures below the boiling points of both pure liquids.

In cases 2 and 3 it is not possible to separate the two liquids by fractional distillation. The effect of boiling is to obtain a **constant-boiling point mixture**.

Theory of fractional distillation. The separation of oxygen and nitrogen from liquid air is an example of outstanding importance, and this will be considered in some detail. Fig. 104 shows the curves of boiling point against percentage composition of the liquid (lower curve) and vapour (upper curve). The letters A, B, C refer to stages in the fractionating column of Fig. 105.

(a) *To obtain pure nitrogen.* Suppose liquid air, containing 76·7 per cent. nitrogen and 23·3 per cent. oxygen, is produced at −193° C. and allowed to attain equilibrium with its vapour at A (Figs. 104 and 105). Following the horizontal line for −193° C. to the left,

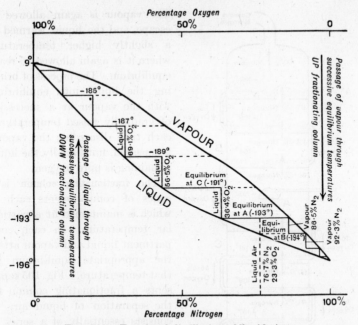

FIG. 104.—Fractional distillation of liquid air.

it is seen that the composition of the liquid is 63·6 per cent. nitrogen, while following it to the right, the composition of the vapour at this temperature is 86·5 per cent. nitrogen. The liquid is now discarded, and the vapour cooled to − 194° C., and allowed to attain a new vapour-liquid equilibrium in which the composition of the vapour is 92·3 per cent. nitrogen and that of the liquid is 76 per cent. nitrogen at B. If the liquid is again discarded and the vapour is again cooled, a new equilibrium is attained in which the vapour is still richer in nitrogen. By repetition of this process, vapour consisting of pure nitrogen is eventually obtained.

(b) *To obtain pure oxygen.* As before, a start is made with liquid air at − 193° C., containing 23·3 per cent. oxygen. When equilibrium is attained, the vapour has the composition 13·5 per cent. oxygen, and the liquid 36·4 per cent. oxygen. The vapour is allowed to escape, and the liquid warmed to, say, − 191° C.; at this temperature there is equilibrium between vapour containing 26·1 per cent. and liquid containing 56·5 per cent. oxygen, at C.

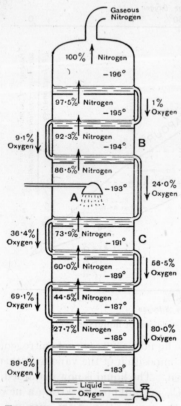

FIG. 105.—Fractionating column for liquid air.

The vapour is again allowed to escape, and the liquid warmed to a slightly higher temperature, where it is again allowed to reach equilibrium. The process of bringing the liquid into equilibrium with the vapour at a succession of gradually raised temperatures, each time discarding the vapour, is repeated, until finally the liquid remaining is pure oxygen.

The fractionating column is a series of compartments each of which is maintained at a particular temperature. In each compartment liquid and vapour attain the appropriate equilibrium for that temperature. Fig. 105 represents a fractionating column for the separation of liquid air. It consists essentially of a series of trays, the temperatures of which range from −196° C. at the top to −183° C. at the bottom. At each of these temperatures, when the liquid and vapour are in equilibrium, the liquid is richer in oxygen and the vapour is richer in nitrogen. Overflow pipes allow the liquid to trickle down from each tray to the one below it, and the overflow from successive trays becomes progressively richer in oxygen going downwards. Holes in the floor of each tray allow the vapour to rise to the tray above, and the vapour from each successive tray going upwards is richer in nitrogen. Boiling liquid air at −193° C. enters the column at the point A. From this, vapour containing 86·5 per cent. nitrogen and 13·5 per cent. oxygen rises into B which is at −194° C., while liquid containing 63·6 per cent. nitrogen and 36·4 per cent. oxygen falls down to C. Pure gaseous nitrogen is withdrawn from the top of the column, and pure liquid oxygen from the bottom.

QUESTIONS ON CHAPTER V

1. Describe how you would determine the relation between the pressure and volume of (a) an unsaturated, (b) a saturated vapour, and state clearly what results you would expect to obtain.

Three identical barometer tubes are filled with mercury and inverted with their lower ends dipping into a large dish of mercury and their upper ends 90 cm. above its surface. The initial reading of all three barometers is 740 mm. A small quantity of volatile liquid is introduced into the Torricellian vacuum of the second and it then reads 730 mm. Rather more of the same liquid is introduced into the third so that some remains unevaporated, and it reads 650 mm. If the atmospheric pressure increases by 10 mm., what will be the readings of the three barometers? (B.)

2. Explain in general terms the kinetic theory of liquids and gases, and apply it to explain the phenomena of evaporation, boiling, saturated and unsaturated vapours, and the pressure of gases. (C.)

3. What do you understand by the vapour pressure of a liquid, and how would you measure its variation for temperatures between 0° C. and 100° C.? How do you take account of vapour pressure in problems in which both a gas and the vapour of a liquid are enclosed in the same volume?

A diving bell is lowered into water until the level of the water inside leaves half the volume of the bell still unoccupied by water. The temperature of the bell and its surroundings may be taken as 20° C. throughout, and the mercury barometer at the surface of the water stands at 750 mm. Find the depth to which the bell has been lowered.

[The vapour pressure of the water at 20° C. is 17 mm. and the density of mercury is 13·6 gm. per c.c.] (C.S.)

4. How would you verify experimentally that the boiling point of a liquid is that temperature at which its vapour pressure is equal to the atmospheric pressure?

A small quantity of (a) water, (b) dry air, is introduced into the space above the mercury in a barometer. Discuss how the accuracy of the barometer is affected in each case. (O. & C.)

5. Describe an experiment to determine the vapour pressure of water at 25° C.

Explain how water can be made to boil at 90° C. and describe the difference between the processes when water is boiling at 90° C. and when it is merely evaporating at this temperature. (C.)

6. What is meant by the vapour pressure of a liquid? Describe in general terms, from the view-point of the kinetic theory, why you would expect the temperature of a liquid to fall when it evaporates, and the vapour pressure to increase with temperature.

Describe an experiment by which you could investigate the variation of vapour pressure with temperature of a volatile liquid. (O. & C.)

7. State and explain the meaning of Dalton's law of partial pressures.

A litre of air originally saturated with water vapour at 100° C. is cooled to 50° C. while the total pressure is maintained unaltered at 100 cm. of mercury. What volume will it now occupy, if the saturated vapour pressure of water vapour at 50° C. is 9·2 cm. of mercury?　(O.)

8. State Dalton's Law of Partial Pressures.

Show how the variation of the vapour pressure of a liquid with temperature may be found by measuring at different temperatures the volume of air contained in a tube closed at one end, the air being enclosed by an index of the liquid.　(C.S.)

9. A vessel contains a mixture of gas and a vapour in contact with excess of the liquid. How will the pressure in the vessel change (a) if the volume is changed at constant temperature, (b) if the temperature changes at constant volume?

A closed vessel contains a mixture of air and water vapour in contact with excess of water. The pressures in the vessel at 27° C. and 60° C. are respectively 77·7 cm. and 98·1 cm. of mercury. If the vapour pressure of water at 27° C. is 2·7 cm. of mercury, what is the vapour pressure at 60° C.?　(O. & C.)

10. What is meant by saturation vapour pressure?

Some air is contained in a narrow tube between the closed end and a water index. The volume of the contained air is measured at various temperatures. Show how, from these measurements, if the saturation vapour pressure at one temperature is known, it may be calculated for the other temperatures. Point out any sources of error, and indicate any precautions you would take.　(C.)

11. Explain what is meant by the statement that the vapour pressure of ether at 20° C. is 44 cm. of mercury.

A glass tube closed at one end is completely filled with mercury and inverted in a bowl of mercury, so that the top of the tube is 32 cm. above the level of the mercury in the bowl. Describe and explain what will happen if a little ether is introduced into the tube, the temperature being 15° C. and the barometric height 76 cm. What will happen if the temperature is gradually increased to 40° C.? The boiling point of ether is 35° C.　(O & C.)

12. The graph of p against 1/v obtained in an experiment to verify Boyle's law was found to consist of an approximately straight line through the origin joined to another approximately straight line of smaller slope for large p. What conclusions do you draw from these results, and what further experiments would you make to test your conclusions?　(O.S.)

13. Explain the meaning of *saturation vapour pressure of water* and *dew-point*.

Describe a method of determining the dew-point of the air in the laboratory, and explain how the value is used in calculating the relative humidity.　(J.M.B.)

14. Explain what is meant by the "dew-point", and describe an accurate method of determining its value.

The saturated vapour pressure of water at 11·25° C. is 1 cm. of mercury, the density of dry air at 76 cm. pressure and 25° C. is

0·001184 gm. cm.³, and the density of water vapour relative to that of air at the same pressure and temperature is 0·624. Find the weight of a litre of moist air at 25° C., if the barometer stands at 76 cm., and the dew-point is 11·25° C. (C.W.B.)

15. Describe in some detail how you would determine the relative humidity of the air in a laboratory.

Some air in a flask is saturated with water vapour. The pressure of the mixture is 80·0 cm. of mercury at 10° C. What will it be at 50° C. if the volume has remained unchanged and the air is still saturated? The saturation vapour pressure of water in cm. of mercury is 0·9 at 10° C. and 9·2 at 50° C. (O.)

16. Describe, with the aid of a diagram, some form of refrigerator and explain its action. (C.)

17. Explain the physical principles underlying the working of any form of domestic refrigerator. Give a sketch showing the essential features of the apparatus. (L.)

18. Explain the action of a refrigerator in which the cooling is produced by evaporation.

Vapour from alcohol boiling at 78° C. is passed into 50 gm. of alcohol at 20° C. contained in a copper calorimeter of mass 30 gm. What will be the temperature of the calorimeter and its contents when 5 gm. of vapour have been added? [Sp. ht. of alcohol = 0·6 ; sp. ht. of copper = 0·1 ; latent heat of vaporization of alcohol = 205 cal. per gm.]
(J.M.B.)

19. Discuss the following : (a) A small drop of water will evaporate in a space in which water vapour is in equilibrium with a plane surface. (b) Boiling by bumping. (J.M.B., part question)

20. Describe how you would show the effect on the boiling point of a liquid of (a) change of pressure, (b) the addition of soluble matter to the liquid.

Describe one practical application of (a).

How could you use a thermometer to test whether a boiling liquid is pure? (J.M.B.)

21. What is meant by a *cooling curve*?

Describe how the melting point of a solid can be determined by the cooling curve method, and explain the shape of the curve obtained in the experiment. (J.M.B.)

22. By considering the equilibrium of a liquid which has risen in a fine capillary tube, obtain a relation between the surface tension, the vapour pressure over a flat surface, and that over a curved surface whose radius of curvature is r.

Hence calculate the radius of a capillary tube from which water will not evaporate when the humidity is 99 per cent. [Surface tension of water = 80 dynes per cm.] (O.S.)

CHAPTER VI

HEAT AND WORK

THE statement that heat is a form of energy, or is one of the many forms in which energy can exist, scarcely requires demonstration to a generation which has grown up surrounded by innumerable applications of this idea. It has even been found expedient, in Chapter II of this book, to anticipate (or rather take for granted) some of the points which are often delayed to this stage in the usual sequence of presentation, simply because the use of electrical energy as a means of supplying heat is so generally understood and accepted nowadays. But the statement requires some explanation, since it can bear two quite different senses. First, it describes the experimental fact that the absorption of heat may produce mechanical work or some other means by which mechanical work may ultimately be performed, and that the dissipation of mechanical or other forms of energy may liberate heat; this forms the study of the present chapter. Secondly, it may be read as a statement as to the nature of the heat possessed by a material body, which is believed (if we delve no further into the ultimate structure of things than the molecule) to be the sum of the mechanical kinetic energies of vibration, translation, or rotation, of the particles of which it is composed. According to this, heat is simply a branch of mechanics, and the study of "Heat" as a separate subject is merely a matter of convenience because this particular kind of mechanical motion happens to affect our senses, and the instruments devised to aid our senses, in a particular way.

Law of conservation of energy. The law of conservation of energy, which states that the total energy of a closed system remains constant, is used in elementary mechanics to solve artificial problems on frictionless machines, bodies falling freely *in vacuo*, and so on. When it is applied to an actual simple machine of any kind as the closed system, it is found that

energy expended by effort = work done in raising load and moving parts
+ work done in overcoming friction.

228

The work done in overcoming friction generates heat, and the work done in raising the load supplies the load with potential energy. Hence the equation can be written

energy expended by effort = mechanical potential energy supplied to load, etc. + heat energy produced by friction,

the assumption being that the heat generated is exactly equivalent to the mechanical work used in its production.

Is this kind of statement justified? Years of patient experiment were needed to establish its validity, and to prove beyond all possible question that when mechanical work is completely converted into heat, or heat is completely converted into mechanical work, for each unit of work that is converted into heat a definite quantity of heat is produced, and for each unit of heat converted into work a definite quantity of work is furnished.

The statement in black type is known as the **First Law of Thermodynamics**. In symbols, if W units of work are converted into H units of heat energy, $W = JH,$

where J is a constant called the **mechanical equivalent of heat.**

It is now customary, on account of certain practical difficulties connected with the absolute values of electrical units, to distinguish between the mechanical equivalent proper (symbol J) for the conversion of mechanical energy directly into heat, and the electrical equivalent (symbol J') used when W is energy measured by electrical means (see p. 64).

The absolute mechanical unit of energy is the erg, and one joule is 10^7 ergs. This is the *absolute joule.* The volt and the ampere are so defined that the energy in joules dissipated by an electric current equals the product *volts × amperes × seconds.* But the present practical standards of P.D. and current, the international volt and international ampere, differ slightly from the true volt and true ampere of the definition. The standards themselves can be reproduced, and measurements in terms of them made, with greater accuracy than that to which the true values of the standards are at present known. Thus another unit, the international joule, is introduced such that *international volts × international amperes × seconds = international joules.* One international joule equals nearly 1·0002 absolute joules.

Direct determinations of J give the value in absolute joules per calorie. Determinations of J' measure the value in international joules per calorie; the result multiplied by 1·0002 gives J' in absolute joules per calorie. It can be seen that the values of J in absolute units and J' in international units stand independent of any later revaluation of the electrical standards, while the value of J' in absolute units is subject to revision of the factor 1·0002.

Early views as to the nature of heat. Many of the earlier experimenters believed that heat was a weightless, highly elastic, self-repellent fluid, indestructible and uncreatable. This fluid they named *caloric*. The caloric theory offered a quite scientific explanation of the facts then known. Hot bodies emitted heat because the particles of caloric repelled one another strongly. Differences in specific heat were due to the different attracting powers of different substances for the fluid. Expansion occurred because the self-repellent fluid tended to increase the volume of any body in which it was lodged. Latent heat was supposed to enter into combination with the particles of the material; thus *water = ice + latent heat*. If a simple theory of this kind served to explain all the observed facts, it was quite reasonable to look no further.

But the generation of heat by percussion and by friction presented difficulties. The theory stated that the rise in temperature of a block of lead when hammered was due to the extrusion of caloric under pressure, much as water issues from a sponge when it is squeezed. The rise in temperature of two bodies when rubbed together was due to the diminution of the bodies themselves, as the small particles rubbed off had a smaller power of attracting caloric, which was thereby freed—that is, the specific heat of a finely powdered substance was less than that of the same substance in one solid mass. No attempt seems to have been made to detect this diminution of specific heat, and this argument could not possibly explain the generation of heat by the churning of a liquid.

Rumford in 1798 did a series of experiments in which heat was generated by rotating a blunt cannon borer in a large mass of gun-metal. He observed that a large quantity of heat (sufficient to raise nearly 27 lb. of water from the freezing point to the boiling point in one experiment) was evolved for the abrasion of a very small quantity of metallic dust, and he found that the specific heat of this dust was not appreciably different from that of the solid material, which showed that the caloric theory was false on this point at least. Further, the supply of heat appeared to be in-exhaustible, and it was clear that no closed system could supply unlimited amounts of any material substance.

In a paper published in 1799, Davy reported that rubbing two blocks of ice together in a vacuum, using a clockwork mechanism, caused the ice to melt at the surfaces in contact. As it was well known that considerable latent heat is required to turn ice into water, and as no other possible source of heat was available, this experiment was claimed to demonstrate that heat was evolved here by mechanical action only. Also, the specific heat of the product (water) is approximately double that of the solid used. Although this work has been accepted for many years, it seems very doubtful if Davy, then nineteen years of age, could have carried out such an experiment, which would tax the ingenuity of any trained physicist (see Prof. E. N. da C. Andrade, *Nature*, March 9, 1935).

J. Mayer, in 1842, assuming the equivalence of heat and work, calculated a value of J from the difference between the two principal specific heats of a gas. Before discussing this important result, however, it is best to consider the experimental evidence for the existence of the equivalent, and to examine some of the important experiments for its direct determination.

EXPERIMENTAL DETERMINATION OF THE MECHANICAL EQUIVALENT OF HEAT

Joule's experiments. Joule's * work on the equivalence of heat and work can be divided into two periods.

During the first, from 1838 to 1843, he did a great variety of experiments to establish that such equivalence did in fact exist. In 1843 he stated his conviction that *whenever mechanical work is converted into heat, an equivalent quantity of heat is always obtained*. His later researches, from 1843 until 1878, were chiefly devoted to the determination of the value of this mechanical equivalent.

The following brief descriptions of his two famous determinations of J by the churning of water by paddles are taken from Preston's accounts. The first of these experiments (1847) was made with

* The essay on Joule by J. G. Crowther in " British Scientists of the Nine-teenth Century " gives an excellent summary of his life and work, and Preston's " Theory of Heat " (3rd edition), pp. 289-297, describes two of his experiments in full detail.

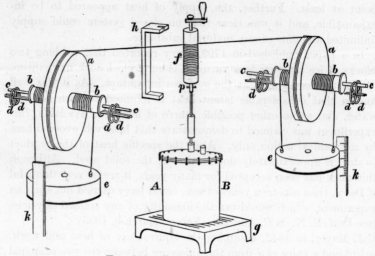

FIG. 106.—Joule's 1847 apparatus.

the apparatus shown in Fig. 106. The copper vessel (calorimeter) AB contained a known mass of water. The water-tight lid had one tubulure for the axis of the revolving paddle and another for the thermometer. The brass paddle had eight sets of revolving arms a, which worked between four sets of stationary vanes b fixed to the frame of the vessel, shown in the vertical and horizontal sections of the calorimeter of Fig. 107. A cylinder of boxwood d prevented conduction of heat along the axis of the paddle system. Referring now to Fig. 106, the paddle was revolved by lead weights e, e

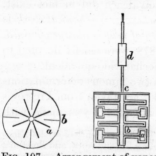

FIG. 107.—Arrangement of vanes in calorimeter.

suspended by string from the rollers bb, bb of the wooden pulleys a, a. These pulleys were supported by steel axles c, c on brass friction wheels d, d. The weights were suspended over the pulleys by fine twine, which was wound doubled on the central roller f, so that the parts passing over the pulleys left the roller at the same level and produced a steady couple round its axis. The roller could be detached from the paddle by withdrawing the pin p, so that the weights could be wound up without turning the paddle. The wooden stool g was perforated by a number of slits, so that the metal came into contact with the wood at only a few points, while the air had free access round every part of it. This reduced losses by conduction, and a large wooden screen intercepted radiation from the body of the experimenter.

The water equivalent of the calorimeter and the mass of water contained in it were known. The temperature of the calorimeter was found, the weights were wound up by placing the roller f in the stand h, and the roller was then pinned to the axis of the paddle. The height of the weights above the ground was read from the graduated slips of wood k, k, and the roller then allowed to revolve until the weights reached the floor. The velocity of the weights on reaching the ground was noted. The roller was then unpinned, the weights wound up again, and the fall repeated. After twenty such falls, the final temperature of the thermometer was read. The mean temperature of the room at the beginning, middle, and end of each experiment was found. Just before each experiment the change of temperature of the calorimeter due to gain of heat from, or loss of heat to, the surroundings was found, and this operation was repeated immediately after the end of each experiment.

Correction was made for the kinetic energy of the weights on reaching the floor. After allowing for this, the work done by the falling weights represented the mechanical energy converted into heat by friction.

In the calculation, Joule worked in British units. Let M be the total water equivalent, in lb. of water, of the calorimeter and its contents, $\theta_1°$ F. the initial temperature, and $\theta_2°$ F. the final temperature, both duly corrected for loss or gain of heat due to the surroundings. The heat evolved is thus $M(\theta_2 - \theta_1)$ B.Th.U. Let W be the total *weight* in lb. wt. of the two leaden weights, h ft. the distance travelled in a single fall, corrected for the kinetic energy on reaching the ground by subtracting from the observed height the fall needed to give the weights this velocity, and n the number of falls. The work done is Whn foot pounds.

$M(\theta_2 - \theta_1)$ B.Th.U. of heat are given by Whn foot pounds of mechanical work,

$$\therefore \ 1 \text{ B.Th.U. is given by } \frac{Whn}{M(\theta_2 - \theta_1)} \text{ foot pounds.}$$

It must be remembered that as the acceleration of gravity is different in different places, the absolute value of the foot pound varies from place to place. Joule's result was that the number of foot pounds required to raise 1 lb. of water 1° F. is 773·64 in the latitude of Manchester.

Careful corrections for several sources of error were made. The work done in rotating the pulleys and overcoming the rigidity of the string was found, and allowance was made for the fact that the motion of the paddles did not cease when the weights hit the ground, as the elasticity of the strings caused a slight "over-running".

The rise in temperature obtained was of the order of only half a degree, but Joule used specially constructed thermometers which he could read to a few thousandths of a degree.

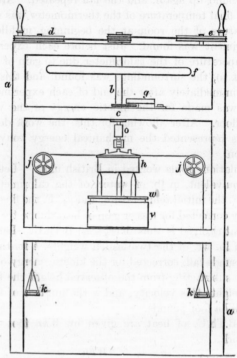

Fig. 108.—Joule's 1878 apparatus.

In the second of the water-churning experiments, undertaken at the request of the British Association and completed in 1878, the friction balance principle was used. The general idea of this is that, instead of finding the force required to turn the paddles, the couple required to prevent rotation of the calorimeter is measured. Fig. 108 shows the apparatus, in which h is the calorimeter, upon the rim of which two cords passing over pulleys j, j and carrying weights k, k apply a constant couple. The paddles are rotated by handwheels d and e, and a flywheel f steadies the rotation. The result obtained was 773·369 ft. lb. per B.Th.U. in the latitude of Manchester.

Theory of the friction balance. The friction balance principle of this and similar experiments is worth considering in more detail.

If a force F is applied tangentially to the rim of a wheel of radius r, Fig. 109, a, a couple of moment Fr is really acting, since there is an equal reaction at the axle. Let this couple now turn the wheel through an angle θ radians. The applied force F moves through a distance $s = r\theta$ in its own direction ; the reaction does not move at all ; hence work done $= F \times s = F \times r\theta = Fr \times \theta.$

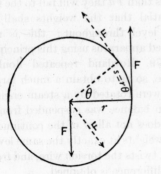

FIG. 109.

(a) Single force applied tangentially, equivalent to couple Fr.

(b) Two applied forces, constituting couple Fd.

If there are two such forces, applied in opposite directions at opposite ends of a diameter as in Fig. 109, b, and in the apparatus of Fig. 108, these forces themselves constitute the couple ; the arm of the couple is the diameter of the wheel, d, the moment of the couple is $F \times d$, and the work done during a rotation θ radians is $Fd \times \theta$; and, in general, the work done by a couple = moment of couple × angle turned through in radians.

In the experiment, the applied forces F *do not* themselves move, the rotation of the paddles exerts a couple C on the contained water, and the work done *by the paddle* rotating through an angle θ radians is thus $C\theta$ (Fig. 109, b).

But, considering the equilibrium of the calorimeter, which does not rotate, the couple applied by the forces F in the strings must balance C. So, if d be the diameter of the groove about which F is applied (the arm of the couple), as this couple just balances C, $C = Fd$ and the work done for a rotation of θ radians is

$$F \, d\theta \text{ units.}$$

As one revolution is 2π radians, in n revolutions of the paddle $\theta = 2\pi n$. Hence the work done in n revolutions of the paddle is $2\pi n Fd$ units.

Only if C exactly equals Fd will the weights which apply the couple remain steady. If C exceeds Fd the weights will be wound up to their fullest extent ; if C is less than Fd they will fall to the full extent of the string. It is essential that the weights shall be maintained exactly at the same level throughout ; this is not difficult to arrange in a hand-operated apparatus using this principle.

Rowland's experiment. In 1879, Rowland repeated Joule's second experiment on a larger scale, so as to obtain a much larger rise in temperature. The paddles were rotated by a steam engine, and the calorimeter with its friction balance was suspended from a torsion wire. Mechanical rotation does not allow of the continuous fine adjustment needed to keep the weights at exactly the same level, but the difference $C - Fd$, or $Fd - C$, twists the torsion wire, and from the observed twist of the wire this difference is obtained.

Rowland found that the quantity of mechanical energy required to raise the temperature of 1 gm. of water through 1° C. varied with the temperature, decreasing at first as the temperature rises, reaching a minimum at about 30° C., and then increasing. The explanation of this is, not that J itself varies, but that the specific heat of water varies with temperature, having a minimum value at about 30° C. The results of Callendar and Barnes by an electrical method lead to a similar conclusion, though the exact temperature of the minimum specific heat was found by them to be 37·5° C. (see p. 246).

Determination of J by a simple friction balance method   Heat is generated by friction between two metal (iron) cones, the inner of which, D, serves as the calorimeter (Fig. 110). This cone can be attached firmly at the centre of a large wooden disc A, round the circumference of which is a light cord carrying a suspended weight.

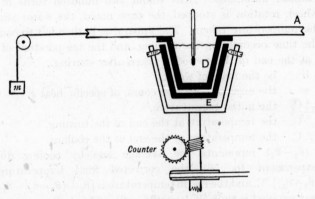

FIG. 110.—Simple friction balance apparatus.

The outer cone is fixed by three ebonite centring screws (which serve as heat insulators) to the inside of a brass block which can be rotated by a belt drive worked either by hand or by machinery. A revolution counter attached to the axle carrying the brass block is desirable ; though a satisfactory substitute for this, if the block is rotated by a handwheel, is to find how many revolutions of the block correspond to one turn of the handwheel, and count the number of hand turns.

It will be noted that the couple which prevents rotation of the inner cone is apparently provided by one force ; the other, as in Fig. 109, a, is the reaction passing through the axis of rotation. This is not entirely satisfactory, and the apparatus tends to rock a little.

The two iron cones are weighed. The inner cone is then fastened securely to the wooden disc, and the outer cone centred in the brass block. The apparatus is assembled, tested to see that it will run properly, and suitable weight to hang on the string found by trial. A known mass of water is placed in the inner cone. For the purpose of this experiment it suffices to run in 20 cc. or 25 cc. from a pipette, taking 1 c.c. as weighing 1 gm. After a minute or two, the water is stirred with the thermometer and the temperature taken. The handwheel is then turned steadily, the time of starting being noted, and the number of turns counted. It is essential to keep the position of the weight as steady as possible, and the speed of rotation has to be varied to secure this. A little practice makes this adjustment almost automatic. After about two hundred turns of the handwheel, rotation is stopped, the time noted, the water stirred, and the temperature taken. The apparatus is then left to cool for half the time occupied in the turning, and the temperature of the water at the end of this period is taken after stirring.

Let W be the mass of water,

    w the mass of both iron cones, of specific heat s,

    $\theta_1°$ C.   the initial temperature,

    $\theta_2°$ C.   the temperature at the end of the turning,

    $\theta_3°$ C.   the temperature at the end of the cooling.

Then $(\theta_2 - \theta_3)$ represents the average loss by cooling during the experiment (p. 56), the corrected final temperature is $[\theta_2 + (\theta_2 - \theta_3)]$ °C. and the rise in temperature is $[\theta_2 + (\theta_2 - \theta_3) - \theta_1]$ °C. The heat evolved is thus $(W + ws)(2\theta_2 - \theta_3 - \theta_1)$ calories.

Let m gm. be the mass of the suspended weight, and r the *radius* (*not diameter*, as the arm of the couple is the radius) of the disc. The couple is then mr gm. wt. cm., or mgr dyne cm.

Let n be the number of turns of the handwheel, and λ the number of turns of the block corresponding to one turn of the wheel. The number of revolutions is then λn, the total angle turned through is $2\pi\lambda n$ radians, and the work done is $2\pi\lambda nmgr$ ergs.

Thus $(W + ws)(2\theta_2 - \theta_3 - \theta_1)$ calories are furnished by the expenditure of $2\pi\lambda nmgr$ ergs, and

$$1 \text{ calorie is equivalent to } \frac{2\pi\lambda nmgr}{(W + ws)(2\theta_2 - \theta_3 - \theta_1)} \text{ ergs,}$$

which is the required value of J.

Results by this method always appear to be a little too high, since there is little opportunity for any of the measured work to be wasted, while it is less easy to correct completely for heat losses.

Constancy of J. Preston gives a table of the results of forty-five separate experiments on the determination of J or J' made between the years 1842 and 1899 by a large number of independent experimenters using a great variety of methods both direct and indirect. *All the results, with the exception of one or two early determinations, agree extremely closely.*

It is upon evidence of this kind that the First Law of Thermodynamics rests. The equivalence of heat and work is no mere speculation ; it has been established as the result of two whole generations of painstaking experimental investigation.

Accurate evaluation of J or J'. While the determination of the electrical equivalent of heat, J', by Callendar and Barnes described earlier (pp. 71-73) is recognised as being very accurate, experiments of greater precision have recently been made. R. T. Birge, who has for many years been engaged on a critical survey of the values of the chief physical constants, has taken three of these as the basis of his computation * of the best values for J and J'.

These three experiments are :

1. The determination of the electrical equivalent J' by Jaeger and Steinwehr (1921).

2. The direct determination of the mechanical equivalent J by Laby and Hercus (1929).

3. The determination of the electrical equivalent J' by Osborne, Stimson, and Ginnings (1939).

The values adopted by Birge for the equivalents are :

For the electrical equivalent J', $4 \cdot 1847 \pm 0 \cdot 0003$ international joules per 15° calorie.

For the mechanical equivalent J, $4 \cdot 1855 \pm 0 \cdot 0004$ absolute joules per 15° calorie.

(The factor converting international joules to absolute joules is $1 \cdot 00020 \pm 0 \cdot 00004$.)

Jaeger and Steinwehr's experiment. These workers used an ordinary calorimetric method, measuring the rise in temperature of a large mass of water (50 kgm.) contained in a thin-walled copper calorimeter. The temperature rise obtained was small, about 1·4°. The water was thoroughly stirred by a system of electrically driven paddles, and the calorimeter was surrounded by an air space, and enclosed in a double-walled metal box, the space between the walls of which contained water at a constant temperature. The current in the electric heating coil was measured by finding the potential drop across a standard 0·1 ohm resistance in series with

---

* Physical Society's *Reports on Progress in Physics*, 1941.

it, and the potential drop across the electric heater was determined. A Weston cell was used as the standard of E.M.F. The time during which the current passed was recorded on a chronograph. The temperature was measured by a platinum resistance thermometer. The accuracy of the whole experiment is within a few parts in ten thousand.

Experiment of Laby and Hercus. Laby and Hercus used what they termed an " induction dynamometer " method. The apparatus is similar in principle to the squirrel cage induction motor, except that (a) the rotating field is produced by actually rotating an electromagnet instead of by phase difference, and (b) the armature is prevented from rotating by the application of a steady couple. Work which would have gone chiefly in rotating the armature against a load in an actual motor is thus entirely converted into heat, by the eddy currents induced in its conductors ; these are in the form of hollow copper tubes through which water flows, so that the heat produced is measured by the method of continuous flow.

A general view of the apparatus is given in Fig. 111. The " rotor " is a case containing an electromagnet energised by a steady current ; it is supported on ball races, and is rotated steadily about

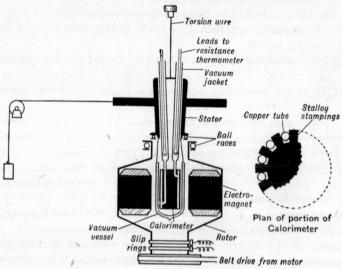

FIG. 111.—Apparatus of Laby and Hercus.

a vertical axis by means of a 1 h.p. 100 volt direct-current motor driven from a battery of fresh accumulators. The electromagnet is carefully aligned so that the axis of rotation is exactly parallel to the axis of the " stator ", and so that there is no component of motion in the direction of this axis at all. The stator is also mounted on a ball race, and is at the same time suspended from a torsion wire. The calorimeter in the stator is a vacuum vessel containing fourteen vertical copper tubes mounted in an armature of stalloy stampings ; a steady stream of water flows through these tubes at such a rate that the flow shall be turbulent, and the inlet and outflow temperatures are observed by means of platinum resistance thermometers so connected as to record the difference with high accuracy. The fundamental interval indication of each thermometer was checked several times during the long period occupied by this set of experiments, and these were found constant to 6 parts in 100,000. The thermometers themselves were surrounded by special silvered vacuum jackets. The couple which prevents rotation of the stator is provided by two weights (one only is shown in the figure) hanging over pulleys with agate knife-edge bearings from fine tungsten wires of 0·0127 cm. diameter which are applied to the edge of an aluminium torsion wheel 20·001 cm. in diameter. The principle on which the mechanical work done is measured is exactly the same as that of the friction balance explained on p. 235. A small mirror on the stator reflects a beam of light on to a scale, so that the steadiness of the stator can be observed.

Great attention was paid to the attainment of perfect steadiness of all the conditions. The speed of the motor was controlled by a centrifugal governor and also by a hand regulator, and its steadiness was ascertained by a stroboscopic method. Special brushes were designed to eliminate variations in speed due to changes in contact resistance. Heat losses to the room were made extremely small by the expedient of regulating the room temperature by electric heaters placed about it so that the room temperature was always that of the mouth of the vacuum flask.

In an experiment, a steadying run of 1 hour preceded the taking of any readings. When the inflow and outflow temperatures $\theta_1°$ C. and $\theta_2°$ C. of the water were steady, the mass of water flowing through the calorimeter during a measured number of revolutions of the rotor was found. Then, if m be the sum of the masses of the two weights hung on the wires, n the number of turns of the rotor, d_θ the diameter of the wheel at room temperature θ, f a factor (very nearly unity) to allow for imperfect centring of the pulleys, the work done is

$$\pi n m g \, d_\theta f \text{ ergs.}$$

If W is the mass of water collected, L the heat lost to the surroundings through the sides of the vacuum flask (a very small correction, of the order 0·001 to 0·003 per cent.), the heat produced is $[W(\theta_2 - \theta_1 - v) + L]$ calories, where a small correction, v, makes allowance for the heating of the water by its turbulent motion through the fine tubes. The value of v, about 0·0016° C., though small, is about 1/3000 of the rise in temperature observed during a run.

Thus $$\pi n m g \, d_\theta f = J[W(\theta_2 - \theta_1 - v) + L]$$

and $$J = \frac{\pi n m g \, d_\theta f}{[W(\theta_2 - \theta_1 - v) + L]} \text{ ergs per calorie,}$$

or $$J = \frac{\pi n m g \, d_\theta f}{[W(\theta_2 - \theta_1 - v) + L] \times 10^7} \text{ absolute joules per calorie.}$$

The value of m was 1000 gm., and in an ordinary run, with $n = 15000$ turns, about 4000 gm. of water was collected, and the steady temperature rise was about 5·4° C.

The result for J finally accepted by Laby and Hercus was

$$J = 4 \cdot 1852 \pm 0 \cdot 0008 \text{ absolute joules, per 15° calorie.}$$

Experiment of Osborne, Stimson, and Ginnings. A quantity of water substance, part liquid and part vapour, is enclosed in a metal calorimeter shell. An electric heater immersed in the water provides means of adding a measured quantity of energy to the calorimeter and its contents. The calorimeter is surrounded by a vacuum jacket, and this in turn is surrounded by a bath of saturated water vapour the temperature of which is kept very close to that of the calorimeter, so that heat losses are very small ; these heat losses are measured and taken into account.

Fig. 112 represents the scheme of the apparatus. The calorimeter C is a copper globe of about 1200 c.c. capacity, fitted with an electric heater H and a circulating pump P. The calorimeter is supported within an evacuated space V, which is surrounded by a bath B of saturated water vapour, to which heat is supplied by the heater E. The temperature of B is elegantly controlled by adjusting the *pressure* within it, since this (p. 179) determines the temperature of water vapour in equilibrium with liquid water. The sample of water is introduced from the container F into the calorimeter as described below; vacuum-pump connections with taps at X and Y enable the calorimeter and the tubing to be evacuated when necessary. A large copper reference block R, to which is attached a platinum resistance thermometer, provides a temperature datum line for the apparatus; this is surrounded by an extension of the steam and vacuum shells. A number of auxiliary thermocouples are used to determine the temperatures of various points on the calorimeter and its surroundings with reference to this block, by having one junction of each thermocouple on the block. Eight thermocouples are used to find the temperature at different points of the calorimeter. Eight more are used to measure the temperature of the inner surface of the vapour bath, so that the very slight difference between the calorimeter and the surroundings is known and the resulting heat leak allowed for. The temperature of the vapour bath itself is regulated automatically by adjusting the *pressure* by a suitable thermostat arrangement. The figure shows the complete apparatus. The vessel K, which could be surrounded

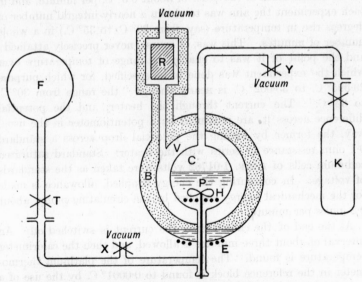

Fig. 112.—Scheme of apparatus of Osborne, Stimson, and Ginnings.

by a bath of liquid air, was employed in another set of experiments, to determine the latent heat of vaporisation of water in joules per gram, the vapour generated by a known energy input being collected as ice for weighing.

In the course of an experiment, pure air-free water is transferred from a still to the previously evacuated and weighed container, which is then weighed and attached to the apparatus. The calorimeter and connecting tubing are then evacuated, the tap T opened, and the water allowed to run into the calorimeter. A little water is left behind in the container and the connecting tubes ; that in the container is allowed for by weighing the container again, while that in the tubing is dealt with by pumping the tubing out through a liquid air trap ; this collects the water vapour as ice, the mass of which is found. In this way the mass of water transferred to the calorimeter is accurately determined ; as a check, the water is pumped out at the end of the experiment and weighed again.

A measured quantity of energy is supplied to the calorimeter and its contents by means of the heater H, which is connected to a battery of storage cells of large current capacity. It is arranged to give a rise of temperature of the order of about 0·5° C. per minute, and in each experiment the aim was to obtain a nearly integral number of degrees rise in temperature (say, from 30° C. to 35° C.) in a whole number of minutes. This was, of course, never precisely attained ; and the point of it was to enable the range of temperature over which the experiment was done to be specified, for which purpose 29·995° C. to 35·002° C. is nearly enough " the range from 30° C. to 35° C." The current through the heater, and the potential difference across it, are measured by a potentiometer in the usual way, the former by finding the potential drop across a standard 0·1 ohm resistance in series with the heater. Standard saturated cadmium cells of E.M.F. 1·01762 volts were taken as the standards of voltage. In computing the energy supplied, allowance is made for the mechanical energy supplied by the circulating pump, about 0·2 joules per minute.

At the end of the chosen time, the current is switched off. An interval of about three minutes is allowed, and then the calorimeter temperature is found. The temperature of the platinum thermometer in the reference block is found to 0·0001° C. by the use of a suitable bridge, and the temperature difference between the various parts of the calorimeter, etc., and this block found by measuring the E.M.F.s of the thermocouples.

The heat capacity of the calorimeter was not determined separately, but was eliminated by doing two sets of experiments over the same temperature range, one with a large mass of water in the calorimeter and the other with a very much smaller quantity. As the temperature range is the same, the difference between the two quantities of energy supplied is used in heating a quantity of water the mass of which is the difference between the larger and smaller masses employed.

The heat supplied to the water in the calorimeter is really used in three ways : (i) raising the temperature of the water ; (ii) producing more water vapour as the temperature rises, and (iii) raising the temperature of the saturated vapour in the space above the water. The heat used in (ii) and (iii) is very small, and the small correction involved can be calculated.

Thus there are known with high accuracy (a) the mass of water, (b) the rise in temperature, and (c) the energy supplied, from which the number of joules required to raise the temperature of one gram of water one centigrade degree is found. At 15° C. this is 4·1858 absolute joules, so the result obtained for J' is 4·1858 absolute joules per 15° calorie.

The Callendar and Barnes experiment. Until recently, the Callendar and Barnes experiment was considered outstanding for its accuracy, to which it was said the continuous-flow method contributed greatly. It is at first surprising to find this experiment omitted from Birge's list ; but there appears to have been some uncertainty about the elimination of heat losses, and Callendar's final estimation of its accuracy was within about 1 part in 4000, which just falls short of being quite comparable in accuracy with the three later determinations.

As to continuous-flow calorimetry, the truth seems to be that with modern equipment and technique, ordinary rise-of-temperature calorimetry is capable of giving results as good as, or better than, this method. Two of the three experiments quoted here used the temperature-rise method ; while Laby and Hercus, who used the continuous-flow method, state explicitly that they chose this for its convenience with their particular apparatus and not because it possessed any particular advantages in itself.

Variation of the specific heat of water with temperature. The experiments of Jaeger and Steinwehr and of Osborne, Stimson, and Ginnings were conducted at many different temperatures, and enabled the number of joules required to raise one gram of water one centigrade degree at different temperatures (that is, the specific heat of water in joules per gram per 1° C.) to be calculated. The results are compared with those of Callendar and Barnes on the graph accompanying, which also shows the result of Laby and Hercus at 15° C. and that of Rowland at 20° C.

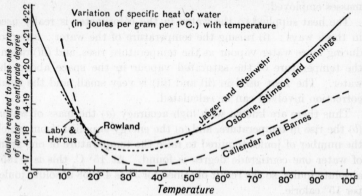

Variation of specific heat of water with temperature (°C.) according to different observers. Rowland's result at 20° C., and that of Laby and Hercus at 15° C., are also shown.

GAS LAWS AND WORK

External work done by an expanding gas. Consider unit mass (one mole) of any gas enclosed in a cylinder (Fig. 113) fitted with a frictionless piston of cross-sectional area A sq. cm. The volume of the gas is V c.c. at pressure p dynes per sq. cm.

Let the gas expand, moving the piston out a distance dx. The change in volume dV is $A\,dx$. Now the force exerted by the gas on the piston is pA dynes, so

$$\text{work done by gas} = pA\,dx \text{ ergs.}$$

But
$$A\,dx = dV.$$

$$\therefore \text{work done by gas} = p\,dV \text{ ergs.}$$

Work done in this way, against an external resistance when a gas expands, is said to be **external work.**

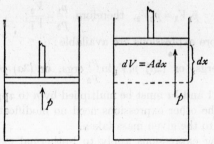

FIG. 113.—Work done by expanding gas.

If the volume of the gas is *reduced* by an amount dV,

$$\text{work done } by \text{ gas} = -p\,dV \text{ ergs,}$$

or $$\text{work done } on \text{ gas} = p\,dV \text{ ergs.}$$

This is for a small expansion by a small element of volume. For a finite expansion from initial conditions p_1, V_1 to final conditions p_2, V_2, the external work done by the gas is

$$\int_{V_1}^{V_2} p\,dV \text{ ergs.}$$

Isothermal change for perfect gas. For a finite expansion from p_1, V_1 to p_2, V_2 *at constant temperature*, Boyle's Law is obeyed, so for all values of p and V, $pV = k$, where k is a constant, and $p = k/V$.

Hence, $$\text{work done} = \int_{V_1}^{V_2} \frac{k}{V}\,dV = k\int_{V_1}^{V_2}\frac{dV}{V}$$

$$= k\,(\ln V_2 - \ln V_1)$$

$$= k \ln\left(\frac{V_2}{V_1}\right) \text{ ergs.}$$

Three alternative expressions can be substituted for the constant k in this expression. If T be the absolute temperature on the ideal gas scale and R the gas constant for one mole of gas,

$$pV = RT = k,$$

also $$p_1V_1 = p_2V_2 = k.$$

Hence, work done by gas is

(1) $RT \ln \dfrac{V_2}{V_1}$ ergs, or (2) $p_1V_1 \ln \dfrac{V_2}{V_1}$ ergs, or (3) $p_2V_2 \ln \dfrac{V_2}{V_1}$ ergs.

As $\qquad p_1 V_1 = p_2 V_2$, therefore $\dfrac{p_1}{p_2} = \dfrac{V_2}{V_1}$;

hence three more expressions are available:

(1a) $RT \ln \dfrac{p_1}{p_2}$ ergs, or (2a) $p_1 V_1 \ln \dfrac{p_1}{p_2}$ ergs, or (3a) $p_2 V_2 \ln \dfrac{p_1}{p_2}$ ergs.

Expressions 1 and 1a must be multiplied by n to apply to n moles of gas, while the other expressions need no modification if the p's and V's apply to the given mass taken.

The foregoing expressions apply to isothermal expansions, but the original equation,

$$external\ work = \int_{V_1}^{V_2} p\, dV \text{ ergs,}$$

always enables the external work to be calculated, whether the expansion takes place under simple conditions or not.

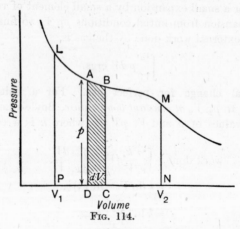

Fig. 114.

Consider the graph of p against V for any change (Fig. 114). Let the pressure at some point such as A be p; let the volume increase by dV to the point B. The area of the strip $ABCD$ is $p\,dV$, so this area represents the external work done by the gas during the small expansion. The whole area $LMNP$ between the curve and the axis of V from V_1 to V_2 thus represents the external work done by the gas in expanding from V_1 to V_2. Such a graph is called a work diagram, or an indicator diagram.

In the isothermal case, the energy to provide the external work must obviously be supplied as heat from outside. There is another important particular case, in which the gas expands in an insulating cylinder so that no heat enters or leaves. Then the heat energy of the gas itself must be drawn upon to furnish the external work, and its temperature falls. Similarly, if the gas is compressed so that no heat enters or leaves, the external work done on the gas is converted into heat which cannot escape and the temperature rises. Such changes are called *adiabatic expansions* and *adiabatic compressions* ; they will be discussed more fully later.

Real gases. Internal work. Van der Waals' equation supposes that in an actual gas the molecules attract one another appreciably. Then, if the volume of the gas increases, work is done by the gas in separating the molecules against these attractive forces. This is called **internal work**, and just as we say that the work done in raising a weight vertically (or separating the weight and the earth against the gravitational attraction between them) supplies *potential energy* to the weight-earth system, we can say that this internal work increases the potential energy of the molecules, or the internal potential energy of the gas as a whole. In Van der Waals' equation, the effect of the attractions is supposed equivalent to a pressure a/V^2. Substituting this for p in the expression $\int_{V_1}^{V_2} p \, dV$, the internal work done by unit mass of a real gas on expanding from V_1 to V_2 should be

$$\int_{V_1}^{V_2} \frac{a}{V^2} \, dV, \quad \text{or} \quad \left(\frac{a}{V_1} - \frac{a}{V_2} \right) \text{ergs.}$$

Law of conservation of energy. The law of conservation of energy can now be applied to the expansion of a gas.

Suppose a small quantity dQ of heat energy is supplied to unit mass of gas. Let the resulting increase in the internal kinetic energy of the molecules (or the increase in the heat content of the gas) be dE, the internal work done against molecular attractions (or the gain in internal potential energy) be dI, and the external work performed by the gas in pushing back an external constraint or expanding against an externally applied pressure be dW. By a fairly general convention the symbol U is used for the total internal energy, the sum of the potential and kinetic energies of the molecules, so $dU = dE + dI$. It seems more instructive here to record

dI as a separate item, instead of working in terms of dU, as one of the chief points discussed in the succeeding sections is whether or not dI can be detected separately.

Then, applying the law of conservation of energy,

$$dQ = dU + dW = dE + dI + dW,$$

all quantities being measured in the same units, either all in work units (ergs or joules) or all in calories.

For a perfect gas, since there is no attraction between the molecules, $dI = 0$; this statement is sometimes called Joule's Law.

The two chief specific heats of a gas. Consider unit mass of a perfect gas, for which $dI = 0$. Initially, let its pressure be p, its volume V, and its absolute temperature T.

Let C_v be the specific heat at constant volume, and C_p the specific heat at constant pressure.

Let the temperature be raised from T to $T + dT$, the volume being kept constant. No external work is done, so $dW = 0$. The heat put in is $C_v \, dT$, so as $dI = 0$ and $dW = 0$, from the equation $dQ = dE + dW + dI$,

$$C_v \, dT = dE.$$

Again, let the temperature be raised from T to $T + dT$, the pressure being kept constant. The volume V then increases to $V + dV$, and external work $dW = p \, dV$ ergs $= p \, dV / J$ calories is done. The heat put in is $C_p \, dT$, and as $dQ = dE + dW$,

$$C_p \, dT = dE + dW.$$

But dE is the same as in the first case, $C_v \, dT$,

so $$C_p \, dT = C_v \, dT + dW,$$

or $(C_p - C_v) \, dT = dW$, the units being calories on both sides.

Now $$dW = p \, dV \text{ ergs} = p \, dV / J \text{ cal.}$$

As $pV = RT$, $p \, dV = R \, dT$ for a constant pressure expansion

$$\therefore \ dW = \frac{p \, dV}{J} = \frac{R \, dT}{J} \text{ cal.}$$

$$\therefore \ (C_p - C_v) \, dT = \frac{R}{J} \, dT, \text{ units being calories on both sides,}$$

or $$C_p - C_v = \frac{R}{J}.$$

Mayer, in 1842, calculated the value of J using this equation.

Note the assumptions that have been made in deriving it. These are :

1. That the law of conservation of energy, $dQ = dE + dW + dI$, holds.

2. That there is no internal work done, so $dI = 0$.

3. That the equation of state of the gas is $pV = RT$.

Internal work done when a real gas expands. If a fixed mass of gas is made to expand in such a way as to do no external work, it should be possible to detect the effect of internal work, since, if internal work is done, the only source available to furnish internal potential energy is the internal kinetic energy, which is thus reduced, so that cooling should result.

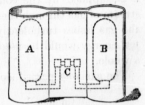

In 1845 Joule carried out an experiment to look for this work. Two copper vessels *A* and *B* (Fig. 115) were connected by a

FIG. 115.—Joule's apparatus.

pipe fitted with a stopcock *C*. The vessel *A* contained dry air at 22 atmospheres pressure, while *B* was exhausted. Both vessels were placed in a water bath, the temperature of which could be read to $1/200°$ F. The temperature of the water was noted, and the stopcock opened. Air passed from *A* to *B* until the pressures in each vessel were the same. The water was stirred, and the temperature taken ; no fall in temperature was observed.

Considering the expansion more closely, the first small quantity of air emerging from *A* expands into a vacuum, and so really does do no external work. But after this, the rest of the air does external work in compressing the air in *B*. The vessel *A* should thus in any event cool. But the air which first reaches *B* is compressed by that which follows it in, so that external work is done on *B* ; *B* should therefore rise in temperature. As the external work done by the gas in *A* equals the external work done on the gas in *B*, the heat loss in *A* equals the heat developed in *B*. Joule performed a second experiment with the same two vessels immersed in separate water baths, and observed that this apparently happened, no cooling of the whole gas attributable to internal work being detected.

In view of the large heat capacity of the apparatus and the small mass of air employed, it is not surprising that Joule failed to detect any internal work effect. The experiment really shows, not that no internal work is done when a gas expands, but that any internal work done must be very small.

A different type of experiment was done by Joule and William Thomson (Lord Kelvin). In this, a stream of the gas under examination was allowed to expand freely through a porous plug of cotton wool or silk fibres. This expansion, of course, does external work ; but (if Boyle's Law is obeyed), this external work is not done at the expense of the internal energy of the gas, since it is supplied by the compressor which maintains the continuous stream of gas through the apparatus. The porous plug ensures that the gas issues turbulently ; since, if it streamed through a single jet, energy would be used in supplying kinetic energy to the jet as a whole.

The gas was passed slowly and uniformly through a long copper spiral immersed in a stirred water bath kept at uniform temperature. At the top of the copper tube a boxwood tube (*bb*, Fig. 116) was fixed, and this tube contained a plug of cotton wool or silk fibres between two perforated brass plates. Outside the tube was an insulating belt of cotton wool *d*. A thermometer bulb was placed with its bulb just above the plug, and this was surrounded by the glass tube.

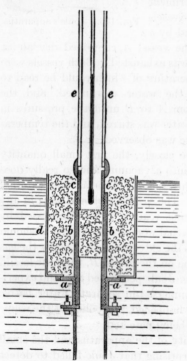

The results may be summarised as follows :

1. All gases show a change in temperature on passing through the plug. This is called the Joule-Kelvin (or Joule-Thomson) effect.

2. This change in temperature is proportional to the difference between the pressures on the two sides of the plug.

3. At ordinary temperatures, all the gases examined, except

FIG. 116.—Porous-plug experiment.

hydrogen, showed a cooling. Hydrogen showed a rise in temperature. The mean values between 0° C. and 100° C. for the temperature change for 1 atmosphere pressure difference are :

Nitrogen	0·249°	cooling
Oxygen	0·253°	cooling
Air	0·208°	cooling
Carbon dioxide	1·005°	cooling
Hydrogen	0·039°	rise in temp.

Later experiments showed that :

4. For every gas there is an *inversion temperature*. If initially above this temperature, the temperature of the gas rises on passing through the plug. Below this temperature, the temperature of the gas falls on passing through the plug. The inversion temperature for hydrogen is about 190° K., and for helium about 30° K. For the other common gases it is well above ordinary temperatures.

Explanation of results. If the gas obeys Boyle's Law, there is no external work done by a *free* expansion. But if the gas does not obey Boyle's Law, there will be external work as well as internal work done. Suppose for a moment that the temperature on both sides of the plug is maintained constant (making Boyle's Law relevant) by suitably supplying or removing heat.

Consider a fixed mass of gas at the high pressure p_1 ; let its volume be V_1. The external work done on the gas in passing it through the plug at constant pressure p_1 is $p_1 V_1$; let the volume be V_2 on passing through the plug, and the pressure (atmospheric) be p_2. The work done by the gas in pushing back the atmosphere is thus $p_2 V_2$. If Boyle's Law is obeyed, $p_1 V_1 = p_2 V_2$, and no external work is done. But a real gas only obeys Boyle's Law closely at its Boyle temperature. Above the Boyle temperature, pV is greater at high pressures than at low pressures, and $p_1 V_1$ is greater than $p_2 V_2$. Below the Boyle temperature pV is less at moderately high pressures than at low pressures, and $p_1 V_1$ is less than $p_2 V_2$.

If the temperature is above the Boyle temperature, then $p_1 V_1$ is greater than $p_2 V_2$, and the work done on the gas by the compressor exceeds that done by the gas on the atmosphere, the internal energy of the gas is increased, and heat must be removed to keep the temperature constant, or, if this is not done, a rise in temperature results.

If the temperature is below the Boyle temperature, then $p_1 V_1$ is less than $p_2 V_2$, the external work done by the gas is greater than that done on the gas, and the internal energy of the gas is drawn upon ; heat must be supplied from without if the temperature is to remain constant, and, if this is not done, there is a fall in temperature.

Thus the sign of the external work contribution to the observed effect depends on whether the gas is initially above or below its Boyle temperature. At ordinary temperatures the cooling is the sum of the external work and internal work coolings for most gases. While for hydrogen (and helium) the heating is the difference between the external work heating and the internal work cooling.

Left at this stage, the chief theoretical question seems still unanswered. There still seems no clear proof of molecular attraction since (a) cooling does not invariably occur, and (b) much of the cooling usually observed is attributable in the first instance to another cause, *external* work due to the deviation of the gas from perfect-gas behaviour (though this in itself is supposed partly due to attractions). But it is easy to calculate the external work effect on its own and compare this with the observed Joule-Kelvin effect. From Amagat's results for the variation of pV with p for nitrogen and hydrogen,* the average value of $p_2 V_2 - p_1 V_1$ for one atmosphere pressure difference can be found and this, converted into calories and divided by C_p, gives the temperature change for a pressure difference of one atmosphere. It appears that the external work cooling per atmosphere for nitrogen at $17 \cdot 7°$ C. should be about $0 \cdot 08°$, and the heating for hydrogen about $0 \cdot 05°$. As the observed temperature changes are $- 0 \cdot 249°$ and $+ 0 \cdot 039°$, the true *internal work coolings* are about $(0 \cdot 249 - 0 \cdot 08) = 0 \cdot 169°$ for nitrogen and $(0 \cdot 05 - 0 \cdot 039) = 0 \cdot 011°$ for hydrogen.

Application of Van der Waals' equation. It should be possible to explain the whole of the observations of the Joule-Kelvin effect in terms of the equation of state of a real gas.†

Consider one mole of a real gas, and suppose that the temperature is maintained constant on both sides of the plug. The same symbols as before are used throughout.

* See Preston, " Theory of Heat ", pp. 466, 467.

† The following treatment is taken from Roberts' " Heat and Thermo-dynamics ", Chapter 5.

The Van der Waals' equation assumes that there is molecular attraction causing an effective internal pressure a/V^2.

The external work done by the gas on passing through the plug is

$$p_2V_2 - p_1V_1 \text{ ergs.}$$

The internal work is

$$\int_{V_1}^{V_2} \frac{a}{V^2}\, dV, \quad \text{or} \quad \left(-\frac{a}{V_2} + \frac{a}{V_1}\right) \text{ ergs.}$$

The total work done by the gas is

$$p_2V_2 - p_1V_1 - \frac{a}{V_2} + \frac{a}{V_1} \text{ ergs.}$$

Now, Van der Waals' equation $\left(p + \dfrac{a}{V^2}\right)(V - b) = RT$ when

expanded becomes $pV + \dfrac{a}{V} - pb - \dfrac{ab}{V^2} = RT$.

Neglect the product ab as a small quantity of the second order, and in the first order term a/V substitute the approximate value p/RT for $1/V$, so that the approximate form of Van der Waals' equation becomes

$$pV = RT - \frac{ap}{RT} + bp.$$

Hence $p_1V_1 = RT - \dfrac{ap_1}{RT} + bp_1, \quad p_2V_2 = RT - \dfrac{ap_2}{RT} + bp_2,$

and the external work $p_2V_2 - p_1V_1 = \left(\dfrac{a}{RT} - b\right)(p_1 - p_2).$

Again, substituting p/RT for $1/V$ in the two small terms a/V_2 and a/V_1, $\qquad a/V_2 = p_2/RT \quad \text{and} \quad a/V_1 = p_1/RT$;

so the internal work $\left(-\dfrac{a}{V_2} + \dfrac{a}{V_1}\right) = \dfrac{a}{RT}(p_1 - p_2).$

Hence the total work done is

$$\left(\frac{a}{RT} - b\right)(p_1 - p_2) + \frac{a}{RT}(p_1 - p_2) = \left(\frac{2a}{RT} - b\right)(p_1 - p_2) \text{ ergs.}$$

As p_1 is always greater than p_2, the first bracket determines the sign of this work.

If $\dfrac{2a}{RT} > b$, or $T < \dfrac{2a}{Rb}$, work is done by the gas, and hence to maintain isothermal conditions heat must be supplied ; in the actual porous plug experiment this heat is not forthcoming, and the temperature of the gas falls.

If $\dfrac{2a}{RT} < b$, or $T > \dfrac{2a}{Rb}$, work is done on the gas. Heat must be removed to keep the temperature constant; if it is not removed, the temperature of the gas rises.

The value $T = \dfrac{2a}{Rb}$ clearly gives the inversion temperature of the gas, which we will call T_i.

According to Van der Waals' equation, the critical temperature T_c equals $\dfrac{8a}{27Rb}$. Hence $\dfrac{T_i}{T_c} = \dfrac{2a}{Rb} \div \dfrac{8a}{27Rb} = \dfrac{27}{4} = 6\cdot75$.

Experimentally, according to Ruhemann, the value of $\dfrac{T_i}{T_c}$ is actually about $5\cdot8$ for all gases.

The inversion temperature of the Joule-Kelvin effect must not be confused with the Boyle temperature. At the Boyle temperature, the second virial coefficient B_v is equal to zero. Van der Waals' equation (see p. 170), gives for B_v the expression $B_v = \left(b - \dfrac{a}{RT}\right)$, and the Boyle temperature T_b at which $B_v = 0$ is thus $\dfrac{a}{Rb}$.

Hence
$$\frac{T_i}{T_b} = \frac{2a}{Rb} \div \frac{a}{Rb} = 2.$$

Thermodynamical reasoning beyond the scope of this book (see Birtwistle's "Principles of Thermodynamics") leads to the following expression for the *fall* in temperature per unit pressure difference, which may be written dT/dp, for constant internal energy:

$$\frac{dT}{dp} = \frac{1}{C_p} \left\{ T\left(\frac{dV}{dT}\right)_p - V \right\},$$

where C_p is the specific heat at constant pressure, and $\left(\dfrac{dV}{dT}\right)_p$ is the rate of change of V with T when p is constant.

For a perfect gas,

$$\frac{1}{V_0}\left(\frac{dV}{dT}\right)_p = \frac{1}{273\cdot2} = a \text{ (p. 139)}, \text{ whence } \left(\frac{dV}{dT}\right)_p = aV_0.$$

$$\therefore\ T\left(\frac{dV}{dT}\right)_p = aV_0T = V, \text{ whence } T\left(\frac{dV}{dT}\right)_p - V = 0, \text{ and } \frac{dT}{dp} \text{ is zero.}$$

For a real gas, $T\left(\dfrac{dV}{dT}\right)_p - V$ is not zero, and from a knowledge of its value, obtained by finding $\dfrac{dT}{dp}$ for the Joule-Kelvin effect, the degree of departure from perfect-gas behaviour can be ascertained and the correction which should be applied to a gas thermometer employing that gas can be found.

At the temperature of inversion, as $\dfrac{dT}{dp} = 0$, $T\left(\dfrac{dV}{dT}\right)_p - V = 0$.

This leads to further interesting results for a gas obeying Van der Waals' equation.

Using the reduced form of Van der Waals' equation, $\left(p_r + \dfrac{3}{V_r^2}\right)(3V_r - 1) = 8T_r$, the values of $\left(\dfrac{dV_r}{dT_r}\right)_{p_r}$ and V_r are substituted in the equation $T\left(\dfrac{dV}{dT}\right)_p - V = 0$.

The corresponding values of T_r and p_r satisfying this condition all lie on a smooth curve which is more or less as shown in the figure, and should apply to all gases. It is called the inversion curve. For values of p_r and T_r within the curve, $\dfrac{dT}{dp}$ is positive, and there is cooling. For values of p_r and T_r outside the curve, $\dfrac{dT}{dp}$ is negative, and there is heating. It can be seen that at any given pressure less than the extreme value (p_r about 13) there are *two* inversion temperatures. One is the " ordinary " inversion temperature T_i, at which the heating effect gives place to cooling, and the other a much lower temperature T_j, at which cooling gives place again to heating. According to Birtwistle, the ratio T_i/T_j should be 9 for a gas following Van der Waals' equation.

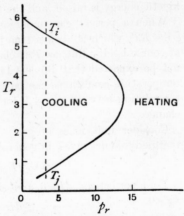

Fig. 116 (a).—" Inversion curve " for Joule-Kelvin effect, plotted in terms of " reduced " pressure and temperature.

ADIABATIC CHANGE

When a gas is expanded or compressed in such a way that no heat enters or leaves the gas, the change is said to be adiabatic. If the gas expands, doing external work, the internal energy of the gas is diminished by an amount exactly equal to the amount of external work done, and the temperature falls. Similarly, if external work is done on the gas by compressing it, the internal energy is increased and the temperature rises.

The kinetic theory enables us to picture how this happens. When a molecule strikes a surface, the velocity *relative to the surface* in a direction normal to the surface is reversed in sense but unaltered in size. If the velocity normal to the surface be u, and the surface is at rest, the rebound velocity in this direction is u. If the surface is receding with velocity v, the rebound velocity is $u - 2v$, while if the surface is approaching with velocity v, the rebound velocity is $u + 2v$. Imagine the gas to be in a cylinder closed by a piston. If the piston move out so that the gas expands, every molecule striking the piston during the motion rebounds with reduced velocity, so the average kinetic energy of the gas is lowered and the temperature falls. Similarly, if the piston move in so that the gas is compressed, every molecule striking it during the motion rebounds with increased velocity ; hence the average kinetic energy is raised, and the temperature rises.

When a perfect gas undergoes adiabatic change, the equation $pV = RT$, which is always true under all possible conditions, must of course hold. But, as T is changing as well as p and V, it must not be expected that Boyle's Law, which only holds for constant temperature conditions, can be applied. The first step is to deduce the relation between p and V for a perfect gas undergoing adiabatic change.

Consider unit mass of gas. The equation of the first law of thermodynamics gives, in general,

$$dQ = dE + dI + dW.$$

For a perfect gas, $dI = 0$, and, since no heat is supplied or removed, $dQ = 0$.

$$\therefore \quad dE + dW = 0.$$

Suppose the volume changes from V to $V + dV$ at constant pressure p, the temperature consequently falling from T to $T - dT$.

Then $\qquad\qquad dE = C_v\, dT$ calories,

$$dW = p\, dV \text{ ergs} = \frac{p\, dV}{J} \text{ calories,}$$

and $\qquad\qquad C_v\, dT + \frac{p\, dV}{J} = 0.$

This equation contains three variables, p, V, and T, and to integrate it the number of variables must first be reduced to two.

As $\qquad\qquad pV = RT, \quad p = \frac{RT}{V}.$

$$\therefore\ C_v\, dT + \frac{RT}{J}\, \frac{dV}{V} = 0.$$

$$\therefore\ C_v\, \frac{dT}{T} + \frac{R}{J}\, \frac{dV}{V} = 0.$$

Now, $\qquad\qquad C_p - C_v = \frac{R}{J}.$

$$\therefore\ C_v\, \frac{dT}{T} + (C_p - C_v)\, \frac{dV}{V} = 0.$$

Dividing by C_v, $\qquad \frac{dT}{T} + \left(\frac{C_p}{C_v} - 1\right) \frac{dV}{V} = 0,$

and writing γ for the ratio C_p / C_v of the two specific heats,

$$\frac{dT}{T} + (\gamma - 1)\, \frac{dV}{V} = 0.$$

Integrating, $\qquad \ln T + (\gamma - 1) \ln V = $ a constant;

or, $\qquad\qquad\qquad \ln T V^{\gamma-1} = $ a constant;

taking antilogarithms, $T V^{\gamma-1} = another$ constant. ....(1)

We can now substitute for T, as $T = pV/R$,

$$\frac{pV}{R} \cdot V^{\gamma-1} = \text{a constant,}$$

or, $\qquad\qquad\qquad p V^{\gamma} = $ a constant. ....(2)

This is the required relation between p and V, the adiabatic equation.

Also, as $\bar{V} = \dfrac{RT}{p}$, substitution in (1) gives

$$\frac{T^{\gamma}}{p^{\gamma-1}} = \text{a constant.} \quad ....(3)$$

External work done during adiabatic change. Consider unit mass of gas initially at pressure p_1 dynes per sq. cm. and volume V_1 c.c. ; let it expand to pressure p_2 and volume V_2 at some other temperature

To find the work done by the gas, integrate the general expression

$$\int_1^2 dW = \int_1^2 p \, dV.$$

For adiabatic conditions it is useless to substitute for p in terms of V and T, as T varies ; hence the adiabatic equation $pV^\gamma = $ constant is used to eliminate p. Write k for the constant.

As $$pV^\gamma = k, \quad p = kV^{-\gamma} ;$$

and the external work done $= \int_1^2 kV^{-\gamma} \, dV$

$$= \frac{k}{1-\gamma} \left[V^{1-\gamma} \right]_1^2 = \frac{k}{1-\gamma} \left[V_2{}^{1-\gamma} - V_1{}^{1-\gamma} \right] \text{ ergs ;}$$

or $$\frac{k}{\gamma - 1} \left[\frac{1}{V_1{}^{\gamma-1}} - \frac{1}{V_2{}^{\gamma-1}} \right] \text{ ergs.} \quad \dots\dots\dots\dots\dots\dots(1)$$

This is the work done *by* the gas ; if V_1 is greater than V_2, external work has been done *on* the gas by a compressor, and then the expression has a negative sign.

The expression may be made neater by substituting $p_1 V_1{}^\gamma = k$, and $p_2 V_2{}^\gamma = k$ in the first and second terms respectively, after removing the bracket.

Then, work done by gas

$$= \frac{p_1 V_1{}^\gamma}{(\gamma-1) V_1{}^{\gamma-1}} - \frac{p_2 V_2{}^\gamma}{(\gamma-1) V_2{}^{\gamma-1}}$$

$$= \frac{1}{\gamma - 1} (p_1 V_1 - p_2 V_2) \text{ ergs.} \quad \dots\dots\dots\dots\dots\dots(2)$$

To express this in terms of the pressures, as $V = \left(\dfrac{k}{p} \right)^{1/\gamma}$, the formula becomes

$$\frac{1}{\gamma - 1} \left[p_1 \left(\frac{k}{p_1} \right)^{1/\gamma} - p_2 \left(\frac{k}{p_2} \right)^{1/\gamma} \right] = \frac{k^{1/\gamma}}{\gamma - 1} \left[p_1{}^{(\gamma-1)/\gamma} - p_2{}^{(\gamma-1)/\gamma} \right] \text{ ergs.} \quad \dots\dots(3)$$

In applying formulae (1) and (3) to problems, the substitution $p_1 V_1{}^\gamma$ is made for k.

Thus, for the external work done by a gas expanding adiabatically from p_1, V_1, to p_2, V_2, we have :

$$\text{work} = \frac{p_1 V_1{}^\gamma}{\gamma - 1}\left[\frac{1}{V_1{}^{\gamma-1}} - \frac{1}{V_2{}^{\gamma-1}}\right] \text{ergs, or } \frac{p_1{}^{1/\gamma} V_1}{\gamma - 1}\left[p_1{}^{(\gamma-1)/\gamma} - p_2{}^{(\gamma-1)/\gamma}\right] \text{ergs.}$$

Adiabatic curves. The graph of p against V for a given heat content has the equation $pV^\gamma = \text{constant}$, and is called an adiabatic curve (Fig. 117). It should be realised that the constant is really a parameter which is constant only for a given heat content, so that there is a complete family of adiabatics for a fixed mass of gas, not just one curve. The adiabatics are steeper than the isothermals, since if the gas expands from the point represented by A to the point represented by B, the temperature falls, say from $T_1{}^\circ$ to $T_2{}^\circ$; so that while A is one point on the $T_1{}^\circ$ isothermal, B is one point on a *lower* isothermal, that

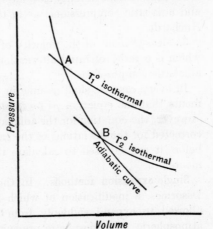

FIG. 117.—Adiabatic curve compared with isothermals.

for $T_2{}^\circ$. In general, the adiabatic passing through the point (p_1, V_1) is steeper than the isothermal through that point.

For the adiabatic, $pV^\gamma = \text{constant}$,

$$\therefore \ V^\gamma \, dp + \gamma p V^{\gamma-1} \, dV = 0,$$

$$\frac{dp}{dV} = -\gamma \, \frac{p}{V}.$$

So the slope of the adiabatic at (p_1, V_1) is $-\gamma p_1/V_1$.

For the isothermal, $pV = \text{constant}$.

$$\therefore \ V \, dp + p \, dV = 0.$$

$$\frac{dp}{dV} = -\frac{p}{V},$$

and the slope of the isothermal at (p_1, V_1) is $-p_1/V_1$.

The gradient of the adiabatic at any point is thus γ times as great as the gradient of the isothermal through the same point.

Determination of γ. Measurements of changes of two of the variables in an adiabatic change enable γ, the ratio of the two specific heats of a gas, to be found directly. The available methods may be classified as :

1. Observation of a single sudden adiabatic expansion or compression, as in the experiment of Clement and Desormes.

2. Observations of fairly slow alternations of adiabatic expansions and adiabatic compressions, as in the oscillating-pellet method of Ruchardt.

3. Measurement of the velocity of propagation of a sound wave, which is a series of rapid alternations of adiabatic expansions and adiabatic compressions.

In every case we shall assume in our descriptions of the experiments that the equation $pV^\gamma = constant$ is true. This equation is, however, the equation for the adiabatic of a perfect gas ; it must be corrected for the deviations of the gas under test from the gas laws before it can be used to calculate the results in accurate experiments.

Single-expansion methods. In the experiment of Clement and Desormes, a modification of which is described below, the gas is allowed to expand suddenly from a pressure p_1, a little above atmospheric, to atmospheric pressure p_0. This expansion is adiabatic. The gas is then allowed to stand to regain the temperature of the surroundings, the pressure rising to p_2. This is the pressure which would have been attained if the original expansion had been isothermal, since the initial and final temperatures of the gas are the same.

Consider the fixed mass of gas left in at the end ; this has expanded from volume V_1 (less than that of the vessel) to V_2 (the volume of the vessel). The three successive stages can be represented by the points A, B, and C on the pV diagram (Fig. 118).

As the expansion from A to B is adiabatic,

$$p_1 V_1{}^\gamma = p_0 V_2{}^\gamma.$$

$$\therefore \frac{p_1}{p_0} = \left(\frac{V_2}{V_1}\right)^\gamma.$$

As the final state at C is that which would have been attained isothermally,

$$p_1 V_1 = p_2 V_2, \quad \therefore \frac{p_1}{p_2} = \frac{V_2}{V_1}.$$

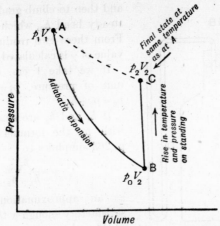

FIG. 118.—Stages in Clement and Desormes' experiment.

Substituting for $\dfrac{V_2}{V_1}$ in the first expression,

$$\frac{p_1}{p_0} = \left(\frac{p_1}{p_2}\right)^{\gamma}.$$

Taking logarithms,

$$\log p_1 - \log p_0 = \gamma(\log p_1 - \log p_2).$$

$$\therefore \ \gamma = \frac{\log p_1 - \log p_0}{\log p_1 - \log p_2}.$$

Thus, if p_1, p_0, and p_2 are measured, the value of γ can be calculated.

The apparatus used in the usual laboratory version to find γ for atmospheric air is shown in Fig. 119. A large vessel A, capacity several litres, is fitted with a wide stopcock B, a tube with a bicycle tyre valve C, and a manometer D containing oil. It is really unnecessary to surround the vessel with insulation, since the expansion is so rapid and the contained air is itself a bad conductor. Air is sent in through C by means of a bicycle pump until the head of oil registered by the manometer is about 10 or 15 cm. The vessel is left to stand until the manometer levels are steady, and the air in the vessel has regained the steady surrounding temperature. The head of oil, h_1 is then observed. The stopcock is opened for a second or so, and quickly closed. The manometer is seen to fall,

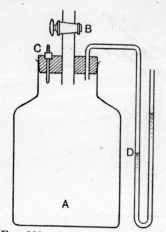

FIG. 119.—Apparatus for Clement and Desormes' experiment.

and then to climb gradually up to a steady head h_2, which is observed. From these two readings alone the value of γ is calculated.

If we take 1 cm. of oil as the unit of pressure, $p_1 = p_0 + h_1$, and $p_2 = p_0 + h_2$.

If h_1 and h_2 are small compared with p_0, the formula deduced on p. 263 simplifies to

$$\gamma = \frac{h_1}{h_1 - h_2}$$

as an approximation, which is satisfactory enough within the limits of this experiment.

Although this approximate formula can be deduced more simply, as is done below, it is worth while to deduce it from the true formula, since this makes clear the size of the approximation made.

If $\qquad p_1 = p_0 + h_1$, and $\quad p_2 = p_0 + h_2$,

$$p_1 = p_0 \left(1 + \frac{h_1}{p_0} \right) \quad \text{and} \quad p_2 = p_0 \left(1 + \frac{h_2}{p_0} \right).$$

Whence $\quad \gamma = \dfrac{\log p_1 - \log p_0}{\log p_1 - \log p_2} = \dfrac{\log p_0 \left(1 + \dfrac{h_1}{p_0} \right) - \log p_,}{\log p_0 \left(1 + \dfrac{h_1}{p_0} \right) - \log p_0 \left(1 + \dfrac{h_2}{p_0} \right)}$

$$= \frac{\log \left(1 + \dfrac{h_1}{p_0} \right)}{\log \left(1 + \dfrac{h_1}{p_0} \right) - \log \left(1 + \dfrac{h_2}{p_0} \right)}.$$

The logarithms could have been taken to any base, and we might just as well write :

$$\gamma = \frac{\ln \left(1 + \dfrac{h_1}{p_0} \right)}{\ln \left(1 + \dfrac{h_1}{p_0} \right) - \ln \left(1 + \dfrac{h_2}{p_0} \right)}.$$

Now, as
$$\ln(1+x) = x - \frac{x^2}{2} + \frac{x^3}{3} \cdots,$$

if we neglect the squares and higher powers of $\frac{h_1}{p_0}$ and $\frac{h_2}{p_0}$,

$$\ln\left(1 + \frac{h_1}{p_0}\right) = \frac{h_1}{p_0}, \quad \ln\left(1 + \frac{h_2}{p_0}\right) = \frac{h_2}{p_0}.$$

$$\therefore \gamma = \frac{h_1/p_0}{h_1/p_0 - h_2/p_0} = \frac{h_1}{h_1 - h_2}.$$

In an experiment h_1 may be about 12 cm. of oil, and p_0 about 1200 cm. of oil, $\frac{h_1}{p_0} = 0\cdot01$ and $\frac{1}{2}\left(\frac{h_1}{p_0}\right)^2 = 0\cdot00005$, so an error of the order

of $0\cdot05$ per cent. in each term is made by the approximation, resulting in an overall error of about this value, which is very much smaller than the experimental error when the experiment is done with the apparatus described above.

The approximate formula can be derived from the fact that the slope at A of the adiabatic through A is γ times the slope of the isothermal through that point. For, if AB and AC are so small that they can be regarded as portions of the tangents to the two curves at A (Fig. 120),

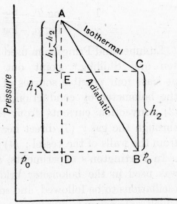

Fig. 120.

$$\text{slope of adiabatic} = \frac{AD}{DB},$$

$$\text{slope of isothermal} = \frac{AE}{CE} = \frac{AE}{DB}.$$

$$\therefore \gamma = \frac{\text{slope of adiabatic}}{\text{slope of isothermal}} = \frac{AD}{DB} \cdot \frac{AE}{DB} = \frac{AD}{AE} = \frac{h_1}{h_1 - h_2},$$

Clement and Desormes used vessels of capacities 3 litres and 10 litres in two sets of experiments, the earlier of which used adiabatic compression, the other being as described here. Later experimenters using the single-expansion principle had much larger vessels.

Apart from minor corrections, such as allowance for the change in volume of the manometer, and for the fact that the gas is not perfect, there is one grave inaccuracy in the method. If the stopcock is sufficiently wide to allow rapid expansion of the air, oscillations occur, and it is impossible to tell when to close the stopcock.

This difficulty is overcome in the method of Lummer and Pringsheim, later developed by Partington, in which the fall in temperature due to the adiabatic expansion is measured by means of a sensitive bolometer, which is a platinum resistance thermometer of very small heat capacity, connected in one arm of a suitable sensitive resistance bridge.

If T_1° K. be the temperature at the initial pressure p_1, and T_0° K. the temperature at p_0, then as $T_1{}^\gamma/p_1{}^{\gamma-1} = T_0{}^\gamma/p_0{}^{\gamma-1}$,

$$\frac{1}{\gamma} = 1 - \frac{\log T_1 - \log T_0}{\log p_1 - \log p_0} \text{ for a perfect gas.}$$

Lummer and Pringsheim used a 90-litre globe of copper. Partington and Shilling* point out that this method is subject to at least four possible sources of error, which were : (1) heating of the bolometer by conduction, from the gas and along the leads ; (2) convection currents from the lower warmer walls ascending through the gas ; (3) direct heating of the bolometer by radiation from the walls of the vessel ; (4) lag of the bolometer.

In Partington's experiments, a short-period string galvanometer was used in the bolometer bridge. This enabled the progress of oscillations to be followed, and so the diameter of the orifice through which expansion took place could be adjusted to a size at which oscillations did not occur. The expansion vessel was of metal and of 130 litres capacity ; it was surrounded by a water bath. The method of experimenting was to unbalance the bridge by a definite amount, corresponding to a fixed but as yet unknown temperature fall, and then find by trial the pressure change needed to give exact balance of the bridge when expansion occurred, the initial and final pressures then being measured. Next, the temperature of the water bath surrounding the metal vessel was lowered slowly until the bridge was exactly balanced again, and this temperature of the bath, as well as the temperature before the expansion, was measured on a standardised mercury thermometer. Thus, corresponding values p_1, T_1 and p_0, T_0 were found ; in computing the value of

* " The Specific Heats of Gases."

γ, the equation of p. 266 was modified to allow for the fact that the actual gas used is not a perfect gas, and Van der Waals' equation was assumed for this modification.

Slow-oscillation method. The experiment in this form was described by Ruchardt in 1929, though earlier experimenters had attempted it with pellets of mercury instead of the metal sphere he used. It cannot be an accurate method, since, if the oscillations are slow enough to be timed, it is unlikely that they will be properly adiabatic. It is described here because the calculation has some instructive features.

A large flask of known volume has an accurately cylindrical glass tube set vertically in its neck. Inside this tube an accurately spherical ball-bearing of the same diameter as the bore of the tube is free to oscillate, as in Fig. 121.

Let m gm. be the mass of the ball ; A sq. cm. the area of cross-section of the tube ; V c.c. the volume of the flask up to the zero position of the ball ; p_0 dynes/sq. cm. the atmospheric pressure ; and p dynes/sq. cm. the pressure in the flask.

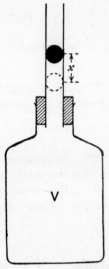

FIG. 121.—Ruchardt's slow-oscillation method.

The ball is at rest when $p = p_0 + \dfrac{mg}{A}$ dynes/sq. cm.

If the ball is depressed a distance x from this mean position, the pressure of the contained gas increases by dp, and the restoring force towards the mean position is $A\,dp$ dynes.

As $pV^\gamma = \text{constant},$ $dp = -\gamma p \dfrac{dV}{V}.$

Now the change in volume, dV, is Ax,

$$\therefore \quad dp = -\gamma p \frac{Ax}{V},$$

whence the restoring force is $-\gamma p \dfrac{A^2}{V} x$ dynes, and the acceleration towards the mean position is

$$-\frac{\gamma p A^2}{mV} x \text{ cm./sec./sec.}$$

As the acceleration is proportional to the displacement x, and is directed towards the mean position, the motion is simple harmonic, the period $T = 2\pi \sqrt{\dfrac{\text{displacement}}{\text{acceleration}}}$ being

$$T = 2\pi \sqrt{\frac{mV}{\gamma p A^2}}; \quad \text{whence} \quad \gamma = \frac{4\pi^2 mV}{A^2 p T^2},$$

or, substituting for p, $\quad \gamma = \dfrac{4\pi^2 mV}{\left[A^2\left(p_0 + \dfrac{mg}{A}\right)\right] T^2}$.

Velocity of sound method. The velocity of sound u in a gas at pressure p and density ρ is given in its simplest form by the equation

$$u = \sqrt{\frac{dp}{d\rho}}.$$

The compressions and rarefactions in sound waves succeed one another so rapidly that they are adiabatic.

As $pV^\gamma = \text{constant}$, and density is inversely proportional to volume we can write $p = c\rho^\gamma$, where c is a constant;

$$\therefore \frac{dp}{p} = \gamma \frac{d\rho}{\rho} \quad \text{and} \quad \frac{dp}{d\rho} = \gamma \frac{p}{\rho};$$

whence $\quad u = \sqrt{\dfrac{\gamma p}{\rho}} \quad \text{and} \quad \gamma = \dfrac{\rho u^2}{p}.$

This expression is only strictly true for the velocity of sound in an unrestricted volume of gas (supposed perfect). In an enclosed tube the value of the velocity is a little different, and corrections which depend on the gas, the tube, and the frequency of the sound have to be made.

In Kundt's Tube experiment (Fig. 122), the source of sound is a rod clamped at its mid point and set into longitudinal vibration by

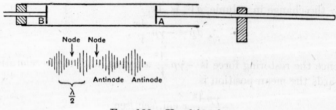

Node   Node

Antinode   Antinode

$\dfrac{\lambda}{2}$

FIG. 122.—Kundt's tube.

stroking with a resined cloth. One end of the rod projects into the
tube of gas, and carries a flat plate A which nearly fills the area
of the tube.

The frequency n of the note emitted when the rod is stroked is
first determined by methods not here described. The other end of
the long tube is closed by a sliding rod, which also carries a flat
disc B.

The wave-length λ of the sound in the gas, the velocity u, and the
frequency n are connected by the equation

$$u = n\lambda.$$

As n is known for the rod, u can be calculated if only λ is
measured.

If the distance AB is suitable, a stationary wave system is set up
in the tube by the superposition of the waves reflected at B upon
those propagated from A. In such a system, points of no
disturbance (nodes) occur at intervals of $\frac{\lambda}{2}$, measured along the
tube, and points of maximum disturbance (antinodes) half-way
between the nodes. The distance between successive nodes is
thus $\lambda/2$, as is also the distance between successive antinodes.

A thin layer of dry lycopodium powder or fine cork dust inside
the tube makes the stationary wave system visible, since this is
thrown into violent agitation at the antinodes, and collects there in
fine transverse streaks when the vibrations stop. The disc B is
moved forwards until a sharply defined pattern, as shown in the
figure, is obtained.

The wave-length λ is determined by measuring the distances
between the dust traces, and u is calculated. The values of ρ and p
are determined, and γ found from the formula $\gamma = \rho u^2/p$.

A later modification of this method is that of Behn and Geiger,
who used a closed tube of the gas under test instead of a solid rod
as the source of sound in a Kundt's tube (Fig. 123). The dust

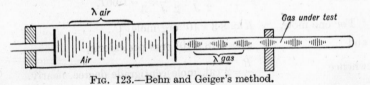

Fig. 123.—Behn and Geiger's method.

pattern inside the source tube is compared with that in the Kundt's tube containing air, and thus the wave-length in the gas is compared with that in air. As n, the frequency of the note of the gas tube is of course the same both in gas and in air, $u_{gas}/u_{air} = \lambda_{gas}/\lambda_{air}$.

Value of γ for a perfect gas. Apart from its importance in calculations on adiabatic changes, knowledge of the value of γ is extremely important, as it helps to decide whether a gas is monatomic, diatomic, or polyatomic.

The experimental results show that, at $0°$ C., and one atmosphere pressure :

for all monatomic gases γ is very close to $1\cdot666$,
for many diatomic gases γ is very close to $1\cdot40$,
for all polyatomic gases γ lies between $1\cdot40$ and $1\cdot0$.

It is possible, by making certain assumptions, to calculate what the value of γ should be for perfect monatomic and diatomic gases.

For a monatomic gas, the internal kinetic energy E is the sum of the kinetic energies of translation of the molecules. Considering one mole, with the usual symbols, $E = \frac{1}{2} N m \bar{c}^2$;

but $$pV = \tfrac{1}{3} N m \bar{c}^2 \quad \text{and} \quad pV = RT.$$

Whence $$E = \tfrac{3}{2} pV = \tfrac{3}{2} RT \text{ ergs} = \frac{3}{2} \frac{R}{J} T \text{ cal.}$$

Let the temperature of unit mass be raised by $dT°$ at constant volume. The heat supplied is $C_v \, dT$ cal., and the increase in internal energy dE is $\dfrac{3}{2} \dfrac{R}{J} dT$ cal.

Thus $$C_v \, dT = \frac{3}{2} \frac{R}{J} dT \quad \text{and} \quad C_v = \frac{3}{2} \frac{R}{J}.$$

Now, $$C_p = C_v + \frac{R}{J}.$$

$$\therefore \ C_p = \frac{3}{2} \frac{R}{J} + \frac{R}{J} = \frac{5}{2} \frac{R}{J},$$

whence $$\gamma = \frac{C_p}{C_v} = \frac{5}{2} \frac{R}{J} \div \frac{3}{2} \frac{R}{J} = \frac{5}{3} = 1\cdot667.$$

For one mole, $$R \simeq 8\cdot3 \times 10^7 \text{ erg/mole/°C.,}$$
and $$J \simeq 4\cdot18 \times 10^7 \text{ ergs per calorie,}$$
whence $$\frac{R}{J} = 2 \text{ cal./mole/centigrade degree, nearly.}$$

Thus the numerical values of the specific heats (the heat capacities of one mole) are approximately

$$C_p = 5 \text{ cal. per mole per centigrade degree,}$$

and $\qquad C_v = 3$ cal. per mole per centigrade degree,

for a perfect monatomic gas.

In deriving the formula $pV = \frac{1}{3}Nm\bar{c}^2$ for point (monatomic) molecules on p. 151, we considered velocities resolved parallel to three independent axes at right angles. The point molecule thus has three mechanical degrees of freedom, and three independent ways of possessing kinetic energy. As there is no reason *a priori* why any one of these should be favoured at the expense of the others, it seems reasonable to suppose that each degree of freedom is associated with one third of the total kinetic energy. That is, each degree of freedom possesses an amount of internal energy $\frac{1}{3}E = \frac{1}{2}RT$. This is known as **Boltzmann's Law of Equipartition of Energy.**

To extend the specific heat calculation to diatomic gases, we may consider what extra degrees of freedom are available for a diatomic molecule. Taking the simplest possible picture of such a molecule, and regarding it as a kind of " dumb bell " (Fig. 124), the moment of inertia about any axis at right angles to AB will be large compared with the moment of inertia about AB. Thus, when the molecule is spinning we can, by resolving the angular velocity into components about the perpendicular axes AB, CD, EF, and retaining only those about CD and

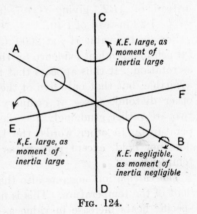

FIG. 124.

EF for which the moment of inertia is appreciable, see that there are two extra degrees of freedom, since kinetic energy of rotation about two independent axes may be possessed in addition to the kinetic energy of translation.

Thus, according to the Law of Equipartition of Energy, if there are five degrees of freedom in all, and each is associated with internal energy $\frac{1}{2}RT$, the total internal energy is $E = \frac{5}{2}RT$;

whence
$$C_v = \frac{5}{2}\frac{R}{J}, \quad C_p = \frac{7}{2}\frac{R}{J},$$

and
$$\gamma = \frac{C_p}{C_v} = \frac{7}{5} = 1\cdot40.$$

For more complicated molecules with x degrees of freedom in addition to those due to translation, this argument should lead to $\gamma = \frac{5+x}{3+x}$, or, if n is the total number of degrees of freedom, $\gamma = 1 + \frac{2}{n}$ which becomes progressively closer to unity as x and n increase.

The argument presented here is obviously shaky. For, if we understand the term "degrees of freedom" to mean independent ways of possessing energy, the diatomic molecule of Fig. 124 has two more. These are kinetic energy of vibration of the individual atoms along the line joining their centres, and the corresponding potential energy of vibration. The total possible number of degrees of freedom for such a molecule is thus *seven* instead of five, and the Law of Equipartition demands a total internal energy of $\frac{7}{2}RT$ instead of $\frac{5}{2}RT$, giving $C_v = 7$ instead of 5 cal./mole/°C., and $\gamma = \frac{9}{7} = 1\cdot29$ instead of 1·40.

For air, the value of γ at 2000° C. is about 1·3. Infra-red spectra furnish independent evidence for the occurrence of vibration as well as rotation. It thus appears that the seven degrees of freedom are available, but that only five of them are effective for air and most other diatomic gases at ordinary temperatures, while the other two are rather grudgingly accorded "acting rank" at high temperatures. In other words, the Law of Equipartition of Energy does not hold, except perhaps as an approximation at very high temperatures.

The calculation suggests also that C_p and C_v should be independent of the temperature. This is not found experimentally, for the specific heats increase in value as the temperature rises. Similar observations equally irreconcilable with calculations based on the Law of Equipartition occur for the specific heats of solids (p. 74), and these alone would have sufficed to discredit it. But in other fields, in particular in radiation problems (p. 390), it leads also to false results. It is best, therefore, to regard the Law of Equipartition as a piece of common-sense intuition which is helpful in that it takes us some way towards an explanation of the way in which γ depends on the atomicity of a gas, but is known to be erroneous as a general physical principle.

Variation of C_p, C_v, and γ with temperature and pressure. The specific heats C_p and C_v both increase, while γ decreases, as the temperature rises. Thus, according to Partington and Shilling, for air at 1 atmosphere and 0° C.,

$$C_p = 6.97, \quad C_v = 4.97 \quad \text{and} \quad C_p - C_v = 2.00 \; ; \text{ hence } \gamma = 1.402,$$

while for air at 1 atmosphere and 2000° C.,

$$C_p = 8.54, \quad C_v = 6.55 \quad \text{and} \quad C_p - C_v = 1.99 \; ; \text{ hence } \gamma = 1.302.$$

The following results for air at 0° C. and 200 atmospheres show the effect of increasing the pressure :

$$C_p = 8.695, \quad C_v = 4.757 \quad \text{and} \quad C_p - C_v = 3.938 \; ; \text{ hence } \gamma = 1.83.$$

It can be seen that calculations for the adiabatic compression and rarefaction of a real gas will not be so simple as those given on p. 259 for a perfect gas. In particular, the use of a constant value of γ in problems on the internal combustion engine, where very high temperatures and pressures occur, must lead to very inaccurate results.

QUESTIONS ON CHAPTER VI

1. Give a short account of the evidence that heat and work are quantitatively interchangeable.

Describe an experiment by which the mechanical equivalent of heat can be determined in the laboratory.   (O. & C.)

2. Describe a non-electrical method of measuring the mechanical equivalent of heat. Explain your calculation.

A roller-skater glides 50 times round the floor of a rink, keeping to a circle of average radius 78 feet, only one skate being on the floor at any one instant. If each skate, of mass 1 lb. and specific heat 0·1, is raised in temperature 20 deg. F., calculate the average force applied by the skater in overcoming friction. Assume that 20 per cent. of the heat generated is received by the skates. ($J = 780$ ft. lb. per B.Th.U.)   (J.M.B.)

3. What are the chief reasons for believing that heat is a form of energy?

Explain the statement that 4.2×10^7 ergs are equivalent to 1 calorie, and describe an experiment involving the conversion of mechanical energy into heat by which it may be checked.

Calculate the number of foot pounds weight which are equivalent to the quantity of heat required to raise the temperature of 1 lb. of water

1 deg. F. Assume that 1 ft. = 30·5 cm. and that the acceleration of gravity = 980 cm. sec.$^{-2}$

(J.M.B.)

4. Give an account of the evidence for our belief that heat is a form of energy.

A lead bullet of mass 20 gm. enters a fixed block of wood with a velocity of 10,000 cm. per second, and is brought to rest in the wood. Calculate (a) the heat developed in gramme-calories, (b) the rise of temperature of the bullet, if it is assumed that two-thirds of the heat produced is absorbed by the bullet.

$(J = 4·2 \times 10^7$ ergs per gramme-calorie. Specific heat of lead = 0·032.)

C.W.B.)

5. What do you understand by the mechanical equivalent of heat? Describe an experiment to determine it, pointing out what precautions must be taken to obtain an accurate result.

A car weighing 1,000 kilograms descends a hill of slope 1 in 10 with the engine disengaged at a uniform speed of 40 kilometres per hour. Find the rate of rise of temperature of the brake drums if all the heat developed by the brakes is retained by the brake drums. The brake drums together weigh 40 kilograms and are made of material of specific heat 0·1. $(g = 1,000$ cm. per sec. per sec.)

(C.S.)

6. Upon what experimental evidence does the extension of the principle of the conservation of energy to include Heat rest? Define specific heat and state how the calorie is related to the erg.

A piece of lead falls from a height of 100 metres on to a fixed non-conducting slab which brings it to rest. Show that its temperature immediately after the collision is raised by approximately 7·7° C.

(The specific heat of lead is 0·0305 between 0° C. and 100° C. 1 calorie = 4·2 × 10^7 ergs.)

(C.S.)

7. Describe a method of measuring the mechanical equivalent of heat.

A bullet moving horizontally strikes a target and comes to rest. The initial temperature of the bullet is 25° C., its melting point 475° C., its specific heat 0·05, and its latent heat of fusion 61·5 calories per gram. Find the minimum velocity at which the bullet may melt completely on striking the target. The mechanical equivalent of heat may be taken as 4·2 × 10^7 ergs per calorie.

(O. & C.)

8. Write an essay on the conservation of energy.

(O. & C.)

9. Explain carefully what is meant by the term " mechanical equivalent of heat ".

Given that one calorie is equivalent to 4·2 × 10^7 ergs, find an expression connecting the difference of temperature at the top and bottom of a waterfall with the height of the fall, assuming the potential energy of the water is all converted into heat.

(O. & C.)

10. Describe, indicating the necessary precautions, how you could determine either (a) the mechanical equivalent of heat, or (b) the heat evolved in the combustion of a given mass of coke. The reaction between carbon and oxygen takes place according to the equation

$$C_{coke} + O_2 = CO_2 + 90,000 \text{ cals.}$$

Compare the cost of heating water in a 70% efficient boiler using coke at £2 per (metric) ton with the cost if a 98% efficient electric heater is used. The electrical energy costs 1/3*d*. per kilowatt-hour. (O.S.)

11. Describe an electrical method of determining J.

In the Callendar-Barnes flow calorimeter, it is found that there is a rise in temperature of 3° C. when the rate of flow is 5 gm. per sec. and a current of 0·75 amp. passes along the heating wire, the difference of potential between its ends being 100 volts. If the rate of flow is reduced to one-third of its former value, a current of 0·5 amp. gives the same rise of temperature. From these data determine the value of Joule's constant. (O. & C.)

12. Define the gram-calorie, and explain what you mean by the mechanical equivalent of heat. Give details of the determination of the latter constant by a constant-flow electrical method. How may this method be used to investigate the variation of the specific heat of water with temperature? (C.S.)

13. How can a value of the mechanical equivalent of heat be deduced from observations on the specific heats of gases? What assumption is made in making this deduction? Describe any experimental test of the correctness of the assumption. (C.S.)

14. Define the mechanical equivalent of heat. Describe a method of measuring this quantity.

Deduce an expression for the difference between the specific heat C_p of a gas at constant pressure and the specific heat C_v at constant volume. Find the value of C_v for gaseous oxygen, given that $C_p = 0·2180$ calories per gm., the density of oxygen at s.t.p. $= 0·00143$ gm. per c.c. and using the normally accepted values for the other data required. (L.)

15. Distinguish carefully between C_v, the specific heat at constant volume and C_p, the specific heat at constant pressure, of a gas. What is the value of $C_p - C_v$ for a gas obeying the equation $p(v - b) = RT$? How would you measure the ratio of C_p to C_v experimentally, and why is this ratio important in the theory of sound propagation in a gas? (C.S.)

16. Describe how the specific heat of a gas under constant pressure has been measured.

Calculate a value for the mechanical equivalent of heat, given that the specific heat of air at constant pressure is 0·237 and at constant volume 0·168, the density of air at 0° C. and 10^6 dynes per sq. cm. pressure 0·001275 gm. per c.c., and the coefficient of expansion at constant pressure 0·00367 per degree C. Point out any assumptions made in the calculation. (C.S.)

17. Describe a direct method of determining the specific heat of air at constant pressure, and explain how the result is calculated from the observations.

If the density of air at N.T.P. is 0·001293 gm. per c.c., and its specific heat at constant volume is 0·169 calories per gm. per degree C., calculate its specific heat at constant pressure. (Density of mercury $= 13·6$ gm. per c.c. at 0° C., $J = 4·2 \times 10^7$ ergs per calorie.) (C.W.B.)

18. Describe a method of finding the specific heat of a gas at constant volume.

Find an expression for the difference of the specific heats of a perfect gas at constant pressure and constant volume. Apply the expression to find an approximate value of this difference for helium. (Density of helium at 0° C. and 760 mm. pressure = 0·18 gm. per litre ; density of mercury = 13·6 gm. per c.c. ; mechanical equivalent of heat = 4·2 × 10⁷ ergs per calorie.) (O. & C.)

19. What is meant by " an adiabatic change " ? Explain how the specific heat of a gas at constant volume is related to its specific heat at constant pressure and the mechanical equivalent of heat. Find a value for the latter, given that the difference of these specific heats for hydrogen is 0·97. (The density of mercury is 13·6 gm. per c.c., that of hydrogen is 0·09 gm. per litre at N.T.P.) (O.)

20. Describe what you consider the best method for the determination of the mechanical equivalent of heat, giving reasons for your choice.

Show that J can be calculated if the difference in the molecular heats at constant pressure and constant volume for a perfect gas is known. Find its value if the volume of a gram-molecule of gas at N.T.P. is 22·4 litres, and the difference in the two molecular heats is 2 calories. ($g = 981$ cm. per sec. per sec., density of mercury = 13·6 grams per c.c.) (O. & C.)

21. What is meant by an adiabatic change?

Describe one method by which the ratio between the two principal specific heats of a gas may be determined.

If the difference between these specific heats in the case of hydrogen is 0·97, obtain a value for the mechanical equivalent of heat. (The density of hydrogen at 0° C. and a pressure of 10⁶ dynes per sq. cm. is 0·09 gm. per litre.) (C.)

22. What is meant by the specific heat of a gas (a) at constant volume, (b) at constant pressure? Deduce a value for the difference between the specific heats in the case of a perfect gas.

Describe a method of measuring the ratio of the two specific heats of a gas directly. Why is a knowledge of this ratio important? (O. & C.)

23. How can the specific heat of a gas at constant volume be measured directly? What information can be deduced about the molecular constitution of a gas from a knowledge of the ratio of its specific heats at constant pressure and constant volume? (C.S.)

24. Describe a method of measuring directly the ratio of the specific heats of a gas at constant pressure and at constant volume.

Why would you expect the value of the ratio to depend on the atomicity of the gas? (O. & C.)

25. Explain how energy supplied in the form of latent heat to a liquid boiling at atmospheric pressure is conserved during the change from liquid to vapour.

The volume of steam produced by the evaporation of 1 gm. of water boiling at 100° C. is 1,650 cm.³ Calculate the internal work done during the change of state.

(Latent heat of steam = 540 cal./gm. $J = 4·2 × 10⁷$ ergs per calorie. Density of mercury = 13·6 gm./cm.³ $g = 981$ cm./sec.²) (B.)

CHAPTER VII

HEAT ENGINES : THE SECOND LAW OF THERMODYNAMICS

ANY device which will convert heat continuously into mechanical work is called a heat engine. Innumerable heat engines can be devised, and, as will be seen later, one of the most fruitful ways of attacking thermodynamical problems is by choosing a suitable imaginary heat engine to fit the requirements of each problem.

The material which, on being supplied with heat, performs mechanical work is called the **working substance**. All practical engines use one of two working substances—either water (in the reciprocating steam engine and the turbine) or air (in the internal combustion engine). We shall first discuss the theory of heat engines in general, without reference to any particular working substance. Next, the theory will be applied to some problems in pure physics. Finally, the theory of one or two practical engines will be discussed.

The ideal heat engine. Carnot's cycle. Consider a fixed mass of any working substance enclosed in a cylinder with non-conducting sides and perfectly conducting base, and fitted with a non-conducting frictionless piston, upon which weights can be placed.

Three stands are available : a perfectly conducting stand X at a high temperature $T_1°$, called the source ; a perfectly non-conducting stand Y ; a perfectly conducting stand Z at a low temperature $T_2°$, called the sink.

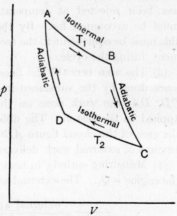

FIG. 125.—Carnot cycle.

The following sequence of operations is carried out ; it is represented on the $p - V$ diagram of Fig. 125.

(1) Starting with the substance at the state represented by the

point A on the diagram, the cylinder is placed on X, weights are slowly removed from the top of the piston, and the substance is allowed to expand isothermally to the state represented by the point B.

(2) The cylinder is then placed on Y, and further expansion is allowed. This expansion is adiabatic, and it is continued until the temperature has fallen to T_2, the state then being represented by the point C.

(3) The cylinder is placed on Z, and weights are slowly added to the top of the piston. External work is done on the substance, which is reduced in volume, and gives out heat isothermally to the sink Z. This is continued until the point D, which lies on the adiabatic through A, is reached.

(4) The cylinder is replaced on Y, and further weights are added to the top of the piston to compress the substance until the point A is reached.

The following observations can be made to begin with :

(1) The substance has been taken through a complete cycle of operations, and its state at the end is exactly the same as at the beginning. It starts at A and ends at A. Whatever has happened to the substance during the cycle is quite independent of the internal energy of the substance at A, and hence also independent of the nature of the working substance used.

(2) A quantity of heat, which we will call Q_1, has been taken in at temperature $T_1°$, and a smaller quantity, which we will call Q_2, has been rejected at temperature $T_2°$. The difference $Q_1 - Q_2$ must be accounted for. By the First Law of Thermodynamics, this must be equivalent to the mechanical work done by the arrangement during the cycle.

(3) The area beneath the lines AB, BC, represents the external work done by the substance in expanding, and the area beneath CD, DA, the work done on the working substance by the load applied to the piston. The difference between these two areas is the area of the closed figure $ABCDA$; and this represents the net amount of external work delivered by the engine during the cycle.

(4) Measuring entirely in heat units, the total energy taken in by the engine is Q_1. The external work delivered is $Q_1 - Q_2$. The ratio

$$\frac{\text{external work delivered}}{\text{total energy absorbed at high temperature}}$$

is called the efficiency of the engine. Thus the efficiency of this engine is $\dfrac{Q_1 - Q_2}{Q_1}$, or $1 - \dfrac{Q_2}{Q_1}$.

The cycle of operations through which the working substance has been taken is called **Carnot's cycle**. There are two important ways in which the Carnot cycle differs from that of any practical engine. First, the heat absorbed is all taken in at one constant temperature, and all the heat rejected to the sink is given out at another constant temperature. In this sense it is *very much simpler* than any practical engine. Secondly, as no work is done at any stage in overcoming friction, and no heat is lost to the surroundings, the cycle is *completely reversible*. This means that if we had carried out the whole sequence of changes in the reverse order, every operation would have been exactly reversed ; by supplying an amount of energy represented by the area $ABCDA$ we could have expanded the substance adiabatically from A to D, caused it to take in a quantity of heat Q_2 along DC, compressed it adiabatically from C to B, and caused it to reject a quantity of heat Q_1 in being compressed isothermally from B to A. In this sense it is an *ideal heat engine*, since in all practical engines work is done in overcoming friction and heat is lost to the surroundings. It can be seen that friction and heat loss both prevent perfect reversibility. If work is done against friction when the piston is depressed, friction (which always opposes motion) does not furnish an equal quantity of work to help the motion when the piston is raised—on the contrary, more work has to be done against friction. If heat is lost to the cooler surroundings when the substance expands, the same cooler surroundings do not supply heat when it contracts—on the contrary, they abstract still more heat. Two other less obvious conditions must be satisfied for complete reversibility. The base must be a perfect conductor of heat, and the operations must be carried out infinitely slowly—otherwise the isothermal stages cannot be realised reversibly.

SECOND LAW OF THERMODYNAMICS

It is a matter of common experience that when two bodies at different temperatures are placed in contact, heat flows from the body at the higher temperature to that at the lower temperature. It is not quite true to say without any qualification that heat always flows from a hot body to a cooler body, since if we operate the Carnot cycle backwards heat will be taken in at $T_2°$ and rejected at $T_1°$, but this is not a normal case, for external work must then be done on the system. The results of experience can be summed up in Clausius' statement:

It is impossible for a self-acting machine, unaided by any external agency, to convey heat from one body to another at a higher temperature · this is one of the forms in which the important fundamental prir known as the **Second Law of Thermodynamics** has been enur

The Second Law of Thermodynamics deals with the of heat for the performance of work. We know from the that if a body can be made to yield up Q heat units, a qu work given by the relation $W = JQ$ can be obtained from it Second Law tells us what prospect we have of making it yie. the heat at all. It is not sufficient merely to have Q_1 heat u. stored in the body at some temperature $T_1°$; arrangements m be made for the flow of some part of it, Q_2, to a body at a l temperature $T_2°$.

The First Law of Thermodynamics, in fact, corresponds to the Rugby Union's ruling that a try shall count three points and a goal five points—very indispensable information for calculating which side has won the match. The Second Law of Thermodynamics corresponds to the whole of the rest of the rules of the game, as they might be deduced by an observant spectator.

Applying the Second Law to reversible heat engines, the following conclusions are reached.

(1) *The efficiency of all reversible engines working between the same two temperatures is the same, whatever the working substance.* Consider two reversible engines E and F, and suppose that both reject Q_2 heat units at $T_2°$, while at $T_1°$, E takes in Q_1 heat units, and F, the more efficient one, $Q_1 + \delta Q$ heat units. If the two are now coupled together so that the less efficient E drives the more efficient F backwards, the combination will work continuously on its own (the Q_2 rejected by E at T_2 being supplied to operate F), and at the same time transfer a quantity of heat δQ (the difference between that absorbed by E and rejected by F) from $T_2°$ to $T_1°$, a feat which is contrary to all experience as expressed by the Second Law. Hence the efficiency of all reversible engines working between two given temperatures is the same, and is independent of the nature of the working substance.

(2) *No engine working between two given temperatures can be more efficient than a reversible one working between those temperatures.* The argument to prove this is essentially the same as that used above. For the more efficient engine could be made to drive the reversible one backwards, and the combination would then be steadily transferring heat from the sink at the lower temperature to the source at the higher temperature and at the same time delivering a balance of useful work, which would be contrary to all experience as expressed in the Second Law.

(3) *The efficiency of a reversible engine is independent of the quantity of heat absorbed at the high temperature and the quantity of the working substance.* This is easily shown, since an engine absorbing $2Q_1$ at T_1 should reject $2Q_2$ at T_2, giving an efficiency $\dfrac{Q_1 - Q_2}{Q_1}$ as before.

THE KELVIN ABSOLUTE SCALE OF TEMPERATURE

The efficiency of a reversible engine working on a Carnot cycle depends only on the two temperatures between which it operates, and is independent of the nature of the working substance. That is, the efficiency of a reversible engine is *a function of the temperatures concerned and of nothing else.* Here we have a property which is absolutely dependent on temperature and on temperature alone. This is the basis of the Kelvin Absolute Thermodynamic Scale of temperature.

Defining a new scale of temperature (and for the present denoting temperatures on this scale by the symbol θ) such that, if a Carnot engine takes in a quantity of heat Q_1 at temperature $\theta_1°$, and rejects a quantity of heat Q_2 at temperature $\theta_2°$, then

$$\frac{Q_1}{Q_2} = \frac{\theta_1}{\theta_2},$$

it is clear that the efficiency $\dfrac{Q_1 - Q_2}{Q_2}$ equals $\dfrac{\theta_1 - \theta_2}{\theta_2}$, and thus the efficiency depends on the temperature alone.

The defining equation $\dfrac{\theta_1}{\theta_2} = \dfrac{Q_1}{Q_2}$ lays down the basis upon which the Kelvin (°K.) scale of temperature is founded. It does not prescribe the numbering of the scale, nor indicate how the scale is to be realised in practice.

For the numbering of the scale, let the size of the degree interval be such that the interval between the ice point and the steam point represents one hundred degrees; let θ_0° be the temperature of the ice point, and $(\theta_0 + 100)^\circ$ that of the steam point. Then if Q_0 and Q_{100} are the quantities of heat absorbed and rejected by a Carnot engine working between the ice point and the steam point,

$$\frac{\theta_0 + 100}{\theta_0} = \frac{Q_{100}}{Q_0}.$$

Assuming that both Q_{100} and Q_0 can be measured, this equation enables us to find θ_0, the thermodynamic temperature of the ice point. The numbering of the scale is thus settled.

To realise the scale in practice, choose as the working substance which is taken through the Carnot cycle in the reversible engine a fixed mass (unit mass) of a perfect gas.

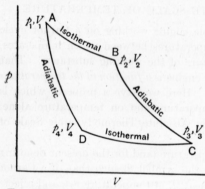

FIG. 126.—Carnot cycle for a perfect gas.

On the $p - V$ diagram (Fig. 126) let the co-ordinates of the points A, B, C, and D be p_1V_1, p_2V_2, p_3V_3, and p_4V_4.

As the gas is perfect, the internal energy is not affected by changes in volume (that is, no internal work against molecular attractions need be considered), and all the heat taken in at the high temperature is used in the performance of external work, while all the external work done at the low temperature on the gas is converted into heat.

Let the temperature of the isothermal on which A and B lie be T_1° *on the perfect gas scale*.

Let the temperature of the isothermal on which C and D lie be T_2° *on the perfect gas scale*.

Then, for the isothermal expansion from A to B, external work done by gas at T_1° on the gas scale

$$= \int_{V_1}^{V_2} p\, dV = RT_1 \ln V_2/V_1.$$

But this equals the heat Q_1 provided, here considered measured in work units, so
$$Q_1 = RT_1 \ln V_2/V_1.$$

For the compression from C to D, isothermally at $T_2°$ on the gas scale,

external work done *by* gas $= \displaystyle\int_{V_3}^{V_4} p\,dV = RT_2 \ln V_4/V_3 \,;$

external work done *on* gas $= -RT_2 \ln V_4/V_3 = RT_2 \ln V_3/V_4\,;$

and if the heat rejected is Q_2 in work units,
$$Q_2 = RT_2 \ln V_3/V_4.$$

Thus, $\dfrac{Q_1}{Q_2} = \dfrac{RT_1 \ln V_2/V_1}{RT_2 \ln V_3/V_4} = \dfrac{T_1}{T_2} \cdot \dfrac{\ln V_2/V_1}{\ln V_3/V_4}.$

Before going further, it is worth noting that if $T_2 = 0$, then $Q_2 = 0$; but on the Kelvin scale, if $Q_2 = 0$, then $\theta_2 = 0$. *Thus the zero of the Kelvin scale is the same as the zero of the ideal gas scale.* Do the two scales coincide completely? They must if $\dfrac{\theta_1}{\theta_2} = \dfrac{T_1}{T_2}$, which is true if $\dfrac{\ln V_2/V_1}{\ln V_3/V_4} = 1$ or if $V_2/V_1 = V_3/V_4$. The next step is to prove that $V_2/V_1 = V_3/V_4$.

As B and C lie on the same adiabatic,
$$p_2 V_2{}^\gamma = p_3 V_3{}^\gamma\,;$$
similarly, considering A and D,
$$p_1 V_1{}^\gamma = p_4 V_4{}^\gamma,$$
so, $\left(\dfrac{V_2}{V_1}\right)^\gamma \cdot \dfrac{p_2}{p_1} = \left(\dfrac{V_3}{V_4}\right)^\gamma \dfrac{p_3}{p_4},$

or, $\left(\dfrac{V_2}{V_1}\right)^{\gamma-1} \dfrac{p_2 V_2}{p_1 V_1} = \left(\dfrac{V_3}{V_4}\right)^{\gamma-1} \dfrac{p_3 V_3}{p_4 V_4}.$

But as A and B lie on the same isothermal, $p_1 V_1 = p_2 V_2$; **and** similarly for C and D, $p_3 V_3 = p_4 V_4$.

Hence, cancelling in the above equation,
$$\left(\dfrac{V_2}{V_1}\right)^{\gamma-1} = \left(\dfrac{V_3}{V_4}\right)^{\gamma-1}, \quad \text{and} \quad \dfrac{V_2}{V_1} = \dfrac{V_3}{V_4}.$$

Thus the equation $\dfrac{Q_1}{Q_2} = \dfrac{T_1 \ln V_2/V_1}{T_2 \ln V_3/V_4}$

becomes $\dfrac{Q_1}{Q_2} = \dfrac{T_1}{T_2}.$

Comparing this with the equation $\dfrac{Q_1}{Q_2} = \dfrac{\theta_1}{\theta_2}$, it can be seen that the Kelvin Absolute Thermodynamic Scale of temperature and the ideal gas scale of temperature are identical—both giving the one really absolute scale of temperature.

From now onwards, therefore, the symbol θ will be discarded in this chapter, and the symbol T used for temperatures on the one absolute scale.

ENTROPY

In the reversible Carnot cycle, taking in heat Q_1 at T_1° K. and rejecting heat Q_2 at T_2° K., $\dfrac{Q_1}{Q_2} = \dfrac{T_1}{T_2}$. Thus $\dfrac{Q_1}{T_1} = \dfrac{Q_2}{T_2}$.

It is necessary now to introduce a new quantity called the entropy, S, such that at any temperature T° K., at which a quantity of heat δQ is taken in, the gain in entropy δS is equal to $\delta Q/T$. The symbols δQ and δS can stand for large finite changes; they are used here chiefly to emphasise that changes in entropy which occur when a system passes from one state to another, and not the absolute value of the entropy at any state, are the important quantities. If it is necessary to evaluate the entropy S for any state, this is usually expressed with reference to the value of S in some chosen state as zero.

For the Carnot cycle, the gain in entropy of the working substance absorbing heat Q_1 at T_1 is $\delta S_1 = Q_1/T_1$. The gain in entropy of the working substance rejecting heat Q_2 at T_2 is $\delta S_2 = -Q_2/T_2$ (the minus sign is used so that this rejection can be written as a gain). Thus,

since $\qquad \dfrac{Q_1}{T_1} = \dfrac{Q_2}{T_2}, \quad \therefore \ \dfrac{Q_1}{T_1} - \dfrac{Q_2}{T_2} = 0 \quad \text{or} \quad \delta S_1 + \delta S_2 = 0.$

So, for the *working substance* taken round a Carnot cycle, the algebraic sum of the gains in entropy is zero. This is not a particularly important deduction, since the working substance is in its initial state again at the end of the cycle, and has not itself changed in any observable respect.

But this can be looked at from the point of view of the *whole system*. The source loses a quantity of heat Q_1 at T_1° K., and so gains entropy δS_1, where $\delta S_1 = -Q_1/T_1$; the sink gains a quantity of heat Q_2 at $T_2°$ K., and so gains entropy $\delta S_2 = Q_2/T_2$. The total gain in the entropy of the combined system of source + sink is

$$\delta S_1 + \delta S_2 = -\frac{Q_1}{T_1} + \frac{Q_2}{T_2},$$

which is zero. That is, for the whole system on which the Carnot engine operates, the algebraic sum of the entropy changes for a whole cycle is zero. This is an extremely important deduction for the system *as a whole*.

Now, any reversible cycle can be regarded as composed of a large number of small Carnot cycles. For example, the cycle of Fig. 127 can be regarded as the summation of a large number of cycles such as $abcda$, $d'c'fed'$, $e'f'ghe'$, and so on, superposed. For each of these small Carnot cycles, the sum of the entropy changes of the system over a complete cycle is zero ; thus for the whole large cycle, the sum of the entropy changes of the system must also be zero.

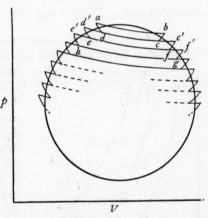

FIG. 127.—Any reversible cycle as summation of Carnot cycles.

That is, for any reversible cycle, the sum of the entropy changes of the system occurring during one complete cycle is zero.

Thus
$$\Sigma \, \delta S = 0$$
or
$$\int dS = 0$$
or
$$\int \frac{dQ}{T} = 0$$
, for a complete cycle.

The idea of entropy is usually a difficult one to grasp. This is perhaps because there seems at first sight to be no need for its introduction. In mechanics, if two bodies of known elastic properties collide, energy considerations enable the total kinetic energy after the impact to be calculated. But the change in the kinetic energies of the individual bodies cannot be calculated at all without using Newton's Third Law of Motion, most simply by introducing momentum, which has the property that the sum of the momentum changes of the two bodies is zero. It is not here suggested that momentum is the mechanical analogue of entropy. All that the two cases have in common is the introduction of some quantity related to, but quite distinct from, energy, to aid the solution of problems on the transfer of energy.

Entropy and adiabatic lines. No heat enters or leaves a system undergoing adiabatic change; that is, $\delta Q = 0$ for a small adiabatic change; therefore $\frac{\delta Q}{T} = 0$, and $\delta S = 0$. So there is no change in entropy during adiabatic change, and the adiabatic lines on the $p - V$ diagram (or on any other indicator diagram) are lines of con-

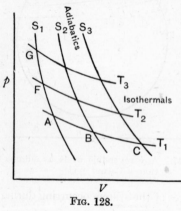

FIG. 128.

stant entropy, or isentropics.

Fig. 128 shows the isothermal lines for temperatures T_1, T_2, T_3, and the adiabatics for entropies S_1, S_2, S_3 (measured above any arbitrary value of S as zero). Moving along the isothermal for T_1 from A to B to C, the entropy changes from S_1 to S_2 to S_3 at constant temperature T_1. Moving up the adiabatic for S_1 from A to F to G, the temperature changes from T_1 to T_2 to T_3 at constant entropy S_1.

Entropy-temperature diagrams. Through any selected point on the usual $p - V$ diagram there can be drawn one isothermal line and one adiabatic line; the point, and the state of the system which the point represents, can be identified just as precisely by stating the value of S and of T for the adiabatic and isothermal which intersect there as by stating the values of p and V for the co-ordinates of the point. Thus the values of S and of T are two co-ordinates which specify the state completely, and changes in the state of the system can be shown just as well on a graph of T against S (a temperature-entropy diagram) as on the usual indicator figure.

On the T-S diagram (Fig. 129), isothermals are lines parallel to the S-axis, and adiabatic lines parallel to the T-axis. The Carnot cycle $ABCD$ is represented by a rectangular figure. Areas beneath the curve on the T-S diagram represent changes in the total energy of the system, since $dQ = T\,dS$ and $\int T\,dS$ thus gives $\int dQ$.

The symbol ϕ is frequently used for entropy; and the temperature-entropy diagram of the meteorologist is known as a "$t\phi$-gram" or tephigram.

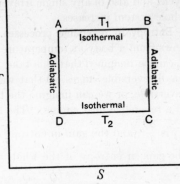

FIG. 129.—Temperature-entropy diagram for Carnot cycle.

Entropy in irreversible cycles.

For a reversible cycle operating between the temperatures T_1 and T_2, the efficiency is given by $\dfrac{Q_1 - Q_2}{Q_1} = \dfrac{T_1 - T_2}{T_1}$, and this is the maximum efficiency attainable by any cycle operating between these two temperatures. For an irreversible cycle the value of the efficiency $\dfrac{Q_1 - Q_2}{Q_1}$ is less than $\dfrac{T_1 - T_2}{T_1}$, where T_1° K. and T_2° K. are the absolute temperatures between which it operates. Considering the whole system of source at T_1°, sink at T_2°, and working substance between these temperatures, at the end of one cycle the working substance is in its initial state, the source has lost entropy $dS_1 = \dfrac{Q_1}{T_1}$, and the sink has gained entropy $dS_2 = \dfrac{Q_2}{T_2}$, so the change in entropy $dS_2 - dS_1$ is $\dfrac{Q_2}{T_2} - \dfrac{Q_1}{T_1}$ for the whole system.

As
$$\frac{Q_1 - Q_2}{Q_1} < \frac{T_1 - T_2}{T_1}, \quad 1 - \frac{Q_2}{Q_1} < 1 - \frac{T_2}{T_1}.$$
$$\therefore \frac{Q_2}{Q_1} > \frac{T_2}{T_1}, \quad \text{and} \quad \frac{Q_2}{T_2} > \frac{Q_1}{T_1},$$
$$\therefore \frac{Q_2}{T_2} - \frac{Q_1}{T_1} > 0.$$

That is, the change in entropy is positive, or the entropy of the whole system has been increased. This is true of any irreversible cycle, and also of any single irreversible process ; the entropy of the whole system increases.

Entropy in reversible processes. When a quantity of heat δQ flows from a body at temperature T_1 to a body at temperature T_2, it can be imagined that this takes place in a series of infinitesimally small reversible stages, so that we can speak of the action as being reversible, or we can imagine the transfer to take place with the aid of a reversible heat engine. The loss of entropy of the hot body at T_1 is $\dfrac{\delta Q}{T_1}$, and the gain in entropy of the cold body at T_2 is $\dfrac{\delta Q}{T_2}$, and the gain n entropy of the whole system is

$$\frac{\delta Q}{T_2} - \frac{\delta Q}{T_1} = \delta Q \left(\frac{1}{T_2} - \frac{1}{T_1} \right).$$

This is positive, since according to the Second Law of Thermodynamics $T_1 > T_2$ if the heat flows naturally without the expenditure of work to cause the transfer.

As was stated in the last section, this is true also of irreversible processes—in fact, the intermediate steps or the mechanism of the action have no effect on the value of the change in entropy, which is concerned only with the quantity of heat δQ and the two temperatures T_1 and T_2. The important conclusion reached is that, whenever heat flows from a body at a high temperature to a body at a low temperature, which is the direction of flow always indicated by the Second Law of Thermodynamics, the entropy of the system as a whole always increases Thus, the Second Law of Thermodynamics leads to the conclusion that **any flow of heat between the parts of a self-contained system always causes the entropy of the system as a whole to increase.**

Entropy and molecular chaos. If a mass of gas is at rest in thermal equilibrium with its surroundings, the final steady state of affairs can be calculated by statistics. At first sight, since no difference in density or temperature can be distinguished for samples, however small, taken from different parts of the gas and subjected to ordinary experiments, it would be reasonable to suppose that the molecules are distributed with perfect uniformity throughout the space of the container, and that all have exactly the same velocity and kinetic energy. But on looking a little more closely, and considering the molecules as individuals, this cannot be true ; for as the molecules are in perpetual random motion and colliding with one another, at any chosen instant a certain fraction of them will be in the act of colliding and momentarily at rest, while they cannot at the same time both move with high speed and also preserve a strict uniformity of arrangement in space.

The prediction of the steady state of affairs was made by Clerk Maxwell. He showed that, for molecules of mass m, of molecular density n per c.c., the number dn with velocities lying between c and $c + dc$ is given by the formula

$$dn = 4\pi n \sqrt{\frac{h^3 m^3}{\pi^3}}\, e^{-hmc^2} c^2\, dc,$$

where e is the base of Napierian logarithms and h is a constant (not to be confused with Planck's Constant which has the same symbol). As the kinetic energy of a molecule is $\frac{1}{2}mc^2$, this formula also shows the way in which the total energy is distributed amongst the individual molecules. It is known as **Maxwell's Distribution Law**.

The distribution can be represented graphically as follows. Write x^2 for hmc^2 ; then

$$dn = n \cdot \frac{4}{\sqrt{\pi}} x^2 e^{-x^2}\, dx, \quad \text{and} \quad \frac{dn}{n} = \frac{4}{\sqrt{\pi}} x^2 e^{-x^2}\, dx.$$

Again, putting y for $\frac{4}{\sqrt{\pi}} x^2 e^{-x^2}$, $\frac{dn}{n} = y\, dx$.

The graph of the function $y = \frac{4}{\sqrt{\pi}} x^2 e^{-x^2}$ when plotted is as **Fig. 130.**

To find the fraction $\frac{dn}{n}$ of the total molecules the velocities of which lie between c and $c + dc$, take the area of the strip beneath the graph and the X-axis lying between x and $x + dx$; as this area is $y\, dx$, this gives the value $\frac{dn}{n}$.

Boltzmann arrived at the same result by a completely different method ; for he showed that the Maxwell distribution of the molecular velocities and energies is the *most probable* distribution. To see what is meant by probability in the thermodynamical sense it is sufficient for our present purpose to understand why one distribution should be called more probable than another. If a handful of ten coins, all distinguishably different, is thrown into the air at random, the most probable distribution of heads and tails when they land is 5 heads and 5 tails. The reason why this is

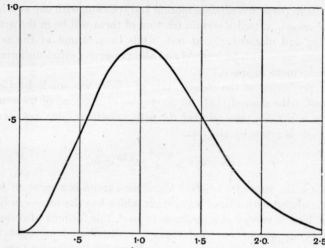

Fig. 130.—Graph of $y = \dfrac{4}{\sqrt{\pi}} x^2 e^{-x^2}$, showing Maxwell's Distribution.

called more probable than any other is simply because the number of different independent ways in which the individual coins can be arranged to give this result is greatest. The number of ways of getting 5 heads and 5 tails is the number of ways in which a *combination* of five distinct events can be chosen from a total of ten distinct events.

This, in the usual algebra notation, is $^{10}C_5 = \dfrac{10!}{5!\,5!} = 252$. For six

heads and four tails, the number of ways is $^{10}C_6 = \dfrac{10!}{6!\,4!} = 210$; for

seven heads and three tails the number of ways is $^{10}C_7 = \dfrac{10!}{7!\,3!} = 120$;

for eight heads and two tails the number of ways is $^{10}C_8 = \dfrac{10!}{8!\,2!} = 45$;

and for nine heads and one tail the number of ways is $^{10}C_1 = 10$.

Similarly, the most probable distribution of the velocities among the molecules of a gas is that which can be realised in the greatest number of independent ways, each molecule being regarded as a distinct individual, and the possession of a given velocity being considered a distinct event for each. The number of ways in which a given state can be realised is a measure of the probability of that state. (This is not the same as the ordinary mathematical probability in which the number of ways of realising an arrangement is divided by the total number of ways of obtaining all possible arrangements.) The Maxwell distribution is that which gives the greatest possible number of ways of arranging the velocities of the molecules amongst the individual molecules, and this is therefore the state of distribution which has the greatest probability.

Now consider two perfectly insulating vessels, each containing unit mass of the same gas, one vessel, A, being at a high temperature $T_1°$, and the other, B, at a lower temperature $T_2°$. The vessels are put into thermal communication, being separated by an extremely thin sheet of an extremely good solid conductor. At the beginning, from the point of view of large-scale operations, it can be said that there is a temperature difference between the two halves of the now united system, and that the system has a definite entropy. From the point of view of molecular probability, the initial state of affairs, with the molecules in one half of the gas possessing very much greater velocities and energies on the average than those in the other half, is one which could only be realised in a relatively small number of different arrangements among all the available molecules; thus it has an extremely small probability.

At the end, the large-scale observation will be that the whole mass of gas is at a uniform temperature T, midway between T_1 and T_2; there has been a flow of heat from vessel A to vessel B, and this has taken place in such a direction that the entropy of the system as a whole has increased. From the point of view of molecular probability, the velocities of the molecules will have attained the Maxwellian distribution for the temperature T. This is the most probable of all the ways in which the total energy available can be distributed among the total number of molecules. The system has moved from a state of very small probability to the state of greatest probability.

Two quantities have increased during the operation. These are (1) the entropy S of the system, and (2) the probability of the state of the molecules, denoted by the symbol ω.

Can there be any connection between these two quantities? Boltzmann suggested that there is such a connection, denoted by the relation $S = f(\omega)$.

To find the form of the function f, consider two quite independent systems, of entropies S_1 and S_2, in states of probabilities ω_1 and ω_2. The total entropy of the two taken together is $S_1 + S_2$; the total probability of the two distributions, of probabilities ω_1 and ω_2, occurring together is $\omega_1\omega_2$.

Thus
$$S_1 = f(\omega_1), \quad S_2 = f(\omega_2),$$

and
$$S_1 + S_2 = f(\omega_1\omega_2);$$

so
$$f(\omega_1) + f(\omega_2) = f(\omega_1\omega_2).$$

This gives a clue to the form of the function, for the equation is obeyed by the logarithms of the ω's; thus

$$\log \omega_1 + \log \omega_2 = \log(\omega_1\omega_2), \quad \text{or} \quad \ln \omega_1 + \ln \omega_2 = \ln(\omega_1\omega_2).$$

Boltzmann showed that the relation between S and ω must be given by the equation $S = k \ln \omega + constant$, where k is a universal constant called Boltzmann's Constant $(k = R/N)$ and the second constant depends on the arbitrary zero from which the value of S is reckoned.

It thus seems that a quite definite physical meaning can be applied to the intangible quantity entropy. It represents the probability, or degree of chaos, or degree of lack of organised arrangement of molecular energies.

This point of view also gives a new meaning to the status of a " law " in physics. The Second Law of Thermodynamics is founded on observation, and no contravention of it on the large scale has ever been observed. But if it were possible to follow the behaviour of every individual molecule in a system closely, there would certainly be continual small variations from the most probable distribution of velocities ; the larger the deviation from the state of highest probability the smaller is the probability of its occurrence. There is a small (exceedingly small) probability that in a mass of gas at temperature T, all the faster moving molecules may at any instant be segregated in one portion of the apparatus, so that one part of the system spontaneously rises to a temperature above T. But the probability of this occurring is so vanishingly small that it is safe to state that it will not be observed. Maxwell imagined that this segregation might be performed by a small and very agile being (" Maxwell's Demon ") able to distinguish the faster molecules and manipulate a frictionless shutter which allowed them through into one part of the apparatus. This is another way of stating that the Second Law of Thermodynamics operates in large-scale actions because the odds against its operation are immeasurably small, but that it has no meaning as applied to the fate of a single molecule and may fail for small-scale actions because the odds against its operation are no longer immeasurably small.

PROBLEMS USING THE EFFICIENCY EQUATION

For a Carnot cycle working between the absolute temperatures $T_1°$ K. and $T_2°$ K., taking in heat Q_1 at $T_1°$ and rejecting heat Q_2 at $T_2°$, we have for the efficiency, $\dfrac{Q_1 - Q_2}{Q_1} = \dfrac{T_1 - T_2}{T_1}$.

Here Q_1 and Q_2 can be measured in any units we please—joules or ergs or calories or any other units, providing that both are measured in the same units.

The Second Law of Thermodynamics is involved in the above statement ; for we have seen that it leads to the conclusion that all reversible engines working between the same two temperatures have the same efficiency. It thus entitles us to say that this equation is true for every kind of reversible heat engine we can imagine.

If the cycle operates over the small range of temperature between $T°$ and $T - \delta T°$, taking in heat Q at the high temperature and rejecting heat $Q - \delta Q$ at the lower temperature, the equation can be re-written $\dfrac{\delta Q}{Q} = \dfrac{dT}{T}$.

The First Law of Thermodynamics can now be used. If the external work done during this elementary cycle be δW, this must be exactly equivalent to the net heat absorbed, δQ. If δW is measured in the same units as δQ (that is, both in heat units or both in work units) we can write $\delta W = \delta Q$, whence

$$\frac{\delta W}{Q} = \frac{\delta T}{T}.$$

This equation will be referred to as the **efficiency equation**. A great number of simple thermodynamical problems are treated by taking the working substance through a small reversible cycle, calculating the heat absorbed at the high temperature and the external work done, and using the efficiency equation in the above form. Some of the standard examples follow below.

The First Latent Heat Equation. The curves of Fig. 131 represent two isothermals of a substance below its critical temperature. The line $XABY$ is the curve for the temperature $T°$, and the line

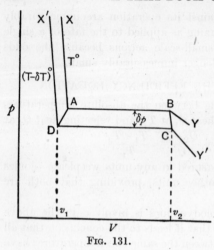

FIG. 131.

$X'DCY'$ the curve for the temperature $T - \delta T°$. At A and D, the substance is entirely liquid, while at B and C it is entirely vapour.

Let the saturated vapour pressure of the liquid at $T°$ and $T - \delta T°$ be p and $p - \delta p$ respectively.

Let v_1 and v_2 be the volumes of unit mass of liquid and unit mass of vapour respectively; let L be the latent heat of evaporation of the liquid at $T°$.

Starting at A, take the unit mass of liquid round the reversible cycle $ABCDA$.

The heat absorbed at $T°$ is the latent heat, so

$$Q = L \text{ calories.}$$

The external work done is given by the area of the strip $ABCD$, and this is $\delta p (v_2 - v_1)$ ergs,

so $$\delta W = \delta p (v_2 - v_1) \text{ ergs} = \frac{\delta p (v_2 - v_1)}{J} \text{ calories.}$$

But $$\frac{\delta W}{Q} = \frac{\delta T}{T},$$

so $$\frac{\delta p (v_2 - v_1)}{JL} = \frac{\delta T}{T}, \quad \frac{\delta p}{\delta T} = \frac{LJ}{T (v_2 - v_1)}, \quad \text{or} \quad \frac{dp}{dT} = \frac{LJ}{T (v_2 - v_1)}.$$

This equation is known as the **First Latent Heat Equation**, or the **Clausius-Clapeyron Equation.**

The equation shows how the variation of vapour pressure with temperature, the latent heat of evaporation, the boiling point, and the difference between the volumes of unit mass of liquid and unit mass of vapour are related. We can compute any one of these quantities if the three others are known. As $(v_2 - v_1)$ is always positive, $\delta p / \delta T$ is always positive.

An exactly similar argument holds for the change of state from solid to liquid, and the same equation results.

Thus, if $T°$ K. be the absolute temperature of the melting point of a solid, δT the change in the melting point caused by a change in pressure δp, v_1 the volume of unit mass of solid and v_2 the volume of unit mass of liquid, and L the latent heat of fusion of the solid at $T°$ K., then

$$\frac{\delta p}{\delta T} = \frac{LJ}{T(v_2 - v_1)}.$$

One important general conclusion emerges from this equation. If $v_2 > v_1$, that is, the substance, like wax, expands on melting, then $\delta p / \delta T$ must be positive, so that increasing the pressure raises the melting point. While if $v_2 < v_1$ and the substance, like ice, contracts on melting, $\delta p / \delta T$ is negative, and increasing the pressure lowers the melting point.

The Second Latent Heat Equation. Let s_1 be the specific heat of the liquid, and s_2 that of the vapour. If $\dfrac{dL}{dT}$ is the rate of variation of latent heat with temperature, and the value of the latent heat at $T°$ K. is L, its value at $T - \delta T$ is $L - \dfrac{dL}{dT} \cdot \delta T$.

Still considering Fig. 131, along AB the heat absorbed is L calories, while from B to C the heat given out (supposedly at $T°$) is $s_2 \, \delta T$; thus $Q_1 = L - s_2 \, \delta T$.

Passing from C to D, the heat given out is $L - \dfrac{dL}{dT} \cdot \delta T$ calories, while the heat taken in as the temperature of the liquid rises in passing from D to A is $s_1 \delta T$, so the total heat given out is

$$Q_2 = \left(L - \frac{dL}{dT} \cdot \delta T\right) - s_1 \, \delta T.$$

The total quantity of heat absorbed in the whole cycle (that is, the net absorption represented by δQ or δW in earlier equations) is thus

$$Q_1 - Q_2 = L - s_2 \, \delta T - \left(L - \frac{dL}{dT} \, \delta T\right) + s_1 \, \delta T$$

$$= \left[\frac{dL}{dT} + (s_1 - s_2)\right] \delta T \text{ calories.}$$

But, by the First Law of Thermodynamics, this is equal to the external work done, which has been shown (p. 248) to be $\delta p (v_2 - v_1)$ ergs or $\delta p (v_2 - v_1)/J$ calories ; and the First Latent Heat equation gives, on rearranging, $\quad \dfrac{\delta p (v_2 - v_1)}{J} = \dfrac{L \, \delta T}{T}.$

Substituting for $\dfrac{\delta p (v_2 - v_1)}{J}$,

$$\left[\frac{dL}{dT} + (s_1 - s_2)\right]\delta T = L\frac{\delta T}{T}.$$

$$\therefore \quad \frac{dL}{dT} + (s_1 - s_2) = \frac{L}{T}.$$

$$\therefore \quad s_1 - s_2 = \frac{L}{T} - \frac{dL}{dT} = -T\frac{d}{dT}\left(\frac{L}{T}\right).$$

This is the **Second Latent Heat Equation**, known as the **Equation of Clausius.**

Surface tension and surface energy. The surface tension σ of a liquid is defined as the force in dynes acting at right angles to a line one centimetre long drawn in the surface of the liquid. For all liquids σ decreases as T increases.

Imagine a heat engine formed by a film stretched on a frame. The film, it must be remembered, has two surfaces. Let one side of the frame be in the form of a wire which can be pulled out by an external force or pulled in by the film. Let l be the length of this wire. The force exerted by the film is $2\sigma l$ dynes (σl dynes for each surface) and this force must be applied to extend the film.

At temperature T° K., increase the area of the film by pulling out the wire a distance δx. The work done by the applied external force on the film is $2\sigma l\,\delta x$; the increase in area of both faces together is $\delta A = 2l\,\delta x$, so we can write for the work done on the film during expansion, work done $= \sigma\,\delta A$.

Now reduce the temperature to $T - \delta T$. At $T - \delta T$, the surface tension of the film is $\sigma - \dfrac{d\sigma}{dT}\cdot\delta T$, where $\dfrac{d\sigma}{dT}$ is the rate of variation of surface tension with temperature. Let the film at this temperature contract to the original area again.

Then, work done by film in contracting $= \left(\sigma - \dfrac{d\sigma}{dT}\,\delta T\right)\delta A.$

The net external work done *by the film* is thus

$$\delta W = \left(\sigma - \frac{d\sigma}{dT}\cdot\delta T\right)\delta A - \sigma\,\delta A,$$

$$\therefore \quad \delta W = -\frac{d\sigma}{dT}\cdot\delta T\cdot\delta A.$$

The initial stretching was supposed to take place at constant temperature T; let the quantity of heat which must be supplied from without for each square centimetre in order to maintain the temperature constant be q; thus the total heat taken in is $Q = q \, \delta A$, the heat here being measured in work units.

Now,
$$\frac{\delta W}{Q} = \frac{\delta T}{T},$$

so
$$\frac{-\dfrac{d\sigma}{dT} \cdot \delta T \cdot \delta A}{q \, \delta A} = \frac{\delta T}{T}, \quad \therefore \quad q = -T \frac{d\sigma}{dT}.$$

Thus the heat supplied per unit area is always positive, since $\dfrac{d\sigma}{dT}$ is always negative. Since q is positive and heat must always be supplied to keep the stretching film at a constant temperature, cooling must always occur unless this heat is supplied.

The total work done in producing one square centimetre of new surface is σ units of work. The heat energy taken in from the surroundings to keep the temperature constant is q units of work per square centimetre.

The total energy stored in one square centimetre of surface is thus $E = \sigma + q$.

But
$$q = -T \frac{d\sigma}{dT}; \quad \text{so} \quad E = \sigma - T \frac{d\sigma}{dT}.$$

The quantity E is called the surface energy.

HEAT ENGINES IN PRACTICE

Of all the reversible cycles that can be devised, operating between two given temperature limits T_1° and T_2°, the Carnot cycle is the most efficient. This is because *all* the heat absorbed is taken in at the higher temperature T_1°, and *all* the heat rejected is given out at the lower temperature T_2°. It might be expected therefore that real heat engines would aim at operating on a Carnot cycle, or something closely approaching it.

The working substance in a real engine is either water which is heated in a boiler (the steam engine), or air which is heated by the combustion of gaseous fuel with which it is mixed (the internal combustion engine), and in neither case is it possible to supply the heat which is absorbed at one constant temperature. The temperature of the water is raised in the boiler, and the temperature of the air is raised by the combustion of the fuel gas, heat being supplied continuously during the rise in temperature in each case. Thus, though we can imagine a reversible steam engine, or even (in principle) a reversible internal combustion engine, the reversible cycle on which it works will be less efficient than that of a Carnot cycle operating between the two extreme temperatures, since the average temperature at which the heat is absorbed is much below the maximum temperature. The reversible cycle for any kind of engine represents, as we have seen, the maximum efficiency for that type of engine, and actual engines are therefore compared with their reversible counterparts instead of with the Carnot cycle.

Rankine cycle. The ideal steam engine cycle is the Rankine cycle. The working substance is "water-substance" and not exclusively steam, and for a reversible cycle the following chain of operations must be considered. Suppose for the moment that they all take place in a single ideal cylinder like that of p. 277 with suitable source at $T_1°$ and sink at $T_2°$. Then the cycle is:

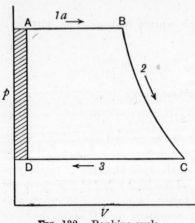

FIG. 132.—Rankine cycle.

1. *Supply of heat to the water*, represented by the point A (Fig. 132); the temperature of the water is rising (this cannot be shown on the figure) but its volume is practically unchanged and its pressure is constant, hence it is represented by a point.

1 (*a*). *Evaporation of the water to steam at constant temperature, $T_1°$*, and its expansion into the cylinder at constant pressure p_1, represented by the horizontal line AB.

2. *Adiabatic expansion of the steam in the cylinder to $T_2°$*, the temperature of the sink; this is represented by BC.

3. *Condensation of the steam to water at constant temperature $T_2°$ and constant pressure p_2*; represented by CD.

4. Omitting the second adiabatic step in the Carnot cycle, *replacing*

the cylinder on the source, represented by the step DA ; this is a vertical jump, because we are dealing with saturated vapours, and the pressure rises from p_2, the s.v.p. at $T_2°$ to p_1, the s.v.p. at $T_1°$ at constant volume.

This differs from the Carnot cycle in the step DA ; for at the point A the water is being raised from $T_2°$ to $T_1°$, and not taking in heat at a constant temperature.

In this imaginary engine, it is supposed that the cylinder itself undergoes no heat change. In practice, such a simple device would be unworkable, for the cylinder itself would be of considerable thermal capacity, and would have to be heated to $T_1°$ and cooled to $T_2°$ again during each cycle. Hence the water is heated and the steam is generated in a separate boiler at the temperature $T_1°$, and is admitted to the cylinder through a valve which is open during the stroke AB; the cylinder is closed and isolated during the adiabatic expansion BC; and at C another valve opens, and the steam already at $T_2°$ is swept out of the cylinder and condensed to water in a separate condenser at $T_2°$. The cycle of operations is completed by a feed pump which returns the water from the condenser to the boiler ; the whole scheme is represented in Fig. 133, which shows an engine designed to take the substance round a cycle. In many actual engines (e.g. locomotives) the condenser is the outside atmosphere, and

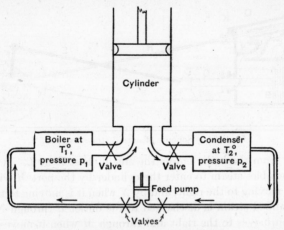

FIG. 133.—Theoretical steam engine.

the working substance is discarded there instead of being conserved.

Early steam engines, while using a separate boiler, condensed the steam inside the cylinder; James Watt's great contribution to the development of the steam engine was the introduction of the separate condenser. Even with the separate boiler and condenser, the supply of heat to, and removal of heat from, the cylinder itself is a source of inefficiency.

The area of the figure $ABCDA$ of Fig. 132 represents the work done by the engine in each cycle. In practice, as the steam cools a little as it enters the cylinder and as the valves do not operate instantaneously, the angles at A, B, C, and D are not sharp, and the curve obtained is of smaller area than that of the ideal curve. The distance of AD from the axis of p represents the volume of the liquid water, and the shaded area the work done by the feed pump in restoring this to the boiler.

Simple form of steam engine. Fig. 134 shows the essentials of a simple form of steam engine. The piston B is moved to and fro in the cylinder A by the steam pressure. The piston rod C and crosshead D move in a straight line, while the connecting rod E and crank F cause the crank shaft G to make one complete revolution while B makes one complete oscillation. A heavy flywheel is attached to G to steady the motion.

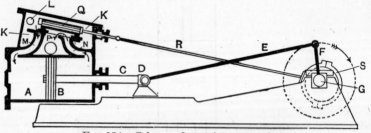

Fig. 134.—Scheme of actual steam engine.

Steam from the boiler enters the steam chest K at L. A sliding valve Q enables steam to enter the cylinder by the port M when the piston is moving to the right, and by N when it is moving to the left. The expanded steam is discharged to the outlet P through N when the piston moves to the right and through M when it moves to the left. The valve Q is operated by the valve rod R which is worked by a small crank on the crank shaft. The expanded steam on passing out through P goes to the condenser, where it is condensed to water; from this, the feed pump restores it to the boiler.

This engine really works as if there were two cylinders, one on each side of the piston. The expansion stroke for the left-hand side is the exhaust stroke for the right-hand side, and matters are reversed when the piston moves to the left.

The tracing of the indicator diagram. The cycle diagram of a steam engine is traced in the following way. A small cylinder containing a piston which moves against a spring of suitable strength is attached in communication with the main cylinder, or with the engine just described, arranged so that it may be connected to either side of the cylinder at will. This piston is acted upon by the steam pressure in the main cylinder, and gives a vertical displacement which is proportional to this pressure, p, to a tracing point which moves over a paper chart mounted on a drum. This drum follows the motion of the piston in the main cylinder, for it is rotated backwards and forwards by a cord connected to the crosshead or some other suitable place; thus the paper receives a horizontal displacement, relative to the tracing point, which depends on the position of the main piston and is proportional to v. The diagram thus obtained is called an **indicator diagram** The scale is superposed on the diagram, and when this has been done, the indicated work per cycle is calculated from the enclosed area as on p. 278.

Internal combustion engines. Internal combustion engines can be broadly classified into two types : those in which the fuel is gaseous when it enters the cylinder, and those in which it is injected as a liquid. Engines using town gas, special gas, or the vapour of petrol or other volatile liquid, belong to the first class ; these may be further subdivided into engines in which the fuel is ignited by the passage of an electric spark, and those in which the heated cylinder walls together with adiabatic compression produce a high enough temperature for ignition ; here only the simple spark-ignition engine is considered. Diesel engines and " heavy oil engines " belong to the second class. It is not proposed to treat either class in great detail. The point here is to show how the action of each class resembles and differs from the ideal Carnot cycle.

The ordinary petrol engine draws its heat supply from the combustion of petrol vapour in the charge of air ; vapour and air are mixed in the carburettor. Suitable mechanism, which will not be described, causes the inlet and exhaust valves to open and close at the appropriate times, and a spark to pass through the compressed charge at the right moment.

The usual cycle on which the petrol engine is designed to work has four strokes of the piston to each cycle ; two of these are devoted to filling the cylinder with a fresh charge of working substance, and sweeping out the used charge with the burnt fuel, and are not really involved in the theory. This is called a *four-stroke* cycle, and it is known as the **Otto cycle**.

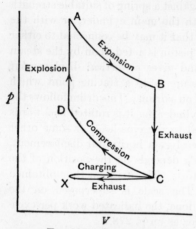

Fig. 135.—Otto cycle.
(The charging and exhaust strokes are separated vertically for clearness.)

Referring to Fig. 135, the operations are :

1. *Charging stroke, XC.* The piston draws in from the carburettor an explosive mixture of about 98 per cent. of air and 2 per cent. petrol vapour, at atmospheric pressure and a temperature of perhaps 70° C. The charge is drawn through an inlet valve which closes at the point C.

2. *Compression stroke, CD.* The piston moves inwards and compresses the charge adiabatically to the point D. The temperature is then about 400° C.

3. *Explosion and expansion, DA and AB.* At D the spark passes, and the fuel is burnt very rapidly, supplying heat very suddenly at constant volume to the charge and raising the pressure to the point A. The temperature is then about 1800° C. Adiabatic expansion then follows, and the piston is driven outwards to the point B. At this point a second valve, the exhaust valve, opens, the pressure falls at once to atmospheric, at C, much of the working substance escaping to the air.

4. *Exhaust, CX.* The piston moves inwards, sweeping the contents of the cylinder out through the exhaust port.

The cycle of operations is then repeated with a fresh charge of air and fuel.

Remembering that it is the air that is the working substance, and that the petrol vapour is simply there as a source of heat which is furnished at an appropriate stage in the cycle, it can be seen that there is no reason in theory why the air itself should be changed ; and we can imagine a fixed mass of air to be taken continuously round the cycle $ABCDA$, with heat supplied at constant volume along DA, and the air being cooled at constant volume along BC (instead of hot air being swept out and replaced by an equivalent amount of cold air at the charging stroke). The cycle $ABCDA$ can then be compared with the corresponding Carnot cycle working between, say 70° C. and 1800° C.

First, the Otto cycle must be less efficient than the Carnot cycle, because heat is being supplied to the working substance throughout the range from 400° C. to 1800° C., instead of entirely at the maximum temperature. Secondly, it has a very great practical advantage ; for if the air were to be raised to 1800° C. by adiabatic compression before any heat were supplied to it, a much greater pressure than that for the point A would be required, so that the whole engine would have to be made stronger, stouter, and heavier ; also, this would be impossible with fuel of the petrol type, which would ignite as if sparked long before so high a temperature was reached. It can be seen, however, that the higher the pressure safely attainable at D, the more closely does the engine approach to the ideal Carnot cycle, and the greater its efficiency should be. Modern motor-car engines are designed to give greater compression than was at one time thought practicable, and modern " anti-knock " fuels, which do not ignite until a high temperature is reached, enable this compression to be utilised ; hence the improvement in efficiency which has enabled the small motor-car to be produced.

Fig. 136 indicates the operations in a four-stroke Diesel engine. This is known as the Diesel cycle. In this, the working substance (air) is raised to a very high temperature by adiabatic compression. The fuel is a heavy oil, much less volatile than petrol. This is injected in liquid form into the cylinder during the first part of the outward motion of the piston. The rate of injection is carefully controlled so that the pressure on the piston during the supply of fuel is maintained constant. Thus the air is heated at constant pressure, instead of at constant volume as in the petrol engine.

The cycle starts with the cylinder full of cold air at atmospheric

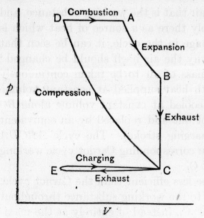

FIG. 136.—Diesel cycle.
(The charging and exhaust strokes separated for clearness.)

pressure. As the piston moves inwards, this is compressed adiabatically from C to the point D, and at this point the fuel is injected. From D to A the burning fuel is supplying heat to the air at constant pressure, and from A to B the remainder of the working stroke takes place adiabatically. At B a valve opens and the pressure drops at once to that of the atmosphere at C. The exhaust stroke CE empties the cylinder, and on the return stroke EC it is filled with fresh air and a fresh cycle starts from C.

The Diesel cycle, while less efficient than the Carnot cycle, is more efficient than an Otto cycle working between the same temperatures. Practical advantages of the Diesel engine include its economy of fuel, and the fact that it runs on crude oil. On the other hand, Diesel engines are heavier than petrol engines of comparable horsepower, and a separate fuel pump to inject the oil into the cylinder at high pressure is required.

Refrigerators. A refrigerator is a heat engine working backwards, or expending work in order to transfer heat from a cold body to one at higher temperature. If a quantity of heat Q_2 be abstracted by a reversible machine from a cold body at temperature T_2, and a quantity Q_1 be transferred to a hot body at temperature T_1, the difference $Q_1 - Q_2$ represents the mechanical work absorbed in driving the refrigerator. The *coefficient of performance* of the refrigerator is the ratio of the heat abstracted to the work supplied from without to operate the machine, and is thus equal to

$$\frac{Q_2}{Q_1 - Q_2}, \text{ or as } \frac{Q_1}{T_1} = \frac{Q_2}{T_2}, \text{ to } \frac{T_2}{T_1 - T_2}.$$

The coefficient of performance is thus greatest when $T_1 - T_2$ is as small as possible.

QUESTIONS ON CHAPTERS VI AND VII

1. Explain the following terms : " adiabatic expansion of a gas ", " reversible heat engine ", " Carnot cycle ", " thermodynamic scale of temperature ".   (O.S.)

2. A compressor driven by an electric motor is used to fill a cylindrical tank with air compressed to 10 atmospheres pressure. Calculate the energy expended in kilowatt-hours if the tank is 9 metres high and 4 metres in diameter.

(One atmosphere = 10^6 dynes/cm.^{2} ; 1 joule = 10^7 ergs. Assume the motor and compressor are perfectly efficient.)   (C.S.)

3. What conditions must be laid down in order that a satisfactory scale of temperature may be established? Illustrate your answer with reference to (a) the mercury-in-glass scale, (b) the platinum resistance scale, (c) the Kelvin scale.   (C.S.)

4. Discuss the effect of changes of pressure on the melting point of a solid and on the boiling point of a liquid. Deduce an expression for the change in the boiling point due to a small change in pressure.

The specific volume of steam at 100° C. and 76 cm. of mercury pressure is 1,601 c.c. per gram, and the latent heat of vaporisation of water 536 calories per gram. Find the change in the boiling point of water due to a change in pressure of 1 cm. of mercury.   (C.S.)

5. Distinguish exactly between the meanings of the three following statements :

      (a) Heat is put into a substance.

      (b) The temperature of a substance is raised.

      (c) Work is done on a substance.

Indicate the relations between these statements by considering (a) a gas in a cylinder, (b) melting ice.   (C.S.)

6. Deduce an expression connecting the pressure and volume of a gas in an adiabatic change.

A litre of hydrogen at 27° C. and 10^6 dynes per sq. cm. pressure expands isothermally until its volume is doubled and then adiabatically until it is redoubled. Find (a) the final temperature and pressure of the gas, (b) the work done during each expansion.

      ($\gamma = 1 \cdot 4$; $(\frac{1}{2})^{0 \cdot 4} = 0 \cdot 76$; $\log_e 2 = 0 \cdot 693$.)   (C.S.)

7. What is meant by a " reversible cycle "? Show that no engine working between two limits of temperature can be more efficient than a reversible one. Discuss the modern tendency to use internal combustion engines in place of steam engines from this standpoint.   (C.S.)

8. How much of the specific heat of hydrogen at constant pressure is due to the external work done in expansion?

(1 g. of hydrogen at standard temperature and pressure occupies 11·2 litres. Specific gravity of mercury = 13·6, $J = 4 \cdot 2 \times 10^7$ ergs/cal.)

      (C.S., *part question.*)

9. Calculate the work done on 1 litre of helium under a pressure of 1 atmosphere, when it is compressed adiabatically to a pressure of 10 atmospheres.   Assume that it behaves as a perfect gas.

(1 atmosphere $= 10^6$ dyne cm.$^{-2}$; $C_p = 5$ and $C_v = 3$ calories per gram-atom.)   (C.S., *part question*.)

10. What is meant by a reversible change?   Give two examples.

Describe a Carnot's cycle, and show that the efficiency of a heat engine working between two given temperatures is a maximum when the engine is reversible.   (C.S.)

11. Explain from the energy point of view the modes of action of two of the following : (*a*) a steam engine, (*b*) a petrol motor, (*c*) a refrigerating machine.   (L.)

12 Explain the factors which govern the efficiency of a heat engine, illustrating your answer by reference to a Carnot engine and a steam engine.

To what extent may an internal combustion engine be regarded as a heat engine?   Why does the efficiency of a petrol engine increase with increasing compression ratio?   (O.S.)

13. Supposing that there were many liquids as common as water, what would be the properties of a liquid selected as the working fluid in the boilers of a power plant?

To what extent does water possess these properties?   (O.S.)

14. Explain as well as you can why a condenser makes a steam engine more efficient.   (O.S.)

15. State the Second Law of Thermodynamics.

A power station driven by an ideal heat engine has to supply on the average each consumer with 3 H.P., and 10 kw. to be used for heating. Discuss whether there will be an increase in thermal efficiency if the power station raises the temperature of its condenser from 17° C. to 78° C. and supplies heat directly to the consumer as exhaust steam.

(Boiler temp., 117° C. ; 1 H.P. = 746 watts.)   (O.S.)

CHAPTER VIII

LIQUEFACTION OF GASES AND PRODUCTION AND MEASUREMENT OF LOW TEMPERATURES

Introduction. In general, there are two ways in which a gaseous substance may be liquefied. The first is to cool the substance to below its critical temperature, and apply a sufficiently great pressure ; the liquefaction of chlorine by Faraday (1823) and carbon dioxide by Thilorier (1835) were early examples of this method. The second method is to cool the gas to a temperature below its normal boiling point, when it will become liquid at atmospheric pressure.

There are three chief ways in which a gas can be cooled. These are (a) directly, by passing it through a tube immersed in a cold liquid or surrounded by a stream of cold gas, or by some similar means, (b) allowing it to expand adiabatically, either in a single expansion or in an engine arranged to deliver mechanical work, and (c) causing it to expand freely through a valve from a high pressure to a low pressure (the Joule-Kelvin effect), which causes a cooling if the initial temperature is below the Joule-Kelvin inversion temperature.

The following table gives a list of the important temperatures for the chief permanent gases.

Gas.	Normal boiling point.	Freezing point.	Critical temp.	Joule-Kelvin inversion temp., approx.
Oxygen -	$-183°$ C.	$-227°$ C.	$-118°$ C.	{ above ordinary
Nitrogen -	$-196°$ C.	$-211°$ C.	$-146°$ C.	{ temperatures.
Hydrogen -	$-253°$ C.	$-259°$ C.	$-241°$ C.	$-80°$ C.
Helium -	$-268·7°$ C.	—	$-268°$ C.	$-243°$ C.
Argon -	$-186°$ C.	$-188°$ C.	$-117°$ C.	—

The following are the commoner refrigerants :

Substance.			Normal B.P.	Critical Temp.
Ammonia	-	-	$-33 \cdot 5°$ C.	$133°$ C.
Sulphur dioxide	-	-	$-8°$ C.	$155 \cdot 4°$ C.
Carbon dioxide	-	-	$-78 \cdot 2°$ C.	$30 \cdot 9°$ C.
Ethylene	-	-	$-103°$ C.	$10°$ C.
Methyl chloride	-	-	$-24 \cdot 1$	—
Methane	-	-	$-164°$ C.	$-82°$ C.

Early work on liquefaction of oxygen. In 1877, oxygen was liquefied by Cailletet and by Pictet, working independently along somewhat different lines.

Cailletet's method was to cool oxygen, compressed to 400 atmospheres pressure, by means of liquid sulphur dioxide ; the pressure was suddenly released, and the resulting cooling by adiabatic expansion caused a mist of liquid oxygen to appear in the experimental tube.

Pictet introduced the method of cascade cooling, using volatile refrigerants. The evaporation of liquid sulphur dioxide was used to cool carbon dioxide to such an extent that it readily liquefied under pressure ; the evaporation of this liquid carbon dioxide was then used to cool oxygen down to $-140°$ C. (which is well below the critical temperature of oxygen, $-118°$ C.), at which temperature it could be liquefied under a pressure of 320 atmospheres. Pictet generated oxygen in a steel retort a (Fig. 137), connected with a steel tube c which was surrounded by a copper vessel d. Carbon dioxide was condensed by means of the pump f into g, and allowed to flow through the tube e into d, where it was evaporated by means of the same set of pumps. The system $dfge$ formed a closed circuit. The liquid carbon dioxide solidified in d, and the temperature reached by its volatilisation was $-140°$ C. The carbon dioxide was cooled and condensed by means of sulphur dioxide, which was circulated through a similar closed system connected with the condenser h. After working for many hours, the cock b was opened, and the pressure, which had risen to 320 atmospheres, was allowed to fall suddenly, producing an even greater degree of cold. On tilting the apparatus, it was seen that liquid oxygen was actually present. In Pictet's experiment, much of the liquid was produced as the result of the final expansion. The continuous production of liquid oxygen

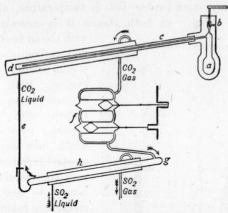

FIG. 137.—Pictet's cascade method.

needs a temperature slightly lower than that obtainable with liquid carbon dioxide.

Later experimenters, notably Dewar in England, and Olzewski and Wroblewski in Poland, used ethylene in place of carbon dioxide ; this gave a temperature of $-169°$ C., and enabled liquid oxygen to be produced continuously. Kamerlingh Onnes, at Leyden, set up a cascade system using methyl chloride in place of sulphur dioxide, and ethylene in place of carbon dioxide, and was able to produce liquid air in quantity.

The cascade process is not at the present time used for the large-scale industrial production of liquid air. The chief objection is that it is cumbersome. It is, however, efficient in its return of liquid air per unit of energy employed. Keesom, who succeeded Kamerlingh Onnes at Leyden, has developed a triple cascade, using ammonia, ethylene, and methane as the successive refrigerants, which is considerably more efficient than the existing commercial processes outlined below. It is possible that this process may be developed further in the future.

MODERN PROCESSES FOR AIR

Modern processes fall into two classes : (a) Hampson and Linde processes, which use the Joule-Kelvin effect alone as the main agent of cooling ; and (b) Claude and Heylandt processes in which the performance of external work in an expansion engine is used to produce a very considerable fall in temperature, aided by the Joule-Kelvin effect. In both classes it is necessary to start with the air freed from water and carbon dioxide, which would solidify and clog the system. Both classes use a continuous circulation system with regenerative cooling; by this means, air which has expanded and escaped liquefaction (though very considerably cooled) is caused to flow round the metal tube taking the stream of air towards the expansion device. Such an arrangement is called a heat exchanger.

Hampson process. The circulating air enters a compressor and, after passing through a water bath which removes the heat generated by compression, passes to the exchanger.

Air at a pressure of 150 atmospheres is allowed to expand through a valve to a pressure of one atmosphere; there is a cooling due to the Joule-Kelvin effect. The expanded air passes back to the compressor through a heat exchanger, cooling the incoming air. After the apparatus has been working for some time, a temperature of about $-188°$ C. is attained at the valve; at this stage, the expanding gas is liquefied.

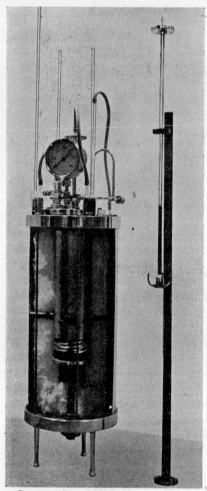

Construction of a Hampson liquefier. A portion of the coiled heat exchanger can be seen. At the right, expansion valve as used in this apparatus.

Reproduced from the Science Museum Handbook, "Very Low Temperatures", by permission of the Controller of H. M. Stationery Office.

Fig. 138 shows the scheme of the process. Details of the apparatus are intentionally omitted from this and the succeeding diagrams, which should be regarded as rather of the same nature as electrical circuit diagrams.

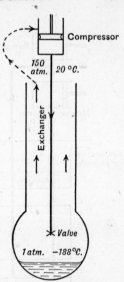

A small apparatus of the simple Hampson type produces about a litre of liquid air per hour ; it is useful where only small quantities of liquid air are required.

Linde process. The chief feature of the Linde process is that the closed circulating system is at a high pressure. The air passing through the valve expands from 150 atmospheres to 40 atmospheres ; consequently, on returning to the compressor it has to be compressed from 40 atmospheres to 150 atmospheres, instead of from 1 to 150 atmospheres.

Now, the work done in compressing a given mass of gas from p_1 to p_2 is a function

Fig. 138.—Scheme of Hampson process.

of the *ratio* p_2/p_1 ; under isothermal conditions, for example, it is proportional to $\ln p_2/p_1$; the fall in temperature produced when a gas expands from p_2 to p_1 freely through a valve is proportional to $(p_2 - p_1)$. The Linde process cuts down p_2/p_1 from 150/1 to 150/40 —that is by a factor of 40. Note that this does not mean that only 1/40 the external work is needed ; if we assume isothermal conditions, when logarithms are taken, the ratio of the " Linde work " to the " Hampson work ' for a given mass of gas comes to about 0·26. On the other hand, the fall in temperature for a pressure difference of $(150 - 40) = 110$ atmospheres is 110/150, or 0·73, of that for a difference of 150 atmospheres. Although these figures involve simple assumptions, perhaps not closely applicable to the actual process, it does look as if the Linde process, giving about $\frac{3}{4}$ the cooling for about $\frac{1}{4}$ the work, is making for greater efficiency and economy in working. Still greater efficiency is obtained by pre-cooling the incoming gas by liquid ammonia ; this is not essential, though as with the Hampson process the heat generated by the compressor must be removed before the gas passes into the interchanger.

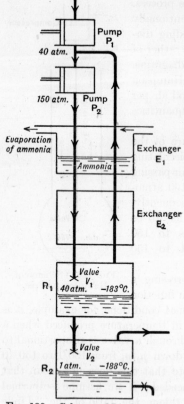

FIG. 139.—Scheme of Linde process.

Fig. 139 gives a "circuit diagram" of the Linde process. The pump P_1 takes in air at one atmosphere pressure and compresses it to 40 atmospheres; but this compression from one atmosphere is not continually operating on air in circulation; the purpose of P_1 is to replace the air which is removed from circulation by liquefaction. The circulating pump P_2 compresses the air in the high-pressure circuit from 40 atmospheres to 150 atmospheres. The compressed air, after cooling in the ammonia bath E_1, passes through the exchanger E_2, and expands through the valve V_1, becoming liquid at a pressure of 40 atmospheres and a temperature of $-183°$ C. That part of the air which is unliquefied streams up through the exchanger E_2 back to P_2 at 40 atmospheres, to be compressed up to 150 atmospheres again; that which has liquefied is replaced by fresh air from P_1. The liquid is removed from the reservoir R_1 by opening the tap V_2; the reservoir R_2 contains liquid air at $-188°$ C. and one atmosphere pressure.

Claude and Heylandt processes. In both these processes, part of the air supplied is cooled by adiabatic expansion in the cylinder of an engine which is actually performing external work. The air thus cooled streams up the exchanger, cooling the remainder of the air, which then expands through a valve as in the Linde process.

Fig. 140 shows the circuit of the Claude process. Air is compressed to 40 atmospheres by the pump P, and after cooling in the

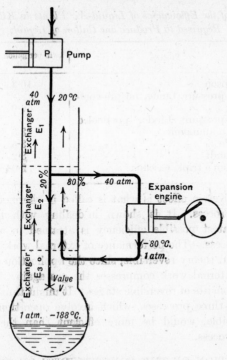

Fig. 140.—Claude process.

exchanger E_1 is divided into two streams; 80 per cent. of the air goes into the expansion engine, and is cooled to $-80°$ C. in doing external work. It then flows up the exchanger E_2, where it cools the other 20 per cent. to $-80°$ C., and finally returns to the intake of the compressor. The part below E_2 is really an ordinary Hampson liquefier. The direct 20 per cent. stream expands through the valve V, and part liquefies and collects in R, while the remainder passes up the exchanger E_3 to cool the incoming air.

In the Heylandt process, the initial pressure is 200 atmospheres; 55 per cent. of the air is expanded in the engine and 45 per cent. in the valve; the exhaust temperature of the engine is $-125°$ C. Apart from these quantitative differences, it is identical with the Claude process; it is slightly the more efficient of the two.

N.H.   x

Comparison of the Efficiencies of Liquid-Air Plants in Kilowatt-Hours Required to Produce one Gallon of Liquid.

Process.	kwh. per gallon liquid air.
Hampson - - - - -	10·3
High-pressure Linde, no pre-cooling - - - - - -	6·0
High-pressure Linde, pre-cooled with ammonia - - -	3·5
Claude - - - - -	3·6
Heylandt - - - - -	3·2
Keesom's triple cascade - -	2·04

The Joule-Kelvin effect is what is called in thermodynamics an irreversible process. It is shown in dealing with heat engines that the greatest possible efficiency is attained in a completely reversible process. The performance of external work by adiabatic expansion is in theory reversible, since the application of a suitable amount of external work compresses the gas again. The cascade system also consists of reversible stages. It might thus be expected that the last three processes, which involve operations which are nearly reversible, would be more efficient than the completely irreversible process.

SEPARATION OF THE CONSTITUENTS OF THE AIR

The air contains about 78 per cent. by volume of nitrogen, 21 per cent. of oxygen, and nearly 1 per cent. of inert gases comprising argon (0·93 per cent.), neon (0·00015 per cent.), helium (0·000014 per cent.), and very much smaller quantities of krypton and xenon. Pure oxygen, nitrogen, argon, and neon are obtained from the air on a commercial scale. Oxygen, which is by far the most valuable of these products on account of its many uses in industry, medicine, and warfare, is sometimes prepared with a fairly high percentage of nitrogen and argon ; for many purposes this is quite satisfactory. On the other hand, for some purposes, such as oxyacetylene cutting, small quantities of argon are injurious and must be removed. Nitrogen, for long considered a waste product, is now used in the synthetic ammonia industry. Argon is used in gas-filled electric lamps, to hinder evaporation of the filament ; as an inert gas it exerts no chemical effect, and as a monatomic gas of fairly high molecular weight it is a fairly good thermal insulator. Neon is used in discharge tubes and lamps. Helium is not extracted from the air on a commercial scale, as better sources are available.

The boiling point of argon (– 186° C.) is intermediate between those of oxygen (– 183° C.) and nitrogen (– 196° C.), consequently special steps have to be taken for its separation. Helium and neon remain gaseous when the other constituents are all liquid, as their boiling points are very low.

In commercial plants for the production of oxygen, the rectifier (based essentially on the fractionating column described on page 224) is assembled as part of the liquefying plant. In particular, the heat exchanger is arranged so that the incoming air provides the latent heat needed for the evaporation of the liquid.

Fig. 141 shows the Linde double column, devised in 1910. It consists essentially of two fractionating columns. The pressure in the lower part *B* is about 5 atmospheres, and that in the upper part *G* a little above one atmosphere. The two columns are separated by a condenser, in which the cooling effect of liquid oxygen in the top column is used to condense nitrogen under pressure in the lower column. At the base of the lower column there is an accumulation of liquid containing about 40 per cent. of oxygen.

Cooled compressed air from the heat exchanger is liquefied in the coil *A* immersed in the liquid bath at the base of the pressure column *B*, and after expansion at the valve *C* is admitted to about the middle of the high-pressure column. It flows down the column from plate to plate, to the bath at the bottom. The vapour from

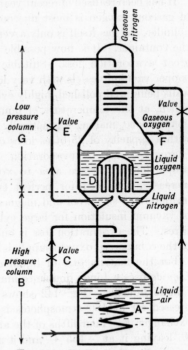

FIG. 141.—Linde double column.

this bath of liquid boiling at the base of B passes up through B, and by the time it reaches the condenser tubes D at the top consists of practically pure nitrogen. The pressure in the lower column is great enough to allow this nitrogen to condense in the tubes, which are cooled on their outsides by liquid oxygen boiling at slightly above atmospheric pressure. About half the liquid nitrogen so produced flows backwards down the high-pressure column, to wash oxygen from the rising vapour, while the other half is expanded to the top of the upper column G through the valve E. The liquid condensing at the bottom of the pressure column has 40 per cent. of oxygen, and is sent to a suitable point in the upper column. Pure liquid oxygen collects at the bottom of G, and about a fifth of the vapour coming from the boiling liquid is conducted away from F through a heat exchanger which cools the incoming gas ; this vapour constitutes the output of the plant.

It has been realised of recent years that the handling and transport of gaseous oxygen is most uneconomical. In an ordinary oxygen cylinder, the gas itself is only a very small fraction of the weight of the container. It is now possible to handle liquid oxygen without great evaporation loss. Suitable containers are large spherical copper vacuum vessels with very long necks, the space between the walls being well polished, highly evacuated, and containing charcoal which, at the temperature of liquid air, adsorbs any residual gas in the space, making a practically perfect vacuum. Such a vessel with a capacity of 25 litres loses only about 5 per cent. of its full charge per day by evaporation. With larger vessels, since the proportion of surface area to volume decreases as the volume increases, the need for perfect surface insulation is less ; such insulators as slag wool and magnesium carbonate are used instead of vacuum insulation for large cylinders holding several thousand litres. The evaporation loss is only 2–3 per cent. per day. Much of the commercial oxygen supply is (or will be) transported as liquid.

For the manufacture of liquid oxygen the French *Société l'Air Liquide* uses a Linde double-column rectifier in conjunction with a Claude liquefier. Fig. 142 shows the circulating system. Compressed air at 150 atmospheres is cooled to $-30°$ C. in the first exchanger F. Four-fifths of the air is then expanded in the engine E, leaving it at $-165°$ C. and 4 atmospheres pressure, whence it passes directly to the high-pressure column B of the double-column

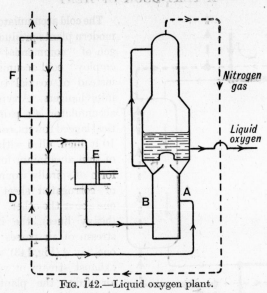

FIG. 142.—Liquid oxygen plant.

rectifier. The remainder of the compressed air is further cooled in D and liquefied by the issuing nitrogen, to be then introduced at a suitable level A in the high-pressure column. Liquid oxygen, 99·5 per cent. pure, is withdrawn from the base of the upper column, while nitrogen drawn from the top of this column cools the incoming stream of air. The yield of such an apparatus is about 300 litres per hour, and the energy consumption about 4 kwh. per gallon of liquid.

Separation of the inert gases. A suitable fractionating column can be designed so that the argon is collected with the oxygen, its boiling point being only a few degrees lower. The argon is then separated from the oxygen by fractionation.

Helium and neon are collected with the nitrogen in a liquid oxygen plant. The nitrogen is removed by passing the mixture under a pressure of 50 atmospheres through a bath of liquid nitrogen ; this causes the nitrogen in the mixture to liquefy. The boiling point of helium is $-269°$ C. and that of neon $-233°$ C. ; that of hydrogen is $-252·5°$ C., so that if the mixture of helium and neon is cooled by liquid hydrogen the neon condenses, leaving the helium still gaseous.

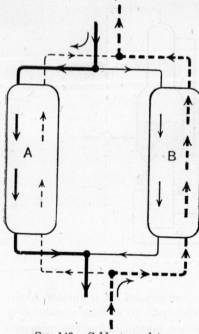

FIG. 143.—Cold accumulator.

The cold accumulator. Some modern plants producing oxygen of " commercial " purity employ " cold accumulators " instead of coaxial tube heat interchangers. A typical cold accumulator is a pair of vertical lagged towers, each about 10 ft. high, filled with $1\frac{1}{4}$ tons of thin aluminium foil in the form of spirally wound strips of corrugated sheet packed one above the other. At first (heavy lines), the incoming stream of air passes through one, say A (Fig. 143), while the exhaust stream of very cold air from the plant passes through the other, B, which it cools to a very low temperature, removing heat from the foil. After 2 minutes, the connections are reversed (thin lines) by suitable taps so that the incoming air passes through B, giving up heat to the very cold foil, while the exhaust stream cools A. Reversal takes place every two minutes. The result is, of course, exactly the same as with an exchanger ; the outgoing cold stream is the means of removing heat from the incoming stream.

The cold accumulator has two great advantages. First, only a very small pressure head is needed to drive the gas through it, and secondly, there is no need for preliminary purification. Ice and solid carbon dioxide are deposited on the foil by the incoming stream ; this sublimes off into the outgoing stream during the " cold " period.

HYDROGEN AND HELIUM

Liquefaction of Hydrogen. The critical temperature of hydrogen is $-241°$ C., which cannot be attained by any independent cooling agent, so the Joule-Kelvin effect is the only way of liquefying hydrogen. The temperature of inversion (for moderate initial pressures) is $-80°$ C. : below this temperature hydrogen is cooled when it expands freely through a valve ; it is necessary to pre-cool the gas below the inversion temperature before expansion.

In Kamerlingh Onnes' hydrogen apparatus, the scheme of which is outlined in Fig. 144, the hydrogen, first carefully purified, is passed through a bath of liquid air boiling under reduced pressure, giving a temperature of $-208°$ C. The hydrogen, at 150 atmospheres pressure, expands through a valve to a pressure

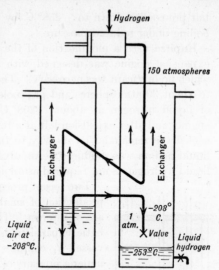

FIG. 144.—Hydrogen liquefaction.

of one atmosphere and is liquefied. The hydrogen must be free from oxygen and nitrogen, as well as other impurities ; otherwise there is the risk of the plant being blocked by solid oxygen or nitrogen, with resulting risk of explosion. This is the main reason for purifying the gas, for the liquid hydrogen is usually required to produce a low temperature rather than for its chemical purity. For this reason Kapitza in 1932 designed a modified form of Onnes apparatus, in which a small quantity of very pure hydrogen is kept circulating round the system, and produces a bath of liquid hydrogen. Commercial hydrogen is then liquefied under pressure in a container immersed in this liquid hydrogen. The commercial hydrogen is drawn off as required for cooling purposes.

Solidification of hydrogen. Solid hydrogen is obtained by using the cooling effect when the liquid is boiled under reduced pressure. The same method will solidify all the permanent gases except helium, for which a different method has to be employed (see p. 322).

Helium. The temperature of inversion of the Joule-Kelvin effect for helium is about $-240°$ C. ; the gas was first liquefied by Kamerlingh Onnes using the same method as for hydrogen, but pre-cooling down to $-258°$ C. by means of a bath of hydrogen boiling under reduced pressure.

Kapitza used a modification of the Claude process, in which the expansion engine was designed with a special grooved piston for which no lubricant was necessary. The purified gas was compressed to about 30 atmospheres and pre-cooled by passing through a bath of liquid nitrogen at about $-208°$ C. ; part then passed to the engine, and after expansion left at a temperature of $-263°$ C. This cooled the remainder on its way to the expansion valve, at which liquid helium was produced. An advantage of this method is that liquid hydrogen is not required as an accessory.

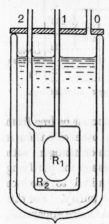

FIG. 145.—Simon's adiabatic expansion method for helium.

Two recent processes devised by Simon for the production of small quantities of liquid helium are of interest. The first method, that of adiabatic expansion, is indicated in Fig. 145. The vessel R_1 contains the helium to be liquefied, under a pressure of 150 atmospheres. The outer chamber R_2, when filled with helium gas, maintains thermal contact between R_1 and the surrounding bath of liquid hydrogen, which is kept boiling under reduced pressure by the application of an exhaust pump to the outlet O. When R_2 is evacuated through 2, the vessel R_1 is perfectly insulated from the bath. The helium in R_1 is then allowed to expand suddenly, and the fall in temperature suffices to liquefy the gas. The adiabatic condition is due to the good thermal insulation rather than the rapidity of the expansion. The whole apparatus is made of metal to withstand the large pressure differences.

The second method employs a new principle, that of adiabatic desorption. When a gas is adsorbed on a solid surface, heat is liberated—an effect analogous with the evolution of latent heat when a vapour condenses. So when adsorbed gas is removed (or "desorbed "), this must result in the removal of heat from the surface. The apparatus is indicated in Fig. 146. The vessel R_1 contains the helium to be liquefied ; the chamber R_2 contains charcoal, and helium gas can be introduced through the tube 2 which also serves for its removal by a vacuum pump. The surrounding vessel R_3 is filled with helium when it is required to place the inner vessels in thermal contact with the surrounding bath of liquid hydrogen boiling under reduced pressure, and is evacuated when they are to be insulated.

The sequence of operations is then as follows. The vessel R_1 is full of helium ; R_2 is supplied with helium which is adsorbed on the charcoal, liberating heat which is conveyed outwards through R_3, which also contains helium to conduct this heat away. The vessel R_3 is then evacuated, so that R_2 and R_1 are now insulated. Next, the vacuum pump is applied to 2 to remove the adsorbed helium from R_2. The fall in temperature produced is sufficient to liquefy the helium in R_1.

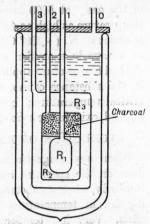

FIG. 146.—Adiabatic desorption method for helium.

Properties of liquid helium. On cooling liquid helium at ordinary pressures, Kamerlingh Onnes observed no sign of solidification. It has been established that a transformation to another form of the liquid takes place at a temperature of $2 \cdot 186°$ K., which is called the λ-point. Above $2 \cdot 186°$ K., the liquid is Helium I ; below this temperature, Helium II. The two forms are strikingly different in physical properties ; helium II has a smaller density, greater latent heat of evaporation, and smaller surface tension. Observers have stated that the viscosity is exceedingly low, and the rate of flow through tubes practically independent of the pressure difference. Helium II has an extraordinarily high coefficient of thermal conductivity—190 C.G.S units, as compared with $0 \cdot 9$ for copper ; but this only persists for temperatures above $0 \cdot 5°$ K. It has been suggested that the very low viscosity of the liquid may have some bearing on this abnormal figure.

Daunt and Mendelssohn (*Nature*, Nov. 12, 1942) point out the striking analogy between the flow of helium *atoms* practically unhindered by *viscous resistance* at this very low temperature in Helium II, and the phenomenon of electrical superconduction, (p. 325), when *electrons* travel through a material unhindered by *electrical resistance*.

Solid helium was first obtained by Keesom, who subjected liquid helium to high pressures. The solid is obtained at a pressure of 250 atmospheres at 4·2° K. Further experiments showed that at a high enough pressure, solid helium could be obtained in equilibrium with the vapour at temperatures well above the critical temperature of the gas ; at 5800 atmospheres, solid helium is obtainable at a temperature as high as 42° K. (− 231° C.) ; the critical temperature is about 5° K. (− 268° C.). Other gases have since been observed to behave in a similar way, hence it must be assumed that the critical temperature applies only to the liquid-vapour change. That is, the substance cannot exist in the *liquid state* at all above the critical temperature ; but it may, if sufficiently great pressure is applied, exist in the *solid state* above this temperature.

PRODUCTION OF EXTREMELY LOW TEMPERATURES

When any magnetic material is magnetised, external work is done on the specimen and this results in a rise in temperature. Similarly, when a substance is demagnetised, there is a corresponding fall in temperature. This is known as the magneto-caloric effect. Very low temperatures, within a very small fraction of a degree of absolute zero, have been obtained by demagnetising samples of suitable materials adiabatically—that is, in an isolated thermally insulated space.

The ratio $\dfrac{\text{intensity of magnetisation of specimen}}{\text{intensity of magnetising field}}$

for any material is called the susceptibility of the material, χ. Substances can be classified as *paramagnetic* (magnetisation in same direction as magnetising field, χ positive) and *diamagnetic* (magnetisation in opposite direction to field, χ negative) ; a few *ferromagnetic* materials such as iron, nickel, cobalt, exhibit very great susceptibility below a certain temperature called the Curie point, different for each substance, but above this temperature behave as ordinary paramagnetics. The susceptibility of diamagnetic substances is independent both of the field strength and the temperature. The susceptibility of paramagnetic substances does not depend on the field strength, but does depend on the temperature.

For paramagnetic substances the relation between susceptibility χ and absolute temperature T is given by the relation $\chi = C/T$, where C is a constant. This is known as Curie's Law.

Thus, at very low temperatures the susceptibility of paramagnetics is very considerably greater than it is at ordinary temperatures. The size of the magneto-caloric effect also increases as the initial temperature is lowered.

In 1926, Giauque and Debye suggested that if paramagnetic salts obeyed Curie's Law at the temperature of liquid helium, the cooling given by adiabatic demagnetisation should be quite large. In 1931, Giauque and McDougall reached a temperature of $0.25°$ K. using gadolinium sulphate, and de Haas, Wiersma, and Kramers reached $0.0034°$ K. using a mixture of chrome-potassium alum and aluminium-potassium alum. For the substances chosen, χ changes rapidly with the temperature.

Fig. 147 gives a general outline of the apparatus used in these experiments. The specimen A is held in the chamber R, which can be filled with helium or evacuated. A test coil surrounds R; this coil is connected in one arm of a A.C. bridge, so that its self-inductance can be measured. The whole is surrounded by liquid helium in a vacuum vessel, which is surrounded by another vessel containing liquid hydrogen or liquid nitrogen. A powerful electromagnet provides the magnetising field.

The procedure is to fill R with helium gas to maintain thermal contact with the outer bath. The initial temperature is of the order 1.2-$1.5°$ K., depending on the pressure above the liquid helium. The specimen is then magnetised in a field of the order of 10,000 oersted.

The heat evolved during the magnetisation is conducted away by the helium gas in R. Next, the chamber R is evacuated. Finally, the magnetising field is switched off.

The method of estimating the temperature reached is interesting. The self-inductance of the test coil depends on the value of χ for the specimen inside it; and if the Curie Law holds, T is proportional to $1/\chi$, which is found from the A.C. bridge

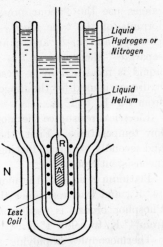

Fig. 147.—Adiabatic demagnetisation.

reading. It is usual in this work to record temperatures on the Curie Scale (defined by the relation $\chi = C/T$), and denote them by the symbol T^*. In the absence of any independent check on the validity of Curie's Law at extremely low temperatures, it would be reasonable to question whether these low temperatures are actually attained or not, but the Curie Law does hold, and the Curie and thermodynamic (Kelvin) scales agree, over the region for which experimental tests have been made.

Measurement of very low temperatures. The following temperatures have been established as additional subsidiary fixed points on the International Temperature Scale :

Boiling point of nitrogen		$-195 \cdot 808°$ C.
,, ,, neon		$-246 \cdot 087°$ C.
,, ,, hydrogen		$-252 \cdot 780°$ C.
,, ,, helium		$-268 \cdot 928°$ C.

all at one standard atmosphere pressure.

The helium gas thermometer can be used to interpolate between these fixed points, and also below the standard boiling point of helium, down to $1°$ K., when the pressure at which it is operated has of course to be below the vapour pressure of the liquid helium.

Other practical forms of thermometer over limited temperature ranges use the vapour pressure of liquefied gas. An empirical formula of the type $\log P = a + bT - c/T$, where P is the vapour pressure and a, b, and c are constants, is used. Actually, no separate " thermometer " is used ; the vapour pressure over the liquid is measured by a pressure gauge. The vapour pressure of hydrogen is used for the range $20°$ K. to $14°$ K., and that of helium from $4 \cdot 2°$ K. to $1°$ K.

Electrical resistance thermometers suffer from two defects at very low temperatures. First, they are disturbed by magnetic fields, and secondly, superconducting impurities cause the material to give inconsistent results.

Platinum resistance thermometers have been used down to about $14°$ K., and lead resistance thermometers in the range $20°$-$7 \cdot 2°$ K. Phosphor bronze is used from $7°$ K. to below $1°$ K., and carbon from $4°$ K. to below $1°$ K.

Thermocouples employing gold and silver alloys have been used from about $17°$ K. to $2 \cdot 5°$ K.

For temperatures below 1° K., the Curie Scale, depending on the variation of the magnetic susceptibility of a paramagnetic salt with temperature is used. Experiments have been done to determine the relation between the Curie Scale and the Kelvin Scale, the principle of which is to take the material through a thermodynamic cycle, and actually measure the heat absorbed from a beam of γ-rays which is used to raise the material from a low temperature to a higher one. At temperatures within the range of independent thermometers, it is found that the Curie Scale and the Kelvin Scale agree.

Properties of materials at very low temperatures. For all substances the atomic heat tends to zero as the absolute zero of temperature is approached (see p. 73). For paramagnetic substances, the magnetic susceptibility is very nearly inversely proportional to the absolute temperature. Perhaps the most striking effect is that of superconduction (or supra-conduction). In 1913, Kamerlingh Onnes found that when mercury was cooled below 4° K. its electrical resistance *vanished*. This effect was also found in lead, tin, and other metals which appear close to these elements in the Periodic Table; but it is not shown by all metals ; for example, copper and gold do not behave in this way, and it appears, like ferromagnetism, a restricted rather than a general property. No trace of electrical resistance is observed in a material which is in the superconducting state. A current once induced in a superconductor continues undiminished in strength for days, indeed so long as the necessary low temperature is maintained. Superconduction ceases in a magnetic field above a certain threshold strength, which depends on the metal and the temperature, but is restored when such field is removed.

QUESTIONS ON CHAPTER VIII

1. Distinguish between a gas and a vapour, and explain what is meant by the critical temperature of a gas.
Give a short account of the method generally used to liquefy air. Suggest a method of measuring the temperature of liquid air. (O. & C.)

2. Describe one good method of liquefying the more permanent gases, and mention the principles on which it depends. Describe a method of measuring low temperatures such as that of liquid air. (C.S.)

3. Write a short essay on the liquefaction of gases and the production

of very low temperatures, mentioning some of the changes in the physical properties of bodies which occur at low temperatures.　(C.S.)

4. Describe briefly the methods employed in liquefying (a) air, (b) hydrogen, and explain the principles involved.　(C.S.)

5. Write a short essay on the liquefaction of gases with special reference to hydrogen and helium.　(C.S.)

6. Describe a method of liquefying hydrogen. How may low temperatures such as that of liquid hydrogen be determined?　(C.S.)

7. Give an account of the liquefaction of gases. Describe the general construction of an apparatus for liquefying hydrogen. Discuss briefly the investigation of one property of matter at low temperatures.　(O.S.)

8. Discuss the physical principles which are applied in the liquefaction of gases. Describe how liquid oxygen can be produced for industrial purposes. Explain the nature of the special difficulties which have been found in liquefying hydrogen and helium and show how they have been overcome.　(J.M.B.)

CHAPTER IX

TRANSFERENCE OF HEAT

THE three principal means by which heat may be transferred from place to place are called **conduction, convection, and radiation.**

Conduction is defined as the transfer of heat through an unequally heated body, without visible motion of any part of the body ; that is, it is the propagation of heat through a material, which itself remains stationary.

Convection is the motion of heated material, which carries its heat with it.

Radiation is the transference of heat from a hot body to a cold body without appreciable heating of the intervening space.

Evaporation of a liquid and condensation of its vapour will transfer heat from a hot liquid to a cold surface ; this, and one or two other similar operations can really, by stretching the definition a little, be classed as particular types of convection.

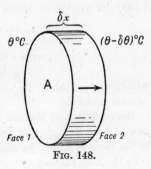

FIG. 148.

Conduction. Coefficient of thermal conductivity. Consider a thin parallel-sided slab of material (Fig. 148) of thickness δx, and area A, with one face (1) maintained steadily at temperature $\theta°$, and the other face (2) at $(\theta - \delta\theta)°$. In this steady state, heat flows at a steady rate from face 1 to face 2, in a direction normal (that is, at right angles) to the faces. Experiments have shown that, under these conditions, the rate of flow of heat is :

> proportional to the area A,
> proportional to the temperature *fall* $- \delta\theta$, and
> inversely proportional to the thickness δx.

$$\therefore \text{ Rate of flow of heat} \propto A \frac{-\delta\theta}{\delta x};$$

or, $$\text{rate of flow of heat} = kA \cdot \frac{-\delta\theta}{\delta x},$$

where k is a constant for the material called its **coefficient of thermal conductivity.**

The ratio $\dfrac{-\delta\theta}{\delta x}$ is the temperature gradient across the slab; and, if δx is very small indeed, can be written $-\dfrac{d\theta}{dx}$.

Similarly, if we write δQ for the quantity of heat passing in time δt, the rate of flow of heat is $\dfrac{\delta Q}{\delta t}$, or $\dfrac{dQ}{dt}$ in the limit when δt is extremely small.

Hence, $$\frac{dQ}{dt} = -kA\frac{d\theta}{dx}.$$

This equation can be stated in words as follows : "When heat is flowing normally between the faces of a thin parallel-sided slab of material, and a steady state has been reached, the rate of flow of heat equals the product of coefficient of thermal conductivity, area of slab, and temperature gradient."

Since $$k = \frac{dQ}{dt} \Big/ -A\frac{d\theta}{dx},$$

k may be written in words as

$$k = \frac{\substack{\text{rate of flow of heat in steady state} \\ \text{normal to the faces of a parallel-sided slab}}}{\text{area} \times \text{temperature gradient}};$$

while, if $A = 1$ and $-\dfrac{d\theta}{dx} = 1$, $k = \dfrac{dQ}{dt}$, and the most satisfactory definition of k is :

The coefficient of thermal conductivity, k, of a material is the rate of flow of heat through unit area under unit temperature gradient, normal to the faces of a thin parallel-sided slab of the material, when a steady state has been reached.

The qualifying statements are important, since other considerations affect the rate of flow of heat if they are not fulfilled, as is shown later.

Temperature distribution down a bar of uniform cross-section in the steady state. Consider a long cylindrical bar of uniform cross-sectional area A, the ends of which are maintained steadily at temperatures θ_1 and θ_2, θ_1 being the greater.

First, suppose that no heat escapes from the sides of the bar. This assumes that the sides lose no heat by radiation, and that they

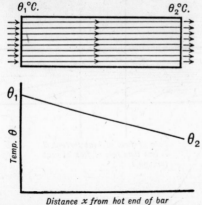

FIG. 149.—Steady heat-flow and temperature distribution for
cylinder losing no heat from side.

are perfectly insulated against loss by conduction and convection,
conditions which are·impossible of fulfilment. If, however, the bar
is made of a very good conductor, the proportion of heat escaping
from the sides is small compared with that passing down the bar ;
while if the radius of the bar, r, is large (as the ratio *surface
area/cross-section*, which is $2\pi r l/\pi r^2$, is proportional to $1/r$) the
proportion of heat escaping from the sides is also reduced. So, for
a *thick bar of a very good conductor* it can be assumed as an approximation that no heat is lost from the sides.

Thus, for a thick bar of a very good conductor the rate of flow of
heat is the same all along the bar. But, for any thin section at
distance x from the hot end, $\dfrac{dQ}{dt} = -kA\dfrac{d\theta}{dx}$; the area A and the
value of k are the same for all values of x. Hence, assuming that k
is independent of the temperature, $d\theta/dx$ is the same for all values
of x. That is, the temperature gradient is the same throughout the
length of a thick bar of a very good conductor, the way in which θ
varies with the distance x being shown in Fig. 149.

If the above conditions are not satisfied and there is an appreciable
escape of heat from the sides, it is easily seen that, as the rate of
flow of heat through a section at distance x decreases as x increases,
then, since k and A are constant, the temperature gradient must
decrease as x increases, as shown in Fig. 150.

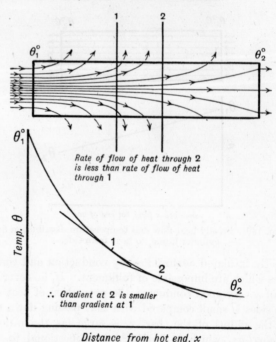

Rate of flow of heat through 2
is less than rate of flow of heat
through 1

∴ Gradient at 2 is smaller
than gradient at 1

Distance from hot end, x

Fig. 150.—Steady heat-flow and temperature distribution for
cylinder losing heat from side.

The calculation of the temperature distribution in the second case
is difficult, but is manageable if certain assumptions are made.
Suppose that the rate of loss of heat at any point is proportional to
the temperature excess at that point, Newton's Law of Cooling being
obeyed. To simplify the notation, let θ stand for the *temperature
excess* above the steady temperature of the surroundings. The
temperature gradient is still properly represented by $d\theta/dx$. Let E
be the heat emitted per sq. cm. per sec. per unit temperature
difference; E is called the *emissivity* of the surface. Let the peri-
meter of the bar be p.

Consider a section of thickness δx lying at distance x from the
hot end of the bar; let the average temperature excess be θ for this
section. Then,

(*rate at which heat flows into face* 1) − (*rate at which heat flows out of
face* 2) = (*rate at which heat is lost from the side*).

Let the temperature gradients at face 1 and face 2 be $\left(\dfrac{d\theta}{dx}\right)_1$ and $\left(\dfrac{d\theta}{dx}\right)_2$.

Rate of flow of heat into 1 $\quad = -kA\left(\dfrac{d\theta}{dx}\right)_1$.

Rate of flow of heat out of 2 $= -kA\left(\dfrac{d\theta}{dx}\right)_2$.

Rate of emission from edge $\quad = E \cdot p\,\delta x \cdot \theta$.

$$\therefore\ -kA\left[\left(\dfrac{d\theta}{dx}\right)_1 - \left(\dfrac{d\theta}{dx}\right)_2\right] = Ep\theta\,\delta x,$$

or,
$$\dfrac{\left(\dfrac{d\theta}{dx}\right)_2 - \left(\dfrac{d\theta}{dx}\right)_1}{\delta x} = \dfrac{Ep}{kA}\,\theta.$$

Now, $\left\{\left(\dfrac{d\theta}{dx}\right)_2 - \left(\dfrac{d\theta}{dx}\right)_1\right\} \Big/ \delta x$ is the change in $\dfrac{d\theta}{dx}$ in going from face 1 to face 2, and this can be written $\delta\left(\dfrac{d\theta}{dx}\right)\Big/ \delta x$, or, in the limit, when δx is extremely small, $\dfrac{d}{dx}\left(\dfrac{d\theta}{dx}\right)$, or $\dfrac{d^2\theta}{dx^2}$.

Writing $\dfrac{d^2\theta}{dx^2}$ for $\dfrac{\left(\dfrac{d\theta}{dx}\right)_2 - \left(\dfrac{d\theta}{dx}\right)_1}{\delta x}$, the equation becomes

$$\dfrac{d^2\theta}{dx^2} = \dfrac{Ep}{kA}\,\theta\ ;\quad \text{and putting}\quad \dfrac{Ep}{kA} = \mu^2,\quad \dfrac{d^2\theta}{dx^2} = \mu^2\theta.$$

This is a differential equation, the solution of which must involve two arbitrary constants.

Let the solution be $\theta = ae^{\mu x} + be^{-\mu x}$, where a and b are constants.

Differentiating, $\qquad \dfrac{d\theta}{dx} = \mu ae^{\mu x} - \mu be^{-\mu x}$,

and again, $\dfrac{d^2\theta}{dx^2} = \mu^2 ae^{\mu x} + \mu^2 be^{-\mu x} = \mu^2(ae^{\mu x} + be^{-\mu x}) = \mu^2\theta$.

Hence $\theta = ae^{\mu x} + be^{-\mu x}$ is a solution satisfying the equation, and a and b are constants determined by the particular case.

Suppose at first that the bar is infinitely long. Then, when $x = 0$, $e^{\mu x} = 1$ and $e^{-\mu x} = 1$, while $\theta = \theta_0$, the temperature *excess* at the heated end.

So $\qquad\qquad\qquad\qquad\qquad \theta_0 = a + b$.

Now, if $\theta = 0$ when $x = \infty$ the right-hand side of the equation must be infinite unless $a = 0$. So $\theta_0 = b$, and the solution is $\theta = \theta_0 e^{-\mu x}$.

The graph of *temperature excess* θ against x is as Fig. 151.

If the bar is not considered infinitely long, suppose that the length is L, and that the far face is at the temperature of the surroundings, so that no heat flows out through the end face, and the temperature gradient at the end is zero.

Then $\dfrac{d\theta}{dx} = 0$ when $x = L$.

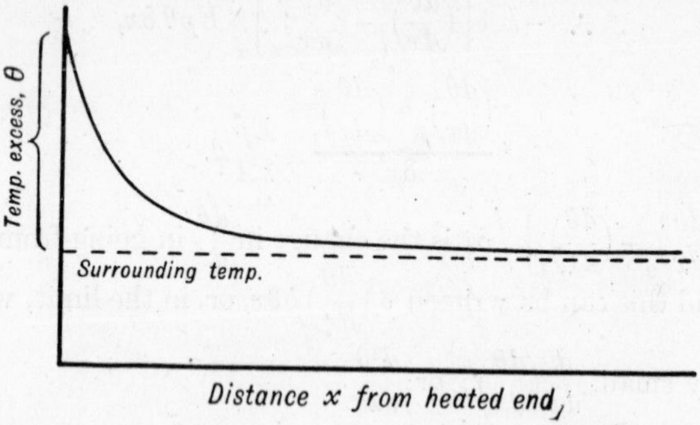

FIG. 151.—Steady distribution of temperature *excess* down bar losing heat from the sides.

Now $\dfrac{d\theta}{dx} = \mu(ae^{\mu x} - be^{-\mu x})$, so if $\dfrac{d\theta}{dx} = 0$ when $x = L$,

$ae^{\mu L} - be^{-\mu L} = 0$ and solving these two equations for a and b.

As before, $\theta_0 = a + b$,

$$a = \frac{\theta_0}{1 + e^{2\mu L}}, \quad b = \frac{\theta_0}{1 + e^{-2\mu L}},$$

and

$$\theta = \theta_0 \left[\frac{e^{\mu x}}{1 + e^{2\mu L}} + \frac{e^{-\mu x}}{1 + e^{-2\mu L}} \right].$$

DETERMINATION OF CONDUCTIVITY

Ingen-Hausz' experiment to compare the conductivities of different materials. The materials to be compared are in the form of long thin rods of equal length, identical in area of cross-section and in surface finish. These are coated with wax, and arranged as in Fig. 152, with one end protruding into a tank A in which water is maintained at the boiling point.

After a steady state has been
reached, the wax is observed to
have melted to distances l_1, l_2,
l_3, ... along the bars 1, 2, 3, ...
of thermal conductivities, k_1, k_2,
k_3 ... .

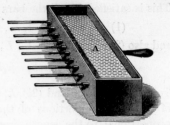

Suppose that the bars are
extremely long compared with
their diameter. Then the equation   FIG. 152.—Ingen-Hausz' experiment.
for the temperature excess at dis-
tance x down each is $\theta = \theta_0 e^{-\mu x}$, where θ_0 is the value of θ for the
tank, and μ stands, as on p. 331, for the factor $\sqrt{Ep/kA}$ for each bar.

Let θ_m be the value of θ for the melting point of wax, the temperature attained when $x = l_1$ for bar 1, $x = l_2$ for bar 2, and $x = l_3$ for bar 3.

For the first bar, $\theta_m = \theta_0 e^{-\mu_1 l_1}$;

for the second, $\theta_m = \theta_0 e^{-\mu_2 l_2}$;

for the third, $\theta_m = \theta_0 e^{-\mu_3 l_3}$; and so on.

Hence, $\mu_1 l_1 = \mu_2 l_2 = \mu_3 l_3$.

But $\mu_1 = \sqrt{\dfrac{Ep}{k_1 A}}$, $\mu_2 = \sqrt{\dfrac{Ep}{k_2 A}}$, $\mu_3 = \sqrt{\dfrac{Ep}{k_3 A}}$ ... ,

E, p, and A being the same for all the bars.

Hence, $\dfrac{l_1}{\sqrt{k_1}} = \dfrac{l_2}{\sqrt{k_2}} = \dfrac{l_3}{\sqrt{k_3}}$ ... .

or $\dfrac{k_1}{l_1{}^2} = \dfrac{k_2}{l_2{}^2} = \dfrac{k_3}{l_3{}^2}$ ... ,

or $k_1 : k_2 : k_3 ... = l_1{}^2 : l_2{}^2 : l_3{}^2 ...$.

This theory would be quite satisfactory for extremely long bars ;
in practice, rods up to about 20 cm. long, with diameters of a few
mm., are used, so it cannot apply to the usual apparatus. Ashford,
(*School Science Review*, vol. 21, p. 83) gives the correct treatment.
If l be the distance at which the temperature excess is θ_m, and L
the exposed length, then the proper equation gives

$$\theta_m = \theta_0 \left[\frac{e^{\mu l}}{1 + e^{2\mu L}} + \frac{e^{-\mu l}}{1 + e^{-2\mu L}} \right].$$

This is satisfied for all the bars if, and only if,

(1) $\mu_1 l_1 = \mu_2 l_2 = \mu_3 l_3 \dots$, or $k_1/l_1^2 = k_2/l_2^2 = k_3/l_3^2 \dots$, as above; and also (2) *either* (a) $L_1 \quad L_2, L_3 \dots$ are infinite

or (b) $\mu_1 L_1 = \mu_2 L_2 = \mu_3 L_3 \dots$, or $\dfrac{k_1}{L_1^2} = \dfrac{k_2}{L_2^2} = \dfrac{k_3}{L_3^2} \dots$.

To satisfy both (1) and (2b), $L_1/l_1 = L_2/l_2 = L_3/l_3 \dots$, thus the lengths of the exposed portions of the bars must be *adjusted* so as to be proportional to the length from which the wax has melted; then the conclusion reached above is strictly applicable, provided the temperature gradient at distance L is negligibly small.

Searle's method for the conductivity of a very good conductor. The absolute determination of k requires three sets of measurements, corresponding to rate of flow of heat, area, and temperature gradient for a thin parallel-sided slab.

For a thick bar of a very good conductor, such as copper, the ends of which are maintained steadily at different temperatures, the temperature gradient is the same throughout. It is therefore possible to measure the temperature gradient at one part of the bar, and the rate of flow of heat at another.

The specimen is a thick bar of copper about 5 cm. in diameter, polished, surrounded by dry felt, and enclosed in a wooden box. Steam circulating through a chamber attached to one end of the bar

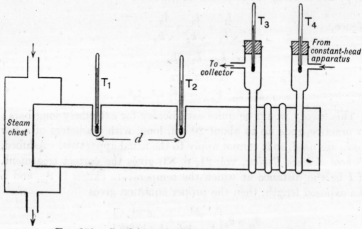

FIG. 153.—Searle's method for conductivity of copper.

maintains this at 100° C. A current of water running from a constant head apparatus through a copper spiral soldered on the other end maintains this end at a steady low temperature, and also enables the rate of flow of heat through the bar to be measured. Thermometers T_1 and T_2 are placed in holes in the bar at a known distance d apart, the holes containing mercury to ensure good thermal contact. Two more thermometers T_4 and T_3 record the inlet and outlet temperatures of the flowing water. Fig. 153 illustrates the apparatus.

The diameter D of the bar is measured with calipers in several places, the value of the area $\pi D^2/4$ calculated in each case, and the average taken. The distance d between the centres of the holes in which the thermometers rest is also taken. The currents of cold water and steam are started, and the apparatus left to attain a steady state. When the readings (θ_1, θ_2, etc.) of all four thermometers are steady, these are observed, and the water flowing through the copper tube in time t seconds is collected and its mass m found. If s be the mean specific heat of water between $\theta_3°$ and $\theta_4°$, the heat supplied in t sec. to this water is $ms(\theta_3 - \theta_4)$ cal., and the rate of supplying heat is $ms(\theta_3 - \theta_4)/t$ cal. per sec.
This is the rate of flow of heat down the bar.

The uniform temperature gradient is $\dfrac{\theta_1 - \theta_2}{d}$ °C./cm.

Hence, as the area, rate of flow of heat, and temperature gradient are all known, k is calculated by substituting in the expression

$$k = \frac{\text{rate of flow of heat}}{\text{area} \times \text{temp. gradient}}.$$

Guard-ring method. The principle of this method, which is applicable to substances which can be classified properly neither as very good or very bad conductors, is indicated in Fig. 154. The material, in the form of a thick slab with parallel faces, has two holes bored for thermometers at a measured distance apart. One face of the slab is steam heated, and the other is in contact with an ice calorimeter. The flow-lines of heat are indicated in the figure; it can be seen that in the centre of the slab these are practically parallel from one face to the other. Thus, if the rate of flow of heat through a known area of the central part of the slab can be found in the steady state, and the uniform temperature gradient along the central part found, k can be determined accurately.

A large part of one wall is maintained at 100° C. by a steam chest ; the central part of this is isolated so that the steam condensing in it, and thus the rate of flow of heat into the central portion, can be found, while the rest acts as a " guard ring ". A corresponding central portion of the ice calorimeter is isolated, so that from the mass of ice melted the rate of flow of heat out of the central portion is found ; the rest of the ice chamber acts as a guard ring. By isolating the centre part, through which the heat flows under the simplest conditions, the simple formula of p. 328 may be used for calculating k. The temperature gradient is $(\theta_1 - \theta_2)/d'$, where $\theta°_1$ and $\theta°_2$ are the readings of the thermometers T_1 and T_2.

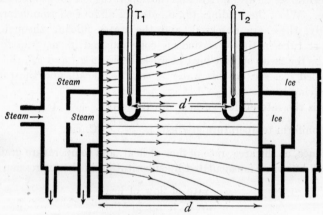

Fig. 154.—Illustrating " guard-ring " method.

The temperature gradient is measured from observations of thermometers within the specimen, with their bulbs in the central flow region. It is not safe to assume that the temperature gradient is $100° - 0°/d$, since there is a film of water on each face of the slab across which there may be an appreciable temperature drop.

The method is quite general in its application. The steady heat supply may be furnished electrically, in which case the heater coil, of which the rate of supply of heat is measured, would be surrounded by a guard-ring heater coil maintained at the same temperature.

It has been stated above that the method is best applied to

materials of the " poor conductor " class. The use of a guard-ring of course adds precision to any determination of k for any kind of conductor. But with a very good conductor, as in Searle's method, side losses can usually be ignored for a specimen of suitable dimensions, while for a very bad conductor it is usually necessary, in order to obtain a substantial rate of flow heat, to have a specimen in the form of a thin slab of large surface area, for which the edge loss is relatively small on account of the small exposed edge area.

Lees' method for the conductivity of a very bad conductor. The apparatus (Fig. 155) consists of a cylindrical steam chest B, the bottom of which is a thick brass block, with a hole bored to receive a thermometer T_1. The specimen S, in the form of a thin circular disc, is sandwiched between the block and a second cylindrical brass block C, in which there is a second thermometer T_2. The block C is suspended from a fixed support by threads shown in the diagram. The only way in which heat can reach C is thus by conduction downwards through the specimen.

The diameter, and the thickness d of the specimen are first measured. The apparatus is then set up, and steam is passed into the chest until the readings θ_1 and θ_2 of T_1 and T_2 are steady. As brass is an extremely good conductor, the thermometers can be taken as recording the temperatures of the faces of the specimen. Thus the temperature gradient in the steady state is $(\theta_1 - \theta_2)/d$.

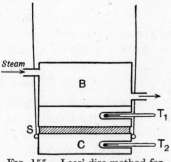

FIG. 155.—Lees' disc method for bad conductor.

Next, the rate of flow of heat through the specimen is found in the following way. The temperature of C is steady ; it is therefore losing heat to the surroundings from its side and base at exactly the same rate as it is receiving heat by conduction through the slab. Thus, the rate of loss of heat from C at temperature $\theta_2°$ equals the rate of flow of heat downwards through the specimen.

The mass m of the block C is found, and the specific heat s of brass obtained from a set of tables. The block is then heated gently by a bunsen burner, and raised to a temperature $\theta_3°$ a few degrees above $\theta_2°$; the specimen alone is placed on top of C, and the time t sec. taken for the temperature to fall to $\theta_4°$, which is as far below $\theta_2°$ as $\theta_3°$ was above it, is found. The average rate of loss of heat over this interval is then $ms(\theta_3 - \theta_4)/t$ calories per second; this is the required rate of flow through the specimen in the steady state.

It is, of course, impossible to reproduce completely during the second part of the experiment the steady-state conditions of the first part. It is usually suggested that the specimen should be retained on the top of C. Another procedure, recommended in Bedford's "Practical Physics", is to allow C to cool uncovered; if S be the area of the curved sides of C, as the area exposed in the second part is $2A + S$ compared with $A + S$ exposed in the first part, the rate of flow through the specimen in the first part is equal to the rate of loss from an area $\dfrac{A + S}{2A + S}$ of that exposed in the second part, whence the rate of flow is then

$$\frac{A + S}{2A + S} \cdot ms \frac{\theta_3 - \theta_4}{t}.$$

The area, rate of flow of heat, and temperature gradient all being known, k is calculated by substituting in the expression :

$$k = \frac{\text{rate of flow of heat}}{\text{area} \times \text{temp. gradient}}.$$

It is assumed that no heat is lost from the curved edges of the specimen in the steady state, so the specimen must be thin. It follows that with this form of apparatus only very bad conductors can be used, since with a thin slice of a moderate conductor the temperature difference would be too small to measure accurately.

The method is used with electric heating, the only modifications being (a) a double sandwich with two slabs of the conductor, and the electric heater mounted in the middle ; and (b) the rate of flow of heat is measured by the rate of dissipation of electrical energy during the steady state, no second part of the experiment being necessary. The whole apparatus is suspended in an evacuated enclosure, and the temperature differences are read by means of thermocouples.

The method can also be adapted to measure k for a liquid, which must of course be retained in position by a solid ring. It is arranged that the heat flows downwards through the liquid, so as to avoid convection effects. A preliminary experiment is done to find the rate of flow of heat through the solid ring, and a second experiment with the ring filled with liquid.

Flow of heat through the walls of a cylindrical tube. Let the internal and external radii be r_1 and r_2, and let the steady temperatures of the inside and the outer side of the tube be $\theta_1°$ and $\theta_2°$, θ_1 being the greater (Fig. 156).

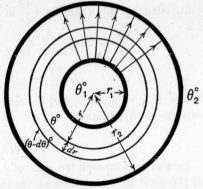

FIG. 156.—Radial heat-flow. The figure can be taken as representing a section across a *cylinder*, or a cross-section of a *spherical shell*.

Let l be the length of the tube.

Consider a thin cylindrical element of radii r and $r + dr$. As this is very thin, and heat flows normally to the faces, this can be regarded as effectively a thin parallel-sided slab, whence

$$\frac{dQ}{dt} = -kA\frac{d\theta}{dr}.$$

As $A = 2\pi rl$, $\therefore \frac{dQ}{dt} = -k \cdot 2\pi rl \cdot \frac{d\theta}{dr} = -2\pi kl \cdot r\frac{d\theta}{dr}.$

Now, as everything is steady, $\frac{dQ}{dt}$ must be the same for all values of r; hence, as k and l are constant, $r\frac{d\theta}{dr}$ must be constant.

Let $\qquad r\frac{d\theta}{dr} = a.$ $\therefore d\theta = a\frac{dr}{r}.$

Integrating, $\theta = a \ln r + b$, where b is a constant.

Now, when $\qquad r = r_1,\ \theta = \theta_1$, and when $r = r_2,\ \theta = \theta_2$,

$$\therefore \theta_1 = a \ln r_1 + b \quad \text{and} \quad \theta_2 = a \ln r_2 + b.$$

$$\therefore \theta_1 - \theta_2 = a(\ln r_1 - \ln r_2).$$

$$\therefore a = \frac{\theta_1 - \theta_2}{\ln r_1 - \ln r_2}.$$

Substituting this value for $r\dfrac{d\theta}{dr}$ in the original equation,

$$\frac{dQ}{dt} = -2\pi kl \frac{\theta_1 - \theta_2}{\ln r_1 - \ln r_2} = 2\pi kl \frac{\theta_1 - \theta_2}{\ln r_2 - \ln r_1}.$$

$$\therefore \frac{dQ}{dt} = k \cdot 2\pi l \frac{\theta_1 - \theta_2}{\ln r_2/r_1}.$$

Hence, if r_1, r_2, θ_1, θ_2, l, and the rate of flow of heat are determined experimentally, k can be found from the expression

$$k = \frac{dQ}{dt} \cdot \frac{\ln r_2/r_1}{2\pi l(\theta_1 - \theta_2)}.$$

Flow of heat through the walls of a spherical shell. Let the inside of the shell be maintained at temperature θ_1, and the outside at temperature θ_2, the internal and external radii being r_1 and r_2. Consider an elementary shell at distance r. The area, A, is $4\pi r^2$, and, as before,

$$\frac{dQ}{dt} = -k \cdot 4\pi r^2 \cdot \frac{d\theta}{dr}.$$

As $\dfrac{dQ}{dt}$ is constant in the steady state, $r^2\dfrac{d\theta}{dr}$ must be constant.

Put $$r^2\frac{d\theta}{dr} = a;\quad \text{then}\quad d\theta = a\frac{dr}{r^2},$$

and, integrating, $\theta = -a/r + b$, where b is a constant.

When $\theta = \theta_1$, then $r = r_1$;

and when $\theta = \theta_2$, then $r = r_2$,

$$\therefore\ \theta_1 = -\frac{a}{r_1} + b.\quad \theta_2 = -\frac{a}{r_2} + b.$$

$$\therefore\ \theta_1 - \theta_2 = a\left(\frac{1}{r_2} - \frac{1}{r_1}\right),$$

and $$a = \frac{\theta_1 - \theta_2}{\dfrac{1}{r_2} - \dfrac{1}{r_1}}.$$

Hence $$\frac{dQ}{dt} = -k \cdot 4\pi \cdot \frac{\theta_1 - \theta_2}{\dfrac{1}{r_2} - \dfrac{1}{r_1}} = 4\pi k \frac{\theta_1 - \theta_2}{\dfrac{1}{r_1} - \dfrac{1}{r_2}}.$$

and the rate of flow of heat is given by

$$\frac{dQ}{dt} = \frac{4\pi k(\theta_1 - \theta_2)r_1 r_2}{r_2 - r_1}.$$

This has been used to determine k for poor conductors. The material is enclosed between two concentric copper shells, the inner of which contains an electric heater. The value of dQ/dt is obtained from the rate of supply of electrical energy in the steady state, where θ_1 and θ_2 at radii r_1 and r_2 are measured by thermocouples.

Determination of thermal conductivity by the tube method. The apparatus is assembled as in Fig. 157. The specimen itself acts as a continuous-flow calorimeter, through which a steady current of water passes from a constant-head supply. Surrounding the specimen is an outer tube through which steam is passed. When a steady state has been reached, the temperatures θ_3 and θ_4 of the thermometers in the inlet and outlet tubes are observed, and the mass m of water flowing through in time t sec. is found.

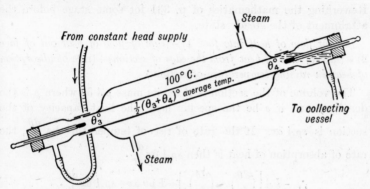

FIG. 157.—Determination of k by tube method.

The rate of flow of heat through the tube, dQ/dt is $m \times 1 \times (\theta_4 - \theta_3)/t$. The average value of θ_3 and θ_4 is taken as the internal temperature θ_1° and the steam temperature, taken as 100° C., is θ_2°. The length l of the part of the tube surrounded by steam is observed. The internal and external radii, r_1 and r_2, of the tube are then measured. This is best done by cutting off a portion of the specimen, and measuring the internal and external diameters with a travelling microscope. The coefficient of thermal conductivity k is then found by substituting in the formula

$$k = \frac{dQ}{dt} \cdot \frac{\ln r_2/r_1}{2\pi l(\theta_2 - \theta_1)},$$

$(\theta_2 - \theta_1)$ being written instead of $(\theta_1 - \theta_2)$, because the heat flows *towards* the axis of the tube instead of *away from* it as on p. 339.

For a thin tube, little error is made by regarding it as a parallel-sided slab which is bent round into a cylinder. For this, the equivalent area is $2\pi \dfrac{r_1 + r_2}{2} . l$, the temperature gradient $\dfrac{\theta_2 - \theta_1}{r_2 - r_1}$, and the formula to be used is

$$k = \frac{dQ}{dt} \cdot \frac{r_2 - r_1}{2\pi \dfrac{r_1 + r_2}{2} l(\theta_2 - \theta_1)},$$

to which the proper formula reduces as an approximation when r_1 is nearly equal to r_2.

Rate of rise of temperature before the steady state is attained. Reworking the mathematics of p. 331 for some stage before the attainment of the steady state,

(*rate of flow of heat into face* 1) $-$ (*rate of flow of heat out of face* 2) $=$ (*rate of loss of heat from the edge of section*) $+$ (*rate of absorption of heat in raising temperature of section.*)

The volume of the section is $A \, \delta x$, its mass $\rho A \, \delta x$ where ρ is the density; and if s be the specific heat, the heat capacity of the section is $s\rho A \, \delta x$. If the rate of rise of temperature be $\dfrac{d\theta}{dt}$, the rate of absorption of heat is then $s\rho A \, \delta x \dfrac{d\theta}{dt}$.

$$\therefore \; -kA \left[\left(\frac{d\theta}{dx} \right)_1 - \left(\frac{d\theta}{dx} \right)_2 \right] = Ep\theta \, \delta x + s\rho A \, \delta x \frac{d\theta}{dt}.$$

So the equation $\dfrac{d^2\theta}{dx^2} = \dfrac{Ep}{kA} \theta$ of p. 331 is amended to

$$\frac{d^2\theta}{dx^2} = \frac{Ep}{kA} \theta + \frac{s\rho}{k} \frac{d\theta}{dt}.$$

If now we assume no emission from the sides,

$$E = 0 \quad \text{and} \quad \frac{d^2\theta}{dx^2} = \frac{s\rho}{k} \cdot \frac{d\theta}{dt},$$

which may be written $\qquad \dfrac{d\theta}{dt} = \dfrac{k}{s\rho} \dfrac{d^2\theta}{dx^2}.$

The quantity $k/s\rho$ is called the **thermometric conductivity** or **diffusivity** of the material. It represents the *change of temperature* produced in *unit volume* of the substance by the quantity of heat which flows in unit time through unit area under unit temperature gradient. It is thus a constant of greater importance than k itself when calculations on the *rate of rise of temperature produced*, rather than the *rate of flow of heat in a steady state*, have to be done.

Conduction through composite walls. Consider two parallel-sided slabs S_1 and S_2 (Fig. 158) of thickness x_1 and x_2, and conductivities k_1 and k_2. When a steady state has been reached, let the temperatures of the outer faces of S_1 and S_2 be θ_1 and θ_2 respectively, and let θ be the temperature of the interface. Let A be the area of cross-section of the slab, and dQ/dt the rate of flow of heat through the composite slab from θ_1 to θ_2.

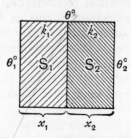

Fig. 158.—Composite walls.

Then
$$\frac{dQ}{dt} = \frac{k_1 A (\theta_1 - \theta)}{x_1} = \frac{k_2 A (\theta - \theta_2)}{x_2}.$$

From these two equations the value of the rate of flow of heat and the temperature of the interface can be found.

We have
$$\frac{k_1 A (\theta_1 - \theta)}{x_1} = \frac{k_2 A (\theta - \theta_2)}{x_2}.$$

$$\therefore \; \theta = \frac{\dfrac{k_1}{x_1} \theta_1 + \dfrac{k_2}{x_2} \theta_2}{\dfrac{k_1}{x_1} + \dfrac{k_2}{x_2}}.$$

Since
$$\theta_1 - \theta = \frac{dQ}{dt} \cdot \frac{x_1}{k_1 A} \quad \text{and} \quad \theta - \theta_2 = \frac{dQ}{dt} \cdot \frac{x_2}{k_2 A}.$$

$$\therefore \; \theta_1 - \theta_2 = \frac{dQ}{dt} \left(\frac{x_1}{k_1 A} + \frac{x_2}{k_2 A} \right),$$

$$\therefore \; \frac{dQ}{dt} = \frac{\theta_1 - \theta_2}{\dfrac{x_1}{k_1 A} + \dfrac{x_2}{k_2 A}}.$$

The same methods enable the interface temperatures and the rate of flow to be found when there are more than two slabs.

Variation of k with temperature for metals. For most pure metals the value of k increases as the temperature rises. The electrical conductivity, σ, also rises with increasing temperature. Wiedemann and Franz stated that the ratio of the thermal and electrical conductivities is the same for all metals at the same temperature; this is known as **Wiedemann and Franz's Law.** Lorenz stated further that the ratio σ/k should be proportional to the absolute temperature T; thus $k/\sigma T$ should have the same value at all temperatures for all metals. Experiments undertaken with the object of testing this relation show that at ordinary temperatures the laws of Wiedemann and Franz and of Lorenz are obeyed, while at low temperatures the value of $k/\sigma T$ falls off.

The numerical value of $k/\sigma T$ can be calculated theoretically, on the supposition that the metal contains free electrons. This ratio is called the **Wiedemann-Franz constant**, and its value is $\dfrac{3R^2}{JN^2e^2}$, where R is the gas constant, N the number of molecules in one mole, and e the value of the charge on an electron. It is thus related to three universal constants. Values of this constant found experimentally agree fairly well with the theory at ordinary temperatures, but the theory fails to predict the fall in the value of $k/\sigma T$ which occurs at low temperatures.

Freezing of a pond. When ice first begins to form on a pond, this is because latent heat from a narrow surface layer at 0° C. is abstracted by the cold air above. The subsequent growth of the ice layer requires that the necessary heat abstraction takes place by conduction through the layer of ice already there. The bulk of the water in the pond is probably at about 4° C.; to form one gram of ice, 4 calories must be removed to obtain water at 0° C., and about 80 calories (L) to freeze this at 0° C. It is not suggested that the water in contact with the lower surface of the ice layer is at 4° C.; the total of about 84 calories is the total heat which must be conducted away somehow for every gram formed at some stage of the proceedings; and the real solution of the problem is of the "composite slab" type, involving the conductivity of the upper layers of water. We shall here consider only the conduction through the ice.

Let ρ gm./c.c. be the density of ice at 0° C., and k c.g.s. units its thermal conductivity. Let the temperature above the ice remain steadily at $-\theta°$ C. At any instant t sec. from the start of freezing, let the thickness of the ice be x cm., and let the thickness increase by a small amount δx in a small further interval of time δt. Consider unit area of the surface. Then, in time δt, volume of ice formed is δx c.c., mass of ice formed is $\rho \, \delta x$ gm., and quantity of heat flowing through the layer above is $L\rho \, \delta x$ cal. So, rate of flow of heat through unit area is $L\rho \dfrac{\delta x}{\delta t}$ cal./sec. The lower surface of the ice is at $0°$ C., and the upper at $-\theta°$ C., so the temperature gradient is $\theta/x°$ C./cm.

As rate of flow of heat through unit area $= k \times$ temperature gradient,

$$L\rho \frac{\delta x}{\delta t} = \frac{k\theta}{x} \, .$$

Thus in the limit, $\qquad \dfrac{dx}{dt} = \dfrac{k}{L\rho} \dfrac{\theta}{x},$

and the rate of thickening of the ice is directly proportional to θ and inversely proportional to the existing thickness x.

Re-arranging and integrating, we have

$$x \, dx = \frac{k\theta}{L\rho} dt, \text{ and } \tfrac{1}{2}x^2 = \frac{k\theta}{L\rho} t,$$

the constant of integration being zero as $x = 0$ when $t = 0$; thus the time to obtain a given thickness is proportional to the square of the thickness, or the thickness attained is proportional to the square root of the time.

Determination of k for a liquid. The effect of convection must be eliminated if the coefficient of thermal conductivity of a liquid is to be measured. This can be done by using a fairly thin horizontal layer of liquid heated from above.

Fig. 159 shows the principle of Lees' apparatus for liquids. The liquid is enclosed in a circular ebonite cell between two copper-plated discs C_1 and C_2; C_3 and C_4 are two more copper discs, separated by an electric heater. Between C_2 and C_3 is a disc of glass of measured thickness and known thermal conductivity. The steady-state temperatures of C_2, C_3 and C_4 are determined by thermo-

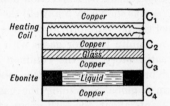

Fig. 159.—Conductivity of a liquid.

couples which are not shown in the figure. The whole apparatus is supported in a constant-temperature enclosure.

As the temperature difference between the faces of the glass plate is known, and also the dimensions and thermal conductivity, the rate of flow of heat into the copper block C_3 is known. Allowance being made for the heat loss from the edge of C_3, the rate of flow of heat through the liquid and ebonite together is calculated. The rate of flow of heat through the ebonite is found by a separate experiment under the same conditions in which the cell contains air, the thermal conductivity of which is known, and the rate of flow of heat through the liquid alone is then obtained. As the rate of flow of heat through the liquid, the area of the cell, the temperature difference between the faces of the liquid, and the depth of the liquid are all determined, the coefficient of thermal conductivity can be calculated.

Conductivity of gases. Gases are very poor conductors, and the determination of k is complicated by the effects of convection and radiation. At ordinary pressures the heat transferred across an enclosure containing a gas is the sum of the heats transferred by (1) conduction, (2) convection and (3) radiation.

The radiation transfer can be estimated by a separate experiment in which the space is highly evacuated, since radiation is the only method operating in a vacuum, and the effect of radiation may be assumed to be the same whether the gas is present or not.

The more difficult problem of convection may be treated in several ways. One way is to arrange that the flow of heat is downwards through a thin horizontal layer of gas, in a manner similar to Lees' method for a liquid. This should eliminate convection entirely. Laby and Hercus employed this method, the layer of gas being about 6 mm. thick. Another way is to use the fact that the transfer by convection depends on the pressure of the gas, while (as was shown by Maxwell) the transfer by conduction is independent of the pressure provided this is not extremely low. This is probably not quite true for gases with many atoms in the molecule, but is satisfactory for the common gases. In the early experiments of Kundt and Warburg, who observed the cooling of a thermometer in a globe containing the gas, it was assumed that at pressures below about one fifth of an atmosphere convection was negligible. The transfer of heat observed at a low pressure was thus supposed due to conduction and radiation only. This is not very accurate, since convection must operate, though to a very limited extent, within the region of reduced pressures at which the conductivity is still constant.

The experiments of Gregory and Archer (1925) disentangled the conduction and convection transfers by an ingenious variation of experimental conditions. These are so instructive that it seems well to describe them in some detail.

The principle of the method is to maintain a temperature gradient between the axis and the walls of a cylindrical tube containing the gas. A wire running along the axis of the tube carries a measured current, and the rate at which energy is supplied to the wire in the steady state equals the rate at which energy is lost from it.

The apparatus is indicated in Fig. 160. Two communicating tubes A and B containing the gas are surrounded by a well-stirred ice bath not shown in the figure. Along the axis of each tube runs a piece of platinum wire, which is connected in one arm of a Callendar and Griffiths bridge. When the bridge is balanced the same current flows through each wire, and the main part of each wire is at the same steady temperature. The cooling at the ends of each wire due to conduction of heat to the leads is the same for both tubes, and so is the loss across the gas from these cooler portions. The diameters of A and B are the same, but B is much shorter than A ; by using the shorter tube B as the " compensating leads " of the bridge, the effect of the cooler end portions is eliminated.

If l_1 is the length of the wire in A and R_1 its resistance, l_2 the length of the wire in B and R_2 its resistance, the bridge really measures the resistance $R_1 - R_2$ (which we will call R) of a wire of length $l_1 - l_2$ (which we will call l), that is, the central portion of A, of which the temperature is uniform. The term " wire ", and the symbols l and R, refer from now on to the main portion of A.

The currents through the arms of the bridge are varied by the rheostat E, and the currents in the wires in A and B are measured using a potentiometer to determine the fall in potential across a standard ohm S in series with each.

Let I be the current in amperes through the wire, θ the steady temperature, r_1 the radius of the wire and r_2 the internal radius of the tube, ϕ the heat loss per second by radiation and ψ the heat loss per second by convection, both from the effective length l of the

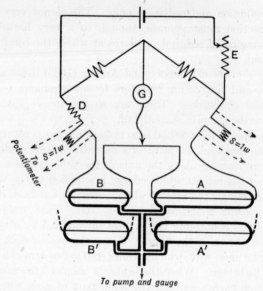

FIG. 160.—Scheme of Gregory and Archer's apparatus. Connections from A' and B' go to a duplicate bridge, which is not shown.

wire at temperature θ. Then, heat supplied electrically per second is I^2R/J' cal.; heat lost by conduction across gas per second is $2\pi kl\theta/\ln r_2/r_1$ cal. (p. 339); heat lost by convection and radiation per second is $\psi + \phi$ cal.; thus

$$I^2R/J' = 2\pi kl\theta/\ln r_2/r_1 + \psi + \phi.$$

The temperature θ was measured by treating the length l of the wire as a platinum resistance thermometer, and was selected by " working backwards "; that is, by placing the galvanometer contact at the required point on the bridge wire and then altering the current through the arms of the bridge until the galvanometer registered zero.

To account for convection, the experiment was repeated with a second pair of wider tubes A' and B', identical in all respects with A and B except that they were both of the same larger radius r_3. These were connected in a duplicate Callendar and Griffiths bridge. The effect of convection for all pressures at which it is appreciable is very much greater in the wide tubes than in the narrow ones,

so that if a pressure can be found
at which the rate of transfer of
heat across the tubes is the same
for both wide and narrow tubes,
it can be concluded that convection has ceased to operate in
both.

If for the moment both ψ and
ϕ are neglected and a value of k
calculated for the narrow tubes
using the expression

$$\frac{I^2R}{J'} = \frac{2\pi kl\theta}{\ln r_2/r_1},$$

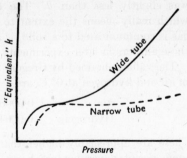

FIG. 161.—Correction for convection
transfer in Gregory and Archer's experiment.

the k obtained is a false value named the "equivalent conductivity"; a corresponding value is obtained with the wide tubes,
using r_3 for r_2. Plotting the value of the equivalent conductivity
against the pressure for both wide and narrow tubes, the two curves
(Fig. 161) are found to coincide over a short range of pressure ; the
value of the equivalent conductivity for which both the wide and
the narrow tubes agree is then the value of the true conductivity
as corrected for convection but not for radiation.

To account for radiation, the experiment is again repeated, this
time with both the wide and narrow tubes highly evacuated and
communicating with tubes containing charcoal immersed in liquid
air to preserve as high a vacuum as possible. Even at this very
low pressure, part of the heat lost from each wire is due to the small
residual conductivity k_r of the gas. If H_N and H_W are the rates of
loss of heat for the narrow and wide tubes respectively, and ϕ the
common radiation transfer for the same temperature θ,

$$H_N = 2\pi k_r \theta / \ln \frac{r_2}{r_1} + \phi$$

and

$$H_W = 2\pi k_r \theta / \ln \frac{r_3}{r_1} + \phi.$$

The radiation transfer ϕ is obtained by eliminating k_r between these
two equations.

Correction had also to be made for the temperature difference
between the inner and outer walls of the glass tube, which meant
that the temperature difference actually maintained across the gas

was slightly less than θ. The question of "accommodation", which really means the extent to which energy conveyed across a gas is communicated to a solid, is a further difficulty considered by these authors in later experiments.

The values obtained by Gregory and Archer for the conductivities of air and hydrogen at 0° C. are :

| Air, | 0·0000583 | c.g.s. units. |
| Hydrogen, | 0·0004043 | c.g.s. units. |

These are appreciably higher than the results of earlier workers ; some recent experimenters have obtained results a little higher still.

Kannuluik and Martin (1934) improved the hot-wire method by using a thick wire (diameter 0·6 mm. to 1·5 mm. in different experiments) along the axis of a vertical metal tube (inside diameter about 2 cm.). The vertical arrangement reduced convection transfer between wire and tube walls ; as the tube was of metal it could be maintained in a constant temperature bath at 0° C., and there was no need to allow for the temperature gradient through the walls of the tube ; while with a thick wire the accommodation uncertainty was reduced. The temperature of the ends of the wires was known exactly, for they were soldered through copper caps at the ends of the tube, and were therefore at the temperature of the bath. The general principle of the method is similar to that of Gregory and Archer. The rate at which heat is supplied electrically to the wire is measured, and the rate of transfer by conduction through the gas found by allowing for the heat lost by conduction along the wire and out through its ends, and also for the effects of convection and radiation. The results obtained for the thermal conductivities of air and hydrogen at 0° C. were :

| Air, | $k = 0·0000576$ | c.g.s. units. |
| Hydrogen, | $k = 0·000413$ | c.g.s. units. |

The conductivity of hydrogen is thus about seven times that of air. Tyndall ("Heat as a Mode of Motion", 1870) describes a beautiful demonstration in which a platinum wire, white hot in a vacuum, is quenched to red heat by admitting air and ceases to glow at all in hydrogen. But he declined to believe that this heat removal could be due to conduction through the gases.

THEORY OF GASEOUS CONDUCTION

The conduction of heat through a gas is a molecular process, the molecules in the hotter regions of the space concerned acquiring greater kinetic energy than those in the cooler parts, and losing this excess of energy by imparting it to the cooler molecules with which they collide. An important factor in this process is the **mean free path**, l, of a molecule, which may be defined as the average distance traversed by a molecule between successive collisions. A value for the mean free path can be calculated approximately as follows.

Let the diameter of a molecule be σ cm. Two molecules collide when their centres come within a distance σ of one another. Let the root-mean-square velocity of the molecules at the temperature considered be $\bar{c}$. Then in one second any chosen molecule travels a distance $\bar{c}$, suppose. The centre of the molecule can be imagined surrounded by a sphere of radius σ; if the centre of another molecule comes within the trajectory of this sphere there is a collision. The volume of the space swept out by this sphere in one second is that of a cylinder of base area $\pi\sigma^2$ sq. cm. and length $\bar{c}$ cm., that is, a volume of $\pi\sigma^2\bar{c}$ c.c. Let n be the number of molecules per c.c. Then the number in volume $\pi\sigma^2\bar{c}$ c.c. is $n\pi\sigma^2\bar{c}$. So our chosen molecule makes $n\pi\sigma^2\bar{c}$ collisions while travelling $\bar{c}$ cm., and the average distance between collisions is $l = \dfrac{1}{n\pi\sigma^2}$ cm. More detailed calculations give the value $l = \dfrac{1}{\sqrt{2}n\pi\sigma^2}$ cm.

The equation for the pressure of a gas given by the kinetic theory (p. 152) becomes, if n denotes the number of molecules *per cubic centimetre*, $p = \frac{1}{3}nm\bar{c}^2$. Thus, at a fixed temperature, p is proportional to n, and as l is inversely proportional to n, l is also inversely proportional to the pressure p. For example, with hydrogen at a pressure of 76 cm., the mean free path is about $1 \cdot 8 \times 10^{-5}$ cm. At a pressure of 1 cm. of mercury it becomes $1 \cdot 4 \times 10^{-3}$ cm., and at a pressure of 10^{-4} cm. of mercury this is 14 cm. Of course, in a container whose linear dimensions are less than 14 cm. this does not mean that a molecule can travel on the average a distance of 14 cm. unimpeded; it does mean that on the average a molecule can travel from one wall of the enclosure to another without the likelihood of a collision on the way, thus

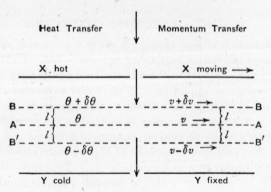

Fig. 162.—Transfer of heat and transfer of momentum across a gas.

the maximum mean free path is attained when the pressure is so low that the calculated mean free path is of the same magnitude as the dimensions of the vessel.

Now consider two parallel plates X and Y, Fig. 162, between which a steady temperature gradient is maintained, the space between being filled with gas. Let m gm. be the mass of each molecule, and C_v the specific heat at constant volume. If the velocities of all the molecules are considered r solved in three directions at right angles, one of these directions being perp ndicular to X and Y, we can consider as before (p. 151) that one-sixth of the total number of molecules is at any instant moving in any given sense along each of these directions. To find the number of molecules crossing unit area of a plane parallel to X and Y per second, imagine a cylinder of height $\bar{c}$ to be erected on this area as base; all the molecules within this cylinder which are moving towards the area will strike it during the succeeding second. The volume of the cylinder is $\bar{c}$ c.c., and the total number of molecules within it is $n\bar{c}$; but of these only one-sixth are moving at right angles to the area and towards it on the average, so the number striking the area per second is $\frac{1}{6}n\bar{c}$.

Consider next unit area of a plane A parallel to X and Y, at temperature θ. In every second $\frac{1}{6}n\bar{c}$ molecules reach this area, having last suffered collision with another molecule (on the average) at the plane B, a distance l away, at which the temperature is $\theta + \delta\theta$. The total mass of the molecules proceeding from the hotter plane B to unit area of A per second is $\frac{1}{6}n\bar{c}m$, and the heat conveyed

($= mass \times specific\ heat \times temperature\ difference$) is $\frac{1}{6}n\bar{c}mC_v\ \delta\theta$ calories per second. Now, downward transfer of heat through the plane A takes place by two processes. The first is by the importation of more energetic molecules from above, and the second is by communicating energy to less energetic molecules arriving from cooler layers below. So an equal transfer of heat in the same direction occurs as the result of $\frac{1}{6}n\bar{c}$ molecules striking unit area of A every second from the plane B', l cm. below, where the temperature is $\theta - \delta\theta$. The total transfer through unit area of A per second, in a downwards direction, is thus $\frac{1}{6}n\bar{c}mC_v\ \delta\theta + \frac{1}{6}n\bar{c}mC_v\ \delta\theta$ or $\frac{1}{3}n\bar{c}mC_v\ \delta\theta$ cal./sec. Now the temperature gradient between B and B' is $\frac{2\ \delta\theta}{2l} = \frac{\delta\theta}{l}$ degrees per centimetre, so the rate of flow of heat through unit area is

$$\tfrac{1}{3}n\bar{c}mC_vl\ \frac{\delta\theta}{l}\ \text{cal./sec.} = (\tfrac{1}{3}n\bar{c}mC_vl \times temperature\ gradient)\ \text{cal./sec.}$$

That is, the coefficient of thermal conductivity of the gas is $k = \frac{1}{3}n\bar{c}mC_vl$.

Providing that the pressure is not so low that the value of l comparable with the dimensions of the vessel, l is inversely proportional to n, and the product nl is independent of the pressure. Thus the coefficient of thermal conductivity of a gas should, except at extremely low pressures, be independent of the pressure. This result was deduced theoretically by Maxwell, and verified to a fair degree of accuracy by the experiments of Kundt and Warburg p. 346) down to 0·1 mm. pressure.

According to the theory, there is a simple relation between the coefficient of thermal conductivity and another important coefficient. If in Fig. 162 we now suppose that the whole is at the same temperature, but that X is moving parallel to itself with a fixed velocity, there will be a force in the direction of the motion of X acting upon Y. Assuming that there is no turbulence of the gas between the plates, there will be a steady velocity gradient across the space XY, the layers of gas near X moving with velocities less than X and these velocities decreasing steadily until Y is reached, when the velocity is zero. The drag experienced by Y is really a molecular effect; the moving plate X gives the molecules in contact with it a momentum parallel to its motion, and this is in part communicated to the plate Y by the molecules striking Y, having been communicated through the successive strata of molecules by molecular collision. By Newton's second law of motion, the rate of transfer of momentum to Y equals the force experienced by this plate. The force per unit area experienced by Y is proportional to the velocity gradient, and the ratio *force per unit area/velocity gradient* is called the coefficient of viscosity of the gas, symbol η.

Consider the plane A, where the velocity is v parallel to the plane itself. The number of molecules arriving at unit area of this plane per second in a direction from above at right angles to A is $\frac{1}{6}n\bar{c}$, and these last suffered collision at B where the velocity is $v + \delta v$, so the downward excess rate of transfer of momentum by means of faster molecules from above is $\frac{1}{6}n\bar{c}m\,\delta v$. But there is also the effect of slower molecules from B', l cm. below, where the velocity is $v - \delta v$; so there is an *upward defect* equivalent to a *downward excess* of a further $\frac{1}{6}n\bar{c}m\,\delta v$. The net rate of change of momentum, which equals the force on the unit area, is thus $\frac{1}{3}n\bar{c}m\,\delta v$. But $\dfrac{\delta v}{l}$ is the velocity gradient, so this force is $\frac{1}{3}n\bar{c}ml \cdot \dfrac{\delta v}{l}$, and the coefficient of viscosity is $\eta = \frac{1}{3}n\bar{c}ml$. Thus, as $k = \frac{1}{3}n\bar{c}mlC_v$, the relation between k and η is $k = \eta C_v$.

Accurate calculations show that this equation is not quite correct, and that the relation between k and η should be $k = a\eta C_v$, where a is a factor which appears to depend on the atomicity of the gas.

APPLICATION OF THE CONDUCTIVITY OF GASES

The katharometer. The conductivity of hydrogen is about seven times as great as that of air under similar conditions, and this has been made the basis of an instrument called the " katharometer " (or purity tester) originally designed by Shakespear and Daynes for detecting the leakage of hydrogen through balloon fabrics.

Two small helices of thin platinum wire, about 0·001 in. in diameter, are enclosed one in each of two cells in a copper block (Fig. 163). Each helix is mounted in a small frame consisting of a loop of copper wire soldered to a ring of copper. One cell is completely closed, and the other communicates to the atmosphere through three small holes ; the helices are maintained in operation at a temperature of about 15° C. above the surroundings, so that the radiation contribution to the heat loss is small, and the small dimensions of each cell reduce convection losses, so that the main heat loss from the wire is by conduction. The two helices are mounted in the adjacent arms of a bridge of the Callendar-Griffiths type.

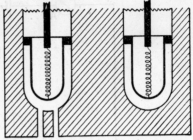

FIG. 163.—Principle of katharometer.

If both helices are surrounded by pure air, the rate of loss of heat from both is the same. But if the apparatus is surrounded by air contaminated by hydrogen, the perforated cell admits this while the other does not, with the result that the helix in the perforated cell loses heat more rapidly than the other, if both are at the same temperature. But the rate at which each wire loses heat must equal the rate of supply when a steady state is attained ; so the temperature of the wire in the open cell falls until at this lower steady state the rate of loss by conduction equals the rate of supply, and the resistance change due to lowered temperature can be measured, and the proportion of hydrogen deduced. It is possible, instead of rebalancing the bridge, to estimate the deflection of the galvanometer, so that the apparatus may be calibrated to give direct readings of the quantity sought. The instrument has a lag of only 15 sec., and it is possible to estimate a proportion of one part of hydrogen in five hundred thousand parts of air.

Flue gas analysis. Though particularly sensitive for the purpose for which it was originally devised, on account of the large conductivity of hydrogen as compared with air, the method can be used for general gas analysis purposes. An important modern application of this principle is the analysis of flue gases in industry. If too little air is supplied to a furnace, all the combustible matter will not be burned, and the gases will contain some carbon monoxide as well as carbon dioxide ; on the other hand, if too much air is supplied, most of the carbon will certainly be turned to carbon dioxide, but valuable heat is wasted in heating up the excess air. There is thus a maximum efficiency which is attained with one fixed air supply ; the degree of efficiency can be estimated from a knowledge of the

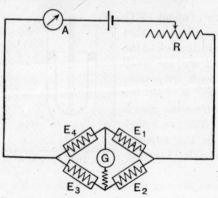

FIG. 164.—Bridge circuit for flue-gas analysis.

percentage of carbon dioxide in the flue gases, together with a knowledge of the flue gas temperature and the percentage of combustible gases. The following section describes the scheme of the Cambridge Instrument Company's flue gas analysis apparatus.

In the electrical carbon dioxide meter, four identical platinum wire spirals are enclosed in separate cells E_1, E_2, E_3, E_4, in a solid metal block, as shown diagrammatically in Fig. 164. Each spiral forms one arm of a Wheatstone bridge circuit. A definite electric current is allowed to flow through the bridge, thereby causing the spirals to become heated and to lose heat to the walls of the cells. If two gases having different thermal conductivities are introduced, one into two of the cells (say E_1 and E_3), and the other gas into the other two cells (E_2 and E_4), the spirals E_1 and E_3 will cool at a different rate from E_2 and E_4, and will therefore be maintained at a different temperature. The consequent difference in the electrical resistance of the spirals will throw the Wheatstone bridge out of balance, causing a deflection of the galvanometer G, the extent of which depends upon the difference in the conductivity of the two gases. The construction is such that changes in the temperature of the metal block affect both sides of the bridge equally. If, therefore, the cells E_2 and E_4 contain a pure gas and the cells E_1 and E_3 the same gas mixed with some other constituent, the extent of the deflection will be an indication of the amount of the second gas present, and the galvanometer can be calibrated to show directly the percentage composition of the mixture.

Since the thermal conductivity of carbon dioxide is only about two-thirds its value for air the method can be used to measure the percentage of carbon dioxide in flue gases. Variations in the proportion of nitrogen and oxygen have very little effect on the readings, as these two gases have practically the same thermal conductivity. The effect of water vapour is compensated by keeping the gases in all the cells saturated. In practice two of the cells are filled with air saturated with water vapour, and the other two are exposed to the gas under test, which is also saturated with water vapour at the same temperature. The difference in conductivity of the gases in the cells then depends solely on the percentage of carbon dioxide in the gas. For measuring the percentage of carbon monoxide and other combustible gases, the flue gases are caused to pass through a small electric furnace where they are completely burnt, and a differential katharometer is used to measure the *increase* in carbon dioxide content, which depends upon the amounts of combustible gases originally present.

A typical carbon dioxide measuring outfit consists of an intake pipe and soot filter for sampling the flue gases, connected by a pipeline to the metering unit, which comprises the carbon dioxide meter proper, a bubbler for washing and saturating the gas and an aspirator for drawing the gas sample from the flue. The metering unit is connected electrically to an indicator or recorder and also to a source of electric current.

The katharometer in the liquid air industry. Large quantities of liquid air are now produced commercially in order to provide oxygen of a high degree of purity, which is extensively used in industrial processes and for medical purposes. Other constituents of liquid air are also used in industry. In addition to being largely used in connection with the manufacture of synthetic ammonia and calcium cyanamide, nitrogen is required as an inert gas for other purposes. Argon and nitrogen-argon mixtures are employed as fillings for lamps and rectifying valves, while helium and neon are used in connection with illuminating signs and in various other forms of lighting.

The thermal conductivity method of gas analysis may be readily applied to the final commercial products and also at various intermediate stages in their production. It is primarily important to measure accurately the purity of the oxygen derived from the liquid air when it is to be used in welding and cutting metals, as small traces, say a few tenths of one per cent., of impurity (chiefly argon) seriously affect the efficiency of the cutting process. The gases issuing from the generator or compressor are cleaned by passing through a filter and, if need be, dried by passage over a desiccating agent, and measurements are then taken with a standard meter using dry air as the comparison gas. The usual range is 95–100 per cent. of oxygen. If the gas is slightly above atmospheric pressure it is caused to flow over the meter at a rate of about 100 c.c. per minute, the rate being controlled by a throttle valve ; if the gas is at, or below, atmospheric pressure, or if it is impossible to obtain a steady flow, it is necessary to draw it from a vessel of large volume by means of an aspirator. A similar method may be used to measure the percentage of oxygen in enriched air. Compensation has to be made for the average proportion of argon in the oxygen, and, if the purity of the oxygen is not constant, suitable corrections have to be applied to the scale reading.

In the nitrogen obtained from liquid air, the only appreciable impurity is oxygen, and, if the nitrogen is to be used as an inert gas or in the production of cyanamide, this impurity should be kept at a low value. It may be measured by causing the oxygen to combine completely with hydrogen added for this purpose, and measuring the loss of hydrogen due to the combustion.

In argon used for commercial purposes, oxygen is usually regarded as the objectionable impurity ; lamp manufacturers sometimes consider a high proportion of nitrogen to be an advantage. The ratio of oxygen to nitrogen in the impurity does not seriously affect the analysis for argon, since the difference in the thermal conductivities of oxygen and nitrogen is small as compared with the difference between the thermal conductivities of these gases and argon. The analysis may be made with an unsymmetrical meter using dry air as the comparison gas. The meter is balanced so as to be independent of current at about the mean argon reading ; the normal range is 80–100 per cent. argon. The thermal conductivity method may also be applied to various intermediate processes in the production of argon. A mixture of helium and neon is obtained which is practically free from other gases, and the percentage of helium or of neon may be measured with an unsymmetrical meter, dry air being used as the comparison gas.

Pirani pressure gauge. At pressures below about 1 mm. of mercury, the product nl (p. 353) is no longer independent of the pressure, because l cannot increase beyond the dimensions of the apparatus. The formula $k = \frac{1}{3}n\bar{c}mC_v l$ shows that, if l is constant, k is proportional to n; or, the conductivity is proportional to the pressure, in this very low pressure region. The Pirani pressure gauge, for use in the region of from 1·0 to 0·0001 mm. of mercury, measures the rate of loss of heat from a filament carrying a current, the measurement being made in the same general way as with the katharometer. Its advantage over the McLeod gauge is that it can be used to indicate and record rapid fluctuations of pressure.

THERMAL INSULATION

One of the chief problems in every-day life is the *prevention* of the transference of heat. There are four main purposes requiring good heat insulators. These are (a) refrigeration and cold storage, (b) building construction, (c) the lagging of steam pipes, and (d) the insulation of furnaces.

The following table, taken from a paper by Ezer Griffiths in the *Journal of Scientific Instruments* (April, 1938) gives a list of some of the more important modern heat insulating materials.

Purpose	Material	Thermal conductivity in British units
Refrigeration	Granulated cork Slag wool Aluminium foil Expanded ebonite	0·29 0·30 0·29 0·28
Building	Light-weight aerated concretes, density 40–100 lb./cu. ft.	1·1–2·8
Steam pipe lagging	Magnesia Asbestos	0·39–0·91 0·36–0·89
Furnace insulation	Diatomaceous brick, density about 30 lb. per cu. ft.	0·6–1·5

The conductivities are expressed in B.Th.U. per hour per square foot per degree Fahrenheit difference per inch thickness (that is, dQ/dt is in B.Th.U. per hour, A in square feet, and $d\theta/dx$ in Fahrenheit degrees per inch). These figures should be divided by 2903 to bring them to the values in c.g.s. units; the student should deduce this relation for himself. It will be found that for refrigerating materials, the value of k in c.g.s. units is about 0·0001, while for building materials k is about 0·0003–0·001. These figures should be compared with those for the conduction across still air, which gives $k = 0·00006$ c.g.s. units (radiation and convection effects eliminated), and with a " vacuum " in which a pressure of 10 mm. of mercury is maintained between silvered faces, for which the equivalent k is 0·000002 c.g.s. units.

In many of the materials listed in the table the effective insulating substance is still air, enclosed in small pockets in the porous material: for example, the light-weight concretes (less dense than water!) are effectively bubbles blown with cement instead of soap solution. The use of aluminium, itself one of the best conductors, for thermal insulation seems surprising; but it is used in the form of very thin foil, which is crumpled up so as to form a large number of very small pockets containing still air. The polished surface prevents radiation across the pockets, and their small size helps in minimising convection in the individual pockets. Aluminium foil is marketed under the trade name of " Alfol "; this material weighs only 3 oz. per cub. ft.; it is used in refrigerated lorries and railway vans.

The vacuum flask. Dewar first used double-walled glass vessels with an evacuated space between the walls for the collection and storage of liquid air. Heat cannot pass across the evacuated space by either conduction or convection, since both of these require a material medium.

In modern "Thermos" flasks, the surfaces facing the evacuated space are silvered. When a hot liquid is placed in the flask, radiation from the hot inner wall to the evacuated space is reduced by the silvering, while the silvered outer wall is a poor absorber; hence transference of heat across the space by radiation is also reduced. The same considerations apply to the entry of heat from the surroundings when the flask contains a cold liquid. If the flask contains a hot liquid, it is usually stoppered to prevent loss of heat by evaporation.

Fig. 165.—Effect of radiation in heat transfer across " Thermos " flasks.

All the vessels contain liquid air. Of the two right-hand vessels evacuated to the same pressure, one is clear and the other has a polished aluminium screen in the vacuum space. Abstraction of heat from the surroundings is shown by the condensation of atmospheric moisture, much reduced when radiation is prevented. The single vessel at the left, silvered on the left half only, shows the same effect.

Reproduced from the Science Museum Handbook, " Very Low Temperatures ", by permission of the Controller of H. M. Stationery Office.

The chief heat transfer which occurs is due to conduction along the material of the walls of the neck—up the inside, round the top to the outside. This is reduced by making the neck long, or by only partially filling the vessel. There is no particular reason why the flask should be made of glass, since by making the walls thinner and the neck longer this exchange by conduction could be made just as small for a metal flask. Modern vacuum flasks for storing liquid air are in fact made of copper or steel, with very long necks ; these are very much more robust than glass flasks. The space between the two walls contains a little charcoal, fastened to the inner wall by wire gauze. This charcoal pocket can just be seen in

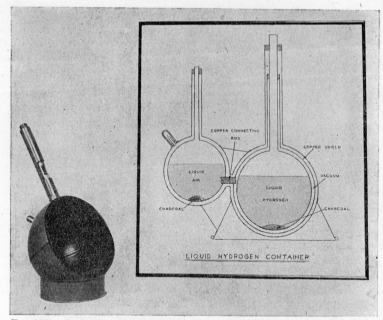

Fig. 166.—A metal vacuum flask in section, and a diagram of Kapitza's double flask for storing liquid hydrogen.

Reproduced from the Science Museum Handbook, " Very Low Temperatures ", by permission of the Controller of H. M. Stationery Office.

the photograph of a sectioned metal flask in Fig. 166. Although it is not clearly shown in the illustration, the charcoal is thus exposed in the space between the walls of the vessels, and *not* to the liquid inside the flask. As charcoal adsorbs gas very efficiently at liquid air temperatures, a very high vacuum is maintained in the space between the walls just when it is most needed.

Kapitza devised a double Dewar vessel for storing liquid hydrogen. Inside the vacuum space of the hydrogen vessel, but not in contact with the walls, was a copper sheath ; this was connected to a bar of copper which, emerging through the side of the outer wall through a suitable seal, had the other end immersed in a second vacuum flask containing liquid air. By this means, the temperature difference against which the hydrogen had to be protected was only about 60 degrees, instead of something of the order of 280 centigrade degrees. The diagram in Fig. 166 gives an idea of the construction of the flask.

CONVECTION

Convection is the transference of heat by a heated material which moves, carrying its heat with it. It can take place only in fluids. *Free or natural convection* always takes place vertically, usually carrying heat upwards (water below 4° C. is a rare exception), and free circulation is necessary for its continuance.

The transfer of heat by free convection can be explained in a general way fairly satisfactorily. Consider the case of a hot body cooling in air. Heat flows from the surface of the body into the adjacent layer of air. The rate of flow of heat per unit area depends on the temperature difference between the body and the air, and upon the *thermal conductivity* of the air.

The rise in temperature produced in this layer of air depends on the specific heat under these conditions.

The change in density resulting from this rise in temperature depends on the *volume coefficient* of the air.

The Archimedes Principle (net) upthrust on this layer of air depends on the change in density.

The upward force on this layer of air accelerates it until it moves at such a speed that the viscous resistance to its motion equals the net upthrust. The *viscosity* is thus involved.

As heated air rises from the surface of the body, a fresh layer of cold air moves up to take its place, thus the cooling continues.

When it comes to the derivation of theoretical formulae, the treatment of the problem by any ordinary means is forbiddingly difficult. Relations between the rate of loss of heat and the various physical constants listed above have been derived by the method of dimensions. In *forced convection* a steady stream of fluid is sent past the hot body by external means, and the problem is a little simpler.

Empirical laws of cooling in air, or other gas. When a heated body is allowed to cool in the air, all three methods of heat transference are of course in operation. But the air is an extremely poor conductor of heat, and radiation is chiefly important for large temperature excesses, so that the chief means by which heat is lost at moderate temperatures under ordinary conditions is by convection.

Still-air cooling is natural convection ; ventilated cooling in a draught is forced convection. For ventilated cooling, in a constant current of air, Newton's Law of cooling is satisfactory for *all* temperature excesses. That is, *for ventilated cooling in a draught, the rate of loss of heat is proportional to the temperature difference between the body and the surroundings.*

In the usual symbols, Newton's Law of cooling is written

$$-\frac{dQ}{dt} = k(\theta - \theta_0).$$

For temperature excesses greater than a few centigrade degrees, the formula is appreciably inaccurate in still air, as might be expected. But in a rapidly moving current of gas it holds up to high temperature excesses, for example, for a motor-cycle cylinder.

The admirable experiments of Dulong and Petit, described in full in Preston's "Theory of Heat", pp. 502-512, and there commended as "one of the most elaborate series of experiments ever conducted" resulted in satisfactory empirical formulae for cooling which take into account both radiation and convection in a still enclosed volume of gas. Their method was to observe the rate of cooling of a thermometer exposed under various conditions, in a large copper globe surrounded by a bath at a known fixed temperature.

First, a set of experiments was done with the globe evacuated. The rate of fall of temperature was then due to radiation alone. The formula found was

$$V_1 = k(a^\theta - a^{\theta_0}),$$

where V_1 is the rate of fall of temperature, k a constant, which depended on the nature of the surface, a a constant (the same for all surfaces), and θ and θ_0 the temperature of the thermometer and that of the enclosure.

Next, a series of experiments was done with different gases at different pressures in the globe. Allowance was made for the cooling due to radiation, which should be the same at a given temperature, whether the space is a vacuum or whether it contains gas. When this allowance was made, the formula deduced for convection alone was

$$V_2 = mp^c(\theta - \theta_0)^{1\cdot233},$$

where p is the pressure of the gas, m and c are constants which have different values for different gases ($c = 0\cdot45$ for air), but are always the same for the same gas, θ and θ_0 have the usual meanings, and the index $1\cdot233$ is the same for all gases.

The full expression for the rate of fall of temperature due to both convection and radiation is thus

$$V = V_1 + V_2 = k(a^\theta - a^{\theta_0}) + mp^c(\theta - \theta_0)^{1 \cdot 233}.$$

The greatest temperature difference employed was about 300 centigrade degrees.

We are interested in the formula $V_2 = mp^c(\theta - \theta_0)^{1 \cdot 233}$, which will be written, in terms of the *rate of loss of heat*, $\dfrac{dQ}{dt} = -k(\theta - \theta_0)^{1 \cdot 233}$, where k is constant for a given body in a given gas at a fixed pressure.

Preston states that the Dulong and Petit convection formula has no theoretical basis, being simply an empirical formula of wider range than Newton's. But Lorentz showed theoretically in 1881 that the rate of loss of heat by convection should be proportional to $(\theta - \theta)^{5/4}$ or $(\theta - \theta_0)^{1 \cdot 25}$, which is not far from the $(\theta - \theta_0)^{1 \cdot 233}$ of Dulong and Petit. Further, Langmuir, investigating the cooling of flat discs in still air, found experimentally that the rate of loss of heat was given by the formula

$$-\frac{dQ}{dt} = k(\theta - \theta_0)^{5/4}.$$

There is thus good evidence, both theoretical and experimental, for believing that the true law of cooling for natural convection is given by this expression, which is often called the **Five-fourths Power Law.**

To sum up, the convection laws are :

Forced convection in a strong draught : Newton's Law of Cooling, namely, *rate of loss of heat* $\propto$ *temperature excess.*

Natural convection in still air : Five-fourths Power Law, namely, *rate of loss of heat* $\propto$ *(temperature excess)*$^{5/4}$.

It is customary to use Newton's Law of cooling to correct for the heat lost in calorimetry experiments, although the calorimeter is *carefully screened from draughts*. It is hard to believe that generations of experimenters would have countenanced the use of an approximation which is unsatisfactory in practice ; the truth is probably that an error in a small correction is often unimportant. Large temperature excesses for which the law is known to be unsatisfactory are simply avoided in elementary work, while in accurate work the exact rate of cooling should be *observed* and not computed.

What order of error is made in using Newton's Law instead of the Five-fourths Power Law for still-air convection cooling for temperature excesses of 10, 20, and 30 degrees, for a given *fixed* value of k?

$10^{5/4} = 17\cdot8$, whence Newton's Law gives 56 per cent. of the true cooling.

$20^{5/4} = 42\cdot3$, whence Newton's Law gives 47 per cent. of the true cooling.

$30^{5/4} = 70\cdot2$, whence Newton's Law gives 43 per cent. of the true cooling.

The difficulty is investigated by C. W. Hansel in " Proceedings of the Physical Society ", vol. 54, p. 162 (March 1942). He states :

" Textbooks of physics often state Newton's Law of cooling as follows :

' The rate of cooling of a body is proportional to its excess temperature above the temperature of the surroundings, provided that this excess temperature is small.'

According to this statement, Newton's law is not a law at all. All that is asserted in this statement is that a short enough part of the cooling curve (i.e. here the graph of rate of cooling against temperature excess) is straight. This is necessarily true, whatever the shape of the curve."

One thing is quite certain. Whether or not it is legitimate to use Newton's law in the cooling correction in calorimetry as an approximation, it is not permissible to use a cooling calorimeter to *demonstrate* Newton's law unless there is forced convection.

Film theory of cooling by convection. The problem of convection is complicated by the fact that the heat eventually convected away has, in the first place, to reach the fluid stream by conduction.

It is believed that the whole surface of the cooling body is covered by a thin layer of stagnant fluid adhering to the wall. The difference between forced and free convection is that this film is more or less continually wiped off and renewed with forced convection if the speed of the fluid current is great enough to cause turbulent motion, while with free convection it is more or less permanent. What happens to the heat after it has escaped by conduction through this film is only part of the problem, which starts with the study of conduction through the film.

According to this theory, the formula for the rate of loss of heat from the surface can be expressed by a " conduction equation " of the form

$$-\frac{dQ}{dt} = hA(\theta - \theta_0),$$

where h is called the " surface coefficient ", and the other symbols have their usual meanings.

Investigation by the method of dimensions shows that for forced convection h is independent of the temperature excess $(\theta - \theta_0)$, so that Newton's Law should be obeyed. The formula obtained for h is called **Nusselt's equation**, and is

$$\frac{hD}{k} = C \left(\frac{DV\rho}{\eta}\right)^b \left(\frac{C_p\eta}{k}\right)^d,$$

where k is the thermal conductivity of the fluid, D a length (the diameter in the case of a flat disc), η the coefficient of viscosity of the fluid, V the velocity of the fluid past the surface, C_p the specific heat at constant pressure, ρ the density of the fluid, and C, b, d are constants. The expression $\left(\frac{DV\rho}{\eta}\right)$ is the well-known **Reynolds' Number** which is involved in many fluid-flow problems. This type of general formula is applicable to *all* fluids, liquids as well as gases.

Now, in forced convection V is constant. In free convection V is determined by the density changes of the fluid, which are themselves determined by the temperature excess. Hence h is not independent of the temperature excess. It has been shown that the formula for h with free convection should be $h = \lambda(\theta - \theta_0)^{1/4}$, where λ is an expression independent of the temperature excess, whence

$$-\frac{dQ}{dt} = \lambda A (\theta - \theta_0)^{5/4}.$$

Different conditions seem to apply if the cooling surface is very large, as this affects the extent of the turbulence of the fluid stream. For very large surfaces it appears that h is proportional to $(\theta - \theta_0)^{1/3}$, whence the rate of loss of heat by free convection is proportional to $(\theta - \theta_0)^{4/3}$.

This section is based on the chapters on Convection in Brown and Marco's " Introduction to Heat Transfer " (McGraw-Hill Book Co., Inc.). A further account of the application of the method of dimensions to convection problems is given in Appendix I.

RADIATION

Radiation was defined by Maxwell as the transfer of heat from a hot body to a cooler body without appreciable heating of the intervening space.

It is now known that thermal radiation, or " radiant heat ", is a means of transferring energy by transverse electromagnetic waves, and is similar in nature to light, radio waves, ultra-violet rays, and X-rays.

It is difficult to imagine the propagation of waves without a medium, and it is still usual to speak of all these waves as waves in the ether, which is regarded as a medium pervading all space. No direct evidence for or against the existence of such an ether has ever been obtained, and it is believed that it is impossible to obtain such evidence. It is also hard to picture transverse waves spreading out in all directions in space. This difficulty can be overcome for the present purpose by considering the simplest possible case of a transverse wave, such as a wave along a string.

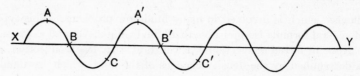

Fig. 167.—Illustration of wave motion.

Fig. 167 represents a portion of an extremely long string, one end of which is executing a linear simple harmonic motion in the plane of the paper at right angles to the line XY. If this end executes ν complete vibrations per second, then in each second ν complete waves are propagated along the string, with a constant velocity v ; ν is called the *frequency* of the wave motion. The *wave-length* λ is the distance between two corresponding points on adjacent waves, such as AA', BB', or CC'. Considering any one second, the wave which is started at the beginning of this interval has travelled a distance v by the end of the second, and the space behind it contains the ν waves each of wave-length λ which have been started during the second. Hence, $v = \nu\lambda$, or $\nu = v/\lambda$. This expression is true for all types of waves.

All electromagnetic radiations travel in free space with the same velocity, the value of which is nearly 3×10^{10} cm./sec.—the " velocity of light ". This is denoted by the symbol c, so that the relation between wave-length and frequency is $\nu = c/\lambda$.

In optics, white light is dispersed by a prism or other means into a spectrum with the colours arranged in increasing wave-lengths from violet $(\lambda = 4 \times 10^{-5}$ cm.) to red $(\lambda = 8 \times 10^{-5}$ cm.). This spectrum is only a small fraction of the total range of electro-magnetic waves, which extend from the γ-rays of artificially radioactive bodies $(\lambda = 10^{-11}$ cm.) to the long-wave radio transmitter $(\lambda = 2000$ metres). For radiations in and close to the visible spectrum, wave-lengths are expressed in terms of the Ångström unit (Å.U.) ; 1 Å.U. $= 10^{-8}$ cm. Longer wave-lengths are usually expressed in terms of the micron μ ; $1\mu = 10^{-4}$ cm.

The characteristic properties of the different types of rays or waves are due to differences in frequency or wave-length.

Suppose that, by means of suitable non-absorbing prisms or gratings a complete spectrum of sunlight as received at the surface of the earth can be cast on a screen. The familiar succession of colours is observed—red, orange, yellow, green, blue, indigo, violet —in order of decreasing wave-length. A sensitive thermal detector moved along the coloured portion shows that the screen is receiving heat as well as light. If the instrument is moved beyond the red end of the spectrum, it indicates strong reception of heat, showing that there is an invisible extension of the sun's spectrum beyond the red end ; this is known as the infra-red region. The same instrument shows that the heating effect extends beyond the violet end of the spectrum, into the ultra-violet. Whenever any radiation, visible or invisible, is absorbed, heat is produced.

This statement is true even at the extreme limits of the complete electromagnetic spectrum, though in general only part of the energy of the radiation is so converted. Radio waves when absorbed by an aerial induce currents in it ; and whenever a current flows in a conductor, heat is produced. Beams of γ-rays of known intensity have actually been used as standard heat supplies in calorimetry experiments at very low temperatures. But, while radiations from all parts of the spectrum may generate heat when absorbed, we shall be thinking chiefly of infra-red radiation in this chapter. Two reasons for this are, that the chief radiation emitted from most practical sources of heat is in the infra-red, and that other radiations such as X-rays and radio waves have remarkable distinctive properties which make their heating effects of trivial interest.

Is radiation or radiant heat a *new form of heat*, or merely a special means of transferring heat? Planck, in his "Theory of Heat" stresses the dual nature of the problem, distinguishing between "radiant heat" and "heat in bodies" (or sensible heat). He points out that the emission of radiant heat occurs by the conversion of heat of the emitting body into radiation, while the reconversion of radiation to "heat in a body" requires the absorption and annihilation of the radiation.

The point may be further emphasised, in that the heat in a body is regarded as the total energy of the oscillating or random-moving particles which compose it, while radiant heat is energy propagated through space with the speed of light. To use a somewhat loose analogy, if we regard the energy of the electric charges executing oscillations in the electric circuit of a small radio transmitter as corresponding to *heat in a body*, the energy radiated from the aerial corresponds to *radiant heat*; when this radiation is absorbed by a conductor, it is transformed again into an oscillating current or particle movement in the conductor.

We are chiefly concerned with the transfer of heat from one body to another in practical problems; that is to say, with the emission and absorption of the radiation rather than with the intervening radiation stage itself.

Optical properties of infra-red radiation. Infra-red radiation, like light, travels in straight lines in a homogeneous medium. On a hot summer day, a person in the shade is out of reach of the sun's heat as well as shielded from its direct light.

Infra-red radiation follows the ordinary rules of photometry, which depend on the rectilinear propagation of light. That is, the intensity of the radiation received on a screen from a small source varies inversely as the square of the distance from screen to source and is proportional to the cosine of the angle of incidence on the screen.

Infra-red radiation travels in empty space with the same velocity as light. When eclipses of the sun occur, the heat is cut off at the same instant as the light.

Many materials which are transparent to light are transparent to the near infra-red ; that is, wave-lengths up to about 5μ. Ordinary glass transmits to 3μ, fluorite to 9μ, rock salt to 15μ. On the other hand, some bodies, such as a solution of iodine in carbon disulphide, while quite opaque to visible light, transmit infra-red radiation well.

Infra-red radiation is reflected and refracted according to the same laws as light, though the refractive index of transparent substances is less than for the visible part of the spectrum. Hence the use of concave mirrors and burning glasses to focus the sun's rays.

Infra-red radiation, like light, is absorbed by dark, rough surfaces, and reflected by light, smooth surfaces. It shows the phenomena of interference, diffraction, and polarisation, which indicate that it is a wave motion of a transverse type, as is light. The radiation also affects suitable photographic plates, sensitised by being bathed in certain dyes, and affects a cæsium photocell.

It is thus concluded that radiant heat, or infra-red radiation, is really a method of energy propagation of the same nature as light, the only real difference being that the human eye is not sensitive to this range of wave-lengths ; or, to put this in another way, infra-red is a " colour " to which everyone is " colour blind ".

Detection of infra-red radiation. The instruments described below are those chiefly used for demonstration purposes. Accurate quantitative instruments are described later.

As has already been mentioned, a thermometer with a blackened bulb may be used to detect thermal radiation.

The ether thermoscope (Fig. 168) has two bulbs, the lower of which is blackened. The space above the ether column in each bulb contains saturated ether vapour. A small rise in temperature in the neighbourhood of room temperature causes a considerable increase in the s.v.p. of ether. Hence, when the blackened bulb is exposed to radiation, which it absorbs, the resulting increase in s.v.p. sends the ether up the tube. Changes in the temperature of the surroundings affect the s.v.p. in both bulbs equally.

Fig. 168.
Ether thermoscope.

FIG. 169.
Crookes' radiometer.

The Crookes' radiometer (Fig. 169) is also a useful demonstration tool. A light windmill with four vertical vanes of mica is mounted to spin on a vertical axis. One face of each vane is blackened, and the blackened sides all face the same way round. The glass enclosure is exhausted to a pressure which is so low that the mean free path of the air molecules is considerable, but which is not an extremely low pressure. The blackened faces absorb radiation better than the polished faces and so, as mica is a poor conductor of heat, the black faces are always hotter than the polished faces. Hence, molecules striking the black faces rebound with an average velocity greater than that for the polished faces, and the reaction causes the mill to spin round with the polished faces leading. A simple analogy to this part of the action is the " catherine wheel ", for as the pressure is so low that the rebounding molecules travel some distance before colliding with other molecules, the effect is as if there were a continuous stream of hot gas coming from the blackened faces.

The thermopile (Fig. 170) consists of a set of thermocouples connected in series. The " hot " junctions are blackened and exposed to the radiation, while the " cold " junctions are covered with a heavy metal cap. The thermopile is connected to a sensitive galvanometer which should have a resistance approximately equal to that of the thermopile. The usual type employs antimony-bismuth couples.

The differential air thermometer (Fig. 171) consists of two equal closed bulbs C and D containing air at ordinary pressure, connected by a U-tube which serves as a liquid manometer. Bulb D is blackened, while C is clear. Both bulbs are affected equally by changes in the temperature of the surrounding air, so any difference between the levels A and B can only be due to the absorption of radiation by D.

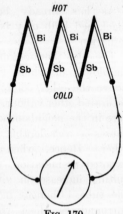

FIG. 170.
Scheme of thermopile.

Using a small electric bowl fire as a source, and any of the above as a detector, simple demonstrations can be devised to show that radiant heat travels in straight lines, obeys the law of inverse squares, obeys the laws of reflection at plane surfaces, is focused by concave mirrors and convex lenses, is transmitted to a considerable extent by a thin sheet of glass, and is absorbed strongly by a cell containing a few centimetres of water. It may also be shown that the radiation from an iron ball, heated to just below red heat, is absorbed by glass much more markedly than that from the much hotter electric fire, indicating that the radiation from sources at different temperatures may differ in *quality* as well as in intensity.

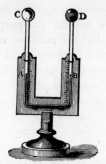

Fig. 171.—Differential air thermometer.

RADIATING POWERS OF DIFFERENT SURFACES

(*a*) **Leslie's Cube.** Different surface finishes are applied to the four vertical faces of a cubical tin box. Face 1 is made a dull black with lamp black, face 2 is coated with black enamel, face 3 is painted a dull white, while face 4 is brightly polished.

Water is maintained steadily boiling in the cube, and a thermopile or some other radiation detector (screened from the direct radiation of the bunsen under the cube) held at exactly the same distance from the centre of each face in turn. The observations show that face 1 is radiating strongly, faces 2 and 3 slightly less strongly, and face 4 very feebly. All the four faces under test are at the same temperature, and considering the two extremes 1 and 4, the experiment shows that a dull black surface radiates much more strongly than a polished silvered surface. We know that a blackened surface absorbs radiation strongly, and a polished silvered surface absorbs only a fraction of the radiation falling on it.

Hence, a dull blackened surface is a good emitter and a good absorber ; a silvered polished surface is a bad emitter and a bad absorber. In general, for all other types of surface, good absorbers are good emitters, and bad absorbers are bad emitters.

In spite of the evidence of this experiment, people often find it hard to believe that a polished surface is a bad emitter. Why is the polished metal reflector used behind the element of an electric fire, if not for the purpose of emitting radiation? The point here is, that the polished surface, just *because it is a poor absorber* of radiation, *reflects* most of the radiation falling upon it. To use an analogy, the Rugby three-quarter with a good pair of hands will be a good absorber of passes and also a good emitter ; the clumsy player who habitually reflects the ball from his chest or his chin is a good reflector of passes, but a bad absorber and a bad emitter.

This " passing " analogy is perhaps closer than at first appears. For a surface is a boundary which faces inwards towards the body as well as outwards towards the surrounding medium, and the generation of the radiation emitted from a body must take place within the body itself. At all temperatures, all parts of a body are oscillating and generating radiation. A blackened surface is at one and the same time absorbing the heat radiated from within the body and " passing " it outwards, while a polished surface reflects back into the body the radiation which strikes its inner surface, absorbing little so that there is little available to be passed out.

(*b*) **Ritchie's experiment.** The two bulbs X and Y of a differential air thermometer are made in the form of two horizontal metal cylinders with flat end faces (Fig. 172). One face P of Y, is silvered, and one face, B, of X, coated with a dull black. A third cylinder, Z, also with one flat face blackened and the other polished, is placed midway between the two bulbs, so that its polished side faces a blackened bulb, and its blackened side faces a polished bulb. The liquid index remains steady, showing that the rates at which X and Y receive radiation are exactly the same. This can be explained as follows.

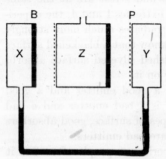

Let E_1 be the energy emitted per second by the blackened face, E_2 that for the polished face. Let A_1 be the fraction of the incident radiation absorbed by the blackened face and A_2 that by the polished face.

For X, the energy emitted by the polished face of the can Z per second is E_1. Of this, a certain fraction α (depending on the separation of the faces) strikes the face of X, so that

Fig. 172.—Ritchie's experiment.

the energy incident on X per second is αE_1. A fraction A_2 of this is absorbed, so the rate of reception of energy by X is $\alpha E_1 A_2$.

For Y, the energy emitted by the blackened face of the can Z per second is E_2, the fraction of this striking the polished face of Y is αE_2, and the fraction absorbed by Y is A_1; so the rate at which Y receives energy is $\alpha E_2 A_1$.

But the two bulbs are receiving energy at the same rate, so

$$\alpha E_1 A_2 = \alpha E_2 A_1.$$

$$\therefore \frac{E_1}{E_2} = \frac{A_1}{A_2}, \quad \text{or} \quad \frac{E_1}{A_1} = \frac{E_2}{A_2}.$$

That is, *the emitting power of a surface is proportional to its absorbing power.*

The quantity E has not been defined precisely here; obviously its value depends on the areas of the surfaces and also the temperatures concerned; but the matter will be put in a more precise way shortly, when this important relation is deduced theoretically.

Prevost's theory of exchanges. Consider a non-conducting enclosure, with walls at a definite temperature, into which are placed several bodies A, B, C, of different materials and surfaces, and at different temperatures (Fig. 173). Suppose that heat interchange between these bodies takes place by radiation only, and that the medium surrounding them is perfectly diathermanous, or transparent to radiation. Suppose that at first A is at a high temperature, B at a moderate temperature, and C at a low temperature. After sufficient time from the start has passed, the whole of the walls and contents of the enclosure will have reached a steady uniform temperature.

At first, A loses heat by radiation to B, C, and the walls; B gains heat by radiation from A, and loses heat to C and the walls. But we cannot suppose that the radiation from B is emitted only in such a direction that it shall select cooler bodies to fall on. During this process, B is emitting heat to A as well as to the rest of the enclosure; the

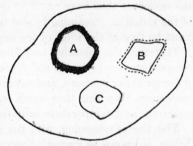

Fig. 173.—Bodies in a uniform temperature enclosure.

temperature of B rises because it gains more heat by radiation than it loses.

When a uniform temperature is reached, the process of radiation does not stop. Each body is radiating to all the other bodies and the walls, and each body is absorbing radiation from all the other bodies and from the walls. All the bodies and the walls are at a constant temperature, because each part is in a state of dynamic equilibrium, absorbing in any interval of time exactly as much radiation as it emits during that interval. There is continually a constant stream of radiation from point to point in all directions in the enclosure.

Now consider the bodies individually, and suppose that A is black, B highly polished, and C a substance which can absorb only radiation of one particular wave-length. The body A absorbs all the radiation falling on it ; it must therefore emit radiation strongly at exactly the same rate as it absorbs it, or its temperature will rise. The body B absorbs very little radiation ; it must emit radiation feebly, at exactly the same rate as it absorbs it, or its temperature will fall. The body C can only absorb radiation of a particular wave-length ; it must radiate at exactly the same rate as it absorbs, and its radiation must take the form of this particular wave-length, for if it did not, the radiation in the enclosure would become more and more deficient in this wave-length, and the temperature of C would fall for lack of the only radiation it can absorb.

Hence, in a uniform temperature enclosure, each body in any interval of time radiates exactly as much energy of exactly the same kind as it absorbs during that interval. Bodies contained in the enclosure thus have no effect on either the kind or the quantity of the radiation streaming to and fro in the enclosure, and the same must be true of the walls of the enclosure.

Therefore the quantity and kind of radiation within a uniform temperature enclosure do not depend on the nature of the materials it comprises or contains, and depend only on the temperature of the enclosure. We can thus speak of the radiation within such an enclosure as " temperature radiation ", or " full radiation ".

This line of reasoning, with the idea of a state of dynamic equilibrium, is known as **Prevost's Theory of Exchanges.**

THE BLACK BODY

Bodies with black surfaces have this appearance in ordinary light because they absorb all the wave-lengths of the visible spectrum. We do not usually speak of shades of black, but if the term " blackness " is used to mean " absorbing power ", we can distinguish between degrees of blackness, ranging from that of a sheet of polished black glass to that of powdered charcoal or black velvet, and it is clear that to obtain the greatest blackness, the surface besides being made of suitable material should be rough, with irregularities which are large compared with the wave-length of the light concerned. There is one further requirement, and that is that the surface must be of appreciable thickness.

In physics, the term black body is used with a definite meaning, to denote a perfect absorber of all radiations.

A perfectly black body, which shall absorb all kinds of electro-magnetic radiations completely, is extremely difficult to picture, but we exclude the extreme regions of the full spectrum here, and consider only ultra-violet, visible, and infra-red radiation. Even here, for the longer wave-lengths, it is difficult to find surfaces which, besides satisfying the other conditions, are rough enough.

But a perfect absorber for the range of radiations we are considering can be manufactured. A cavity in the form of a hollow sphere, with the inside coated with rough black material, and with a small hole in the surface for the admission of radiation, will absorb the whole of the radiation falling on the hole (with the exception of a very small amount indeed, depending on the size of the hole, which may be reflected out). Such a cavity may be regarded as a perfectly black body.

As a perfectly black body is the most perfect absorber of radiation, it must also be the most perfect emitter. The radiation proceeding from such a cavity for any temperature of the walls is called the black body radiation or cavity radiation for that temperature.

Now suppose that a perfectly black body is contained in a uniform temperature enclosure. It absorbs all the radiation falling on it, and the intensity and kind of radiation it emits is exactly the same as the intensity and kind of radiation it absorbs. From this we conclude that the radiation within a uniform temperature enclosure itself is exactly the same in intensity and kind as the radiation absorbed and emitted by a perfectly black body at the same temperature. Further, as the radiation within the enclosure depends only on the temperature, the intensity and kind of the radiation from a perfectly black body depends only on its temperature.

Hence, when speaking of this particular intensity and kind of radiation, which depends solely on the temperature of the radiator, it is referred to as the

$$\left.\begin{array}{l} \text{temperature radiation,} \\ \text{full radiation,} \\ \text{cavity radiation, or} \\ \text{black body radiation} \end{array}\right\} \text{for that temperature.}$$

INTENSITY OF RADIATION

In speaking of the emission of energy by radiation from the surface of a body, we can consider either :

(a) the total energy emitted per square centimetre per second, which is the total emissive power e for that particular temperature, or
(b) the energy emitted per square centimetre per second within a finite wave-length range between wave-lengths λ and $\lambda + d\lambda$, which depends on the size of the wave-length interval $d\lambda$ itself, and is expressed as $e_\lambda d\lambda$, where e_λ is called the emissive power for wave-length λ. (The term emissive power, e, should not be confused with emissivity as defined for other purposes on p. 330.)

For unit area and unit time, the total energy of the radiation of all wave-lengths is e, while the energy between λ and $\lambda + d\lambda$ is $e_\lambda d\lambda$. Clearly e is the sum of all the terms $e_\lambda d\lambda$ for all the wave-lengths concerned, so that $e = \Sigma e_\lambda d\lambda$, or $e = \int e_\lambda d\lambda$ for a continuous range of λ's.

The capital letter symbols E and E_λ will be used instead of e and e_λ when referring to a perfectly black body.

Now, the radiation in a uniform temperature enclosure is travelling through the enclosure and is therefore contained within the space of the enclosure. This space is therefore the seat of a certain fixed quantity of energy at any temperature. To find a meaning for the term "intensity of radiation in an enclosure", consider the radiant energy per unit volume, or energy density u.

Consider one square centimetre of a perfectly black surface

within such an enclosure, and suppose for simplicity that it emits all its radiation normally. The total energy emitted normally in one second is thus E. The velocity of the radiation is c. So the total energy emitted from the surface in one second, supposing that it travelled unimpeded, would fill a cylinder of length c cm. and cross-section 1 sq. cm., that is, a volume c c.c. The energy in 1 c.c. of the medium is thus E/c if this is all that happens.

But in the uniform temperature enclosure, radiation is proceeding towards the surface as fast as it is lost from it, hence, as the same space contains *both* streams of radiation, the total energy density should be twice that calculated; that is, $u = \dfrac{2E}{c}$.

Now the surface actually radiates in all directions, and the proper calculation (which will not be attempted here) takes this into account, and shows that the result should be multiplied by a factor 2.

Thus, the total energy per c.c. of the enclosure is

$$u = \frac{4E}{c};$$

while, for the range λ to $\lambda + d\lambda$, the energy per c.c. is

$$u_\lambda \, d\lambda = \frac{4 E_\lambda \, d\lambda}{c}.$$

The relation between the u's and the E's is thus

$$E = \frac{cu}{4}, \quad E_\lambda = \frac{cu_\lambda}{4}.$$

As the u's are proportional to the E's, the same laws of variation hold for both and either may be used to denote the " intensity " of the radiation concerned. The word intensity as applied to radiation from a surface means the appropriate emissive power, E, e, or $E_\lambda \, d\lambda$, $e_\lambda \, d\lambda$; as applied to an enclosure containing radiation it means the appropriate energy density u or $u_\lambda \, d\lambda$.

Emissive power and absorptive power. Kirchhoff's Law. Consider a body of any type of surface at equilibrium in a uniform temperature enclosure. The energy emitted per square centimetre per second in all directions between wave-lengths λ and $\lambda + d\lambda$ is $e_\lambda \, d\lambda$, where e_λ is the emissive power of that surface for that particular wave-length and temperature.

Let the energy falling on unit area per second within the same wave-length limits be dQ, which depends only on the temperature of the enclosure.

Let the fraction of the incident energy absorbed between the wave-lengths λ and $\lambda + d\lambda$ be a_λ; a_λ is called here the **absorptive power** of the surface. The total energy absorbed by unit area per second is thus $a_\lambda\, dQ$.

As the temperature of the body is constant, the rate of emission of energy equals the rate of absorption,

$$e_\lambda\, d\lambda = a_\lambda\, dQ.$$

$$\therefore\ \frac{e_\lambda}{a_\lambda} = \frac{dQ}{d\lambda}.$$

As $d\lambda$ is a chosen fixed interval, and dQ depends only on the temperature of the enclosure, the right-hand side of this equation must be constant.

So, whatever the nature of the body, the ratio e_λ / a_λ is constant.

If the body happens to be a perfectly black body, we write E_λ for the emissive power, and the absorptive power is 1. So,

$$\frac{e_\lambda}{a_\lambda} = E_\lambda.$$

Hence, at any given temperature, *the ratio of the emissive power of any body for any wave-length to its absorbing power for that wave-length at that temperature is constant, and is equal to the emissive power of a perfectly black body at that temperature.*

This statement is known as **Kirchhoff's Law.**

The ratio e_λ / E_λ is often referred to as the emissivity (a term which is also used with another meaning on p. 330).

As $\dfrac{e_\lambda}{E_\lambda} = a_\lambda$, the emissivity as here defined is equal to the absorbing power.

E_λ increases as the temperature rises; hence it is important to realise that e_λ / a_λ increases as the temperature rises, and is only constant in the sense that it has the same value for all kinds of surface at a fixed temperature and wave-length.

An ideal surface for which a_λ is constant for all wave-lengths (though not equal to unity) that is, for which e_λ is exactly the same fraction of E_λ at all wave-lengths, is called a grey body.

Experimental tests of Kirchhoff's Law. Is it possible to verify Kirchhoff's Law directly? The conditions of the *argument*, a uniform temperature enclosure, are closely reproduced in the heart of a good fire, or inside a long cylinder of graphite raised to red heat electrically. Bodies of different kinds placed inside such an enclosure become indistinguishable from the background, showing that they compensate exactly for the quantity of each radiation they absorb, by the quantity they emit ; so the law holds within a uniform temperature enclosure.

But the law as deduced does not demand that the body shall necessarily be in equilibrium in such an enclosure. How does it apply, say to a piece of red glass at air temperature, exposed to white light? The glass appears red because it absorbs green light strongly. Why does it not emit green light strongly? It is said that if such glass is heated to incandescence it appears green, a statement on which the student would do well to reserve his opinion until he observes for himself the appearance (or non-appearance) of this effect ; but what happens at red (?) heat has nothing whatever (at least directly) to do with Kirchhoff's Law as applied at air temperature. The facts surely are that at air temperature E_λ is infinitesimally small for green light, and e_λ is also infinitesimally small, but approximately the same in value as E_λ. Hence the ratio e_λ/E_λ gives a finite value which is approximately equal to unity, the value of a_λ. The popular misunderstanding of this and other similar points is probably due to confusion between the *emissive power* e_λ and the *emissivity* e_λ/E_λ.

The green radiation absorbed in this case must, of course, be converted into " sensible heat " ; and when the red glass is at a steady temperature, heat is being radiated as fast as it is absorbed, but in the form of long infra-red radiation, for which E_λ at air temperature is appreciable.

It must be remembered that Kirchhoff's Law is a quantitative law, and attempts to apply it qualitatively are useless without some idea of the relative sizes of the quantities concerned.

The best-known illustration of Kirchhoff's Law is the famous line-reversal experiment of Kirchhoff and Bunsen. A source of white light is viewed through a sodium flame by means of a spectroscope. Two fine dark lines are observed in the continuous spectrum, in exactly the same position in the spectrum as the bright yellow lines emitted by sodium. Absorption, given by the relation $a_\lambda = e_\lambda / E_\lambda$ occurs for just these two closely adjacent wave-lengths for which e_λ is large. For all other wave-lengths at this temperature e_λ is zero, and so a_λ is zero.

RADIATION MEASUREMENTS

1. The bolometer. This is really an extremely sensitive platinum resistance thermometer, of very low thermal capacity. The original form, due to Langley, consists of a grid made of very thin platinum foil, blackened to absorb radiation. This grid forms one arm of a Wheatstone bridge, while a similar compensating grid, not exposed to radiation, is placed in the opposite arm. With this compensating grid, changes in the temperature of the surrounding air should cause

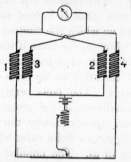

Fig. 174.—Bolometer grid.   Fig. 175.—Connection of bolometer grids in bridge circuit.

no appreciable effect on the balance of the bridge. In an improved form due to Lummer and Kurlbaum, four grids are used, and connected one in each arm of the bridge (Figs. 174 and 175). Changes in room temperature are thus completely compensated, and the two heated strips double the effect of the radiation. The whole is surrounded by a well-lagged box to maintain the temperature constant, the radiation being admitted through a small aperture in the box.

This instrument was used by Lummer and Kurlbaum in their investigation of the distribution of energy in the spectrum of a black body. It gives extremely accurate relative measurements. For spectrum work the actual bolometer strip is a single narrow strip of platinum instead of a grid ; this is called a linear bolometer.

The bolometer has also been adapted for the absolute measurement of radiation. The rate at which electrical energy must be supplied to the unexposed strip to balance the supply by radiation of energy to the exposed strip is measured.

2. **Callendar's Radio-balance** (Fig. 176). This enables absolute measurements of the received radiation to be made by neutralising the heating due to the absorption of radiation by the cooling caused by the Peltier effect at the junction of a thermocouple. The thermocouple is essentially a heat engine, with the hot junction as source and the cold junction as sink; the thermo-electric current itself causes abstraction of heat at the hot junction and liberation of heat at the cold junction, and an externally supplied current similarly heats one junction and cools the other. This is the Peltier effect.

The apparatus consists of two copper cups, 3·5 mm. in diameter and 10 mm. deep, which are connected by a differential copper-constantan thermocouple with one junction soldered to the bottom of each cup. This thermocouple is connected in a circuit containing a battery B, rheostat R, and ammeter A, so that a measured current can be passed through the couple. Connected to the two cups are two other separate sets of thermocouples (or thermopiles) FC, which are shown detached in the diagram for the sake of clearness; these are connected to a sensitive galvanometer G.

When radiation is allowed to fall on one of the two cups, a current is passed from B until G shows no deflection. The two cups are then maintained at the same temperature. The exposed cup is (a) heated by radiation, and (b) heated by the Joule heating effect, and (c) cooled by the Peltier effect at the junction. The other cup is (a) being heated by the same Joule heating effect, and (b) being heated by the Peltier effect, which at this junction causes the liberation of heat. The reading of A is observed.

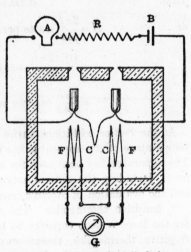

Fig. 176.—Callendar's radio-balance.
By courtesy of the Cambridge Instrument Co., Ltd.

The radiation is then made to fall on the other cup, the previously exposed cup being screened, and a second set of readings taken. The mean of the two current readings is found.

The intensity of the radiation in ergs per sq. cm. per second is calculated as follows. When a charge q coulombs passes through a thermocouple, the heat evolved at one junction and absorbed at the other is πq joules, where π is called the Peltier coefficient for the couple, and is here expressed in volts.

The *difference* between the heats evolved at the two junctions is thus $2\pi q$ joules. As *the charge in coulombs* equals the product *current in amperes* $\times$ *time in seconds*, then in one second the charge q passing equals the current I in amperes.

Hence the difference between the two rates of heating is $2\pi I$ joules per second, or $2\pi I$ watts. This just counterbalances the rate of heating caused when radiation falls on one cup only.

Let H be the rate at which radiant heat energy strikes the apparatus, in joules per sec. per sq. cm. or watts per sq. cm., let A sq. cm. be the mean of the two areas of the apertures, and a the absorption coefficient of the blackened cup.

The rate of absorption of energy is then aAH watts.

Thus
$$aAH = 2\pi I,$$

or
$$H = \frac{2\pi I}{Aa} \text{ watts per sq. cm.}$$

$$= \frac{10^7 \cdot 2\pi I}{Aa} \text{ ergs per sq. cm. per sec.}$$

$$= \frac{2\pi I}{aAJ} \text{ cal. per sq. cm. per sec.}$$

As the Peltier coefficient varies with the temperature, the mean temperature of the apparatus has to be determined to at least $1°$ C. The apparatus has been used for many types of radiation measurement, including the determination of the solar constant (p. 406) and the evaluation of Stefan's constant (p. 390).

3. **Sensitive thermopiles.** The ordinary type of thermopile has far too large a heat capacity to be of use in accurate work. For sensitive thermopiles, thermocouples made of very fine wires of bismuth and silver are used. Arranged so that the " hot " junctions all lie along a line, the linear thermopile has been used to explore

the energy distribution in the spectrum. Modern sensitive thermo-piles are often mounted in evacuated containers to reduce losses from the hot junctions.

A very sensitive radiation detector, called the radio-micro-meter, was designed by C. V. Boys. Fig. 177 shows the general structure of the instrument. One junction of a small antimony-bismuth thermocouple is attached to a small blackened copper disc, shown edgeways, of small thermal capacity, on which the radiation (directed down a horizontal channel in the case) falls. The circuit is completed by a loop of copper, at the upper end of which is a fine glass rod carrying a mirror to reflect a beam of light on to a scale. The whole is suspended from a fine quartz fibre, with the copper loop between the poles of a permanent magnet. The instrument is really a combined thermocouple and galvanometer, as, when the thermoelectric current is generated by radiation falling on the copper disc, the copper loop turns in the magnetic field until arrested by the torsion of the quartz fibre.

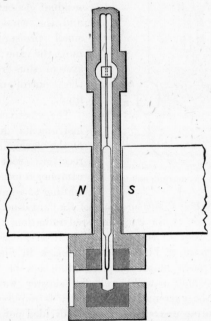

Fig. 177.—Boys' radio-micrometer.

4. **Accurate radiometers.** The vane radiometer designed by Nichols in 1897 is really an accurate modification of the Crookes radiometer. Fig. 178 indicates its construction. Two narrow mica vanes A and B are attached to narrow glass crosspieces and to a fine glass rod carrying a mirror M, the whole being suspended from a fine torsion fibre W. The blackened faces of the vanes are close to the fluorite window of the containing vessel, through which the radiation enters. The container is evacuated to a pressure of about 0·02 mm. of mercury. The radiation falls on one vane A only, the other B (indicated as clear in the figure) being shielded and serving as a compensator for stray radiation. The exposed vane is thus heated to a temperature higher than that of the adjacent fluorite window, and the circulation of the residual gas between the vane and the window sets up a small pressure tending to move the vane; the suspended system thus rotates against the control of the quartz fibre.

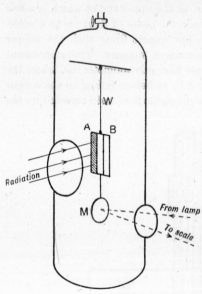

FIG. 178.—Vane radiometer.

The effectiveness of all these instruments depends largely on the blackening of the actual receiver. Soot from burning camphor is usually used. According to an article by A. H. Pfund in Forsythe's " Measurement of Radiant Energy ", camphor soot is unsatisfactory for long infra-red radiation, transmitting as much as 50 per cent. of the incident radiation for wave-lengths of about 11μ. Platinum black and zinc black in films of suitable thickness are much more complete absorbers of long infra-red radiation, absorbing equally well for shorter wave-lengths. If absorption in the extreme infra-red only is required (with transparency at shorter wave-lengths) finely divided powders of quartz, calcite, or fluorite have been used.

Black-body sources. Lummer and Pringsheim, in the course of their investigations on the distribution of the energy in the spectrum of a black body (1897) used as a source a hollow copper sphere coated inside with platinum black, and investigated the radiation emerging from a small hole in its wall. The sphere was heated up to 600° C. in a suitable bath of fused salts. For higher temperatures up to 1300° C. an iron cylinder with blackened inside was used, and the radiation from the inside observed. The same experimenters in later work on the applicability of the radiation laws to the measurement of temperature used a thin tube of carbon, which was heated by an electric current passing along its wall; as before, the radiation from the inside of the tube was observed. This radiator is represented in Fig. 179. The carbon tube R was 34 cm. long, 1·2 mm. thick, and with internal diameter of 1 cm. Copper-plated carbon end-pieces A served as current leads. The back wall of the radiating cavity was formed by the carbon plug P_1, fitting tightly in the tube. Behind this was a second plug P_2, and a third plug P_3 which sealed the tube from the atmosphere at the far end. The tube was gradually destroyed by combination with the oxygen of the air, but precautions were taken to make this process as slow as possible. A current of nitrogen circulated through the shutter F at the open end

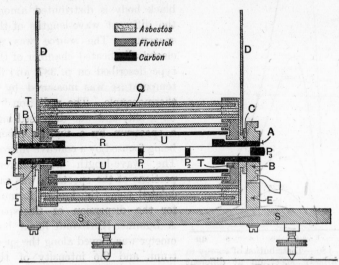

Fɪɢ. 179.—Black-body source of Lummer and Pringsheim.

of the tube, and the whole tube was surrounded by a carbon tube U, which helped to remove oxygen from the air in the neighbourhood of R. This was surrounded by other cylinders of fireclay and asbestos, as indicated in the figure. D and D are plates of copper attached to copper rings C, C, their purpose being to remove heat from the ends of the apparatus. The current passed through R was about 160 amperes, and a steady temperature of about 2300° absolute could be maintained for some hours.

Other forms of black-body radiator all use the principle of radiation from within a hollow space. The interior of refractory tubes immersed in molten platinum, the inside of a V-shaped strip of platinum foil heated electrically, and the inside of an electrically heated metal tube have all been employed as sources.

Distribution of the energy in the spectrum of a black body. A very important series of experiments was performed by Lummer and Pringsheim to determine the way in which the energy emitted by a black body is distributed among the different wave-lengths of the spectrum. The source was an electrically heated chamber of the type described on p. 387, and its temperature was measured by a thermocouple. The radiation fell on a slit, and was dispersed into a spectrum by a fluorite prism, being focused by a concave mirror. The wave-length at different portions of the spectrum was calculated using the known formula for the dispersion of fluorspar. A Lummer-Kurlbaum linear bolometer was moved along the spectrum, and the intensity of the radiation falling on it measured.

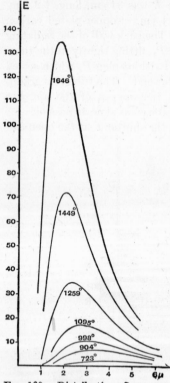

FIG. 180.—Distribution of energy in black-body spectrum at different temperatures.

The bolometer must cover a finite strip of the spectrum, say between wave-lengths λ and $\lambda + d\lambda$, and the recorded intensity depends on the size of the interval $d\lambda$ as well as the emissive power E_λ of the body for wave-length λ. The bolometer readings indicate the emissive power of the source, and the results are shown on the curves of Fig. 180. Here the emissive power, E_λ, for wave-length λ (indicated by E in the figure, which is taken from Preston's " Heat ") is plotted up the Y-axis and the wave-length λ in microns along the X-axis.

Two facts are at once apparent from these curves. The first is, that as the temperature increases the emissive power for every wave-length increases. Secondly, each curve has a definite maximum for E_λ, and with increasing temperature the wave-length at which this maximum occurs shifts steadily towards shorter values of λ; that is, in the direction of the visible spectrum at these temperatures. These observations certainly agree with the well-known facts that as the temperature of an incandescent body is raised it becomes (a) brighter, and (b) whiter in appearance.

In the following sections the theoretical equation for this family of curves is discussed.

Laws of black-body radiation. The total energy emitted per sq. cm. per sec., E, from a perfectly black body depends only on the absolute temperature T. The energy emitted per sq. cm. per sec. between wave-lengths λ and $\lambda + d\lambda$ by a perfectly black body, symbol $E_\lambda\, d\lambda$, depends on the temperature T, the wave-length λ, and the size of the interval $d\lambda$; the emissive power E_λ depends on the temperature T and the wave-length λ only. The use of the capital E to denote two different quantities should be noted carefully; the symbol E alone stands for the total energy of all wave-lengths, while E_λ is the emissive power at wave-length λ.

The dependence of E on T, and of E_λ on T and λ, have been investigated theoretically as well as experimentally. The theoretical work is largely well beyond the scope of this book, though it will be necessary to touch on the main ideas at times. But the most important aspect of the work at this stage is the experimental part.

Dependence of E on T. *Stefan's Law for the total radiation from a black body.* The energy emitted per square centimetre per second is proportional to the fourth power of the absolute temperature. In symbols,

$$E = \sigma T^4,$$

where σ is a constant called Stefan's constant, value

$$5{\cdot}735 \times 10^{-5} \ \text{erg/cm.}^2\text{/sec./deg.}^4$$

This equation refers specifically to *emission*, and not to the *net loss*. If the black body be surrounded by a perfectly black surface at temperature T_0, the gain from the surroundings is $\sigma T_0{}^4$, and the net loss of energy per sq. cm. per sec. is given by

$$E_{\text{net}} = \sigma(T^4 - T_0{}^4).$$

The law is often referred to simply as the **fourth power law**, and is also called the **Stefan-Boltzmann Law**, since while Stefan deduced it empirically from the results of Dulong and Petit, Boltzmann later gave a theoretical proof of it, on thermodynamical grounds.

Dependence of E_λ on T and λ. (a) *Wien's Displacement Law.* Experiments on the distribution of energy in the spectrum of a black body give results as shown in Fig. 180.

The energy distribution curves for all temperatures are of the same general shape, each with a well-marked maximum. The wave-length λ_{max} and the absolute temperature T are connected by the relation

$$\lambda_{\text{max}} T = a \ constant.$$

This is Wien's Displacement Law. The value of the constant is $0{\cdot}293$ cm. degree.

If E_{max} is the value of E_λ corresponding to λ_{max}, then

$$E_{\text{max}} T^{-5} = a \ constant.$$

By combining Stefan's Law and the Displacement Law, the following equation connecting E_λ, λ, and T was obtained by Wien:

$$E_\lambda = \lambda^{-5} f(\lambda T),$$

where $f(\lambda T)$ is some relation between λ and T only. This equation is also referred to as the Displacement Law in some books. It is believed to be rigorously true, and rests on thermodynamical reasoning.

(b) *Distribution formulae.* The three most important attempts to obtain the exact form of the function $f(\lambda T)$ in the equation $E_\lambda = \lambda^{-5} f(\lambda T)$ are those of Wien, of Rayleigh, and of Planck.

Rayleigh's formula is of theoretical importance on account of its *striking failure*. Assuming the Law of Equipartition of energy (p. 271) to hold, its derivation is flawless, and it was deduced independently by Jeans. Yet the formula,

$$E_\lambda = 8\pi k T / \lambda^4,$$

where k is Boltzmann's constant, not only fails to give curves resembling those found experimentally (though there is agreement for very large values of λT) but also predicts that the total radiation from a body at any finite temperature shall be infinite. The theory on which it is based (that is, the initial assumption made) thus fails to survive the test of experiment.

Planck's formula agrees closely with the observed curves. It was deduced by considering the emission of radiation from individual atoms, discarding the idea of radiation as a continuous stream of energy, and the law of equipartition, and assuming that the radiation of each frequency v was composed of quanta of magnitude $e = hv$, where h is a universal constant known as Planck's Constant, its value being $6 \cdot 55 \times 10^{-27}$ in C.G.S. units. These ideas were revolutionary at the time of their introduction. It is now realised that in all investigations of the emission and absorption of energy by individual atoms, energy must also be regarded as atomic.

Planck's formula is

$$E_\lambda = c_1 \lambda^{-5} \cdot \frac{1}{e^{c_2/\lambda T} - 1},$$

where e is the base of natural logarithms, and c_1 and c_2 are constants called the first and second radiation constants respectively. It is not proposed to attempt the theory underlying the equation, but it is worth mentioning that the values of the constants c_1 and c_2 are given by the theory in terms of other known constants. The value of c_1 is $8\pi hc$, and that of c_2 is ch/k, where h is Planck's Constant, c the velocity of light in free space, and k is Boltzmann's Constant R/N (p. 152). Taking the values

$c = 3 \times 10^{10}$ cm./sec. $\qquad R = 8 \cdot 3 \times 10^7$ erg/mole/deg.
$h = 6 \cdot 55 \times 10^{-27}$ C.G.S. units. $\qquad N = 6 \cdot 06 \times 10^{23}$ per mole,

$c_1 = 8\pi \times 6 \cdot 55 \times 10^{-27} \times 3 \times 10^{10} = 4 \cdot 94 \times 10^{-15}$ C.G.S. units, and

$c_2 = 3 \times 10^{10} \times 6 \cdot 55 \times 10^{-27} \times \dfrac{6 \cdot 06 \times 10^{23}}{8 \cdot 3 \times 10^7} = 1 \cdot 43$ cm. degrees.

Wien's formula is

$$E_\lambda = c_1 \lambda^{-5} e^{-c_2/\lambda T},$$

where all the symbols have exactly the same meaning as in Planck's formula. It can be seen that for small values of λT, $e^{c_2/\lambda T}$ is large compared with unity, and the denominator of Planck's formula is approximately $e^{c_2/\lambda T}$, so that $\dfrac{1}{e^{c_2/\lambda T} - 1}$ approximates to $e^{-c_2/\lambda T}$. Wien's formula is thus, as experiment has shown, a satisfactory approximation to the true formula of Planck if the product λT is sufficiently small.

Fig. 181 compares the plotted curves for 1646° K. obtained using Rayleigh's formula, Wien's formula, and Planck's formula. The complete inadequacy of Rayleigh's, and the close agreement between the other two, will be observed.

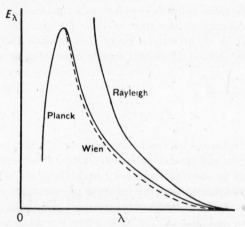

FIG. 181.—Calculated energy distribution for black body at 1646° K., according to the different radiation formulae.

The formula of Wien is in very close agreement with experiment for small values of λT; it is so satisfactory for the visible portion of the radiation from bodies at temperatures up to 2000° absolute or so that it is universally used in optical pyrometry. But it does not accord with experiment for values of λT greater than about 0·3 cm. degree.

It is worth while here to put in some numerical values to show how closely the two formulae agree for the visible spectrum of a body at 2000° absolute, and how considerably they disagree in the infra-red region.

Let T be 2000° K. and $\lambda = 6 \times 10^{-5}$ cm. (red light). Then

$$\lambda T = 0\cdot12 \quad \text{and} \quad \frac{c_2}{\lambda T} = \frac{1\cdot43}{0\cdot12} = 12 \text{ approximately.}$$

Thus $e^{c_2/\lambda T} = e^{12} = 2\cdot2 \times 10^4$; and neglecting the 1 in the denominator of Planck's formula causes an error of about one part in 20,000.

For the same temperature, let λ be 6×10^{-4} cm. (near infra-red). Then

$$\lambda T = 1\cdot2, \quad \frac{c_2}{\lambda T} = 1\cdot2 \text{ approx., and } e^{c_2/\lambda T} = e^{1\cdot2} = \text{approximately } 2\cdot7.$$

Neglecting the 1 in the denominator causes an error of more than one part in three.

When Wien's formula is used in pyrometry, the error caused in its use at 2000° K. is only 0·01°.

SUMMARY OF THE LAWS OF BLACK-BODY RADIATION

1. *Total radiation.*

Stefan's Fourth Power Law : $E = \sigma T^4$,

where E is the total energy emitted per sq. cm. per sec., and $\sigma = 5\cdot735 \times 10^{-5}$ erg/sq. cm./deg.[4]

2. *Distribution of energy in the spectrum.*

Wien's Displacement Law : $\lambda_{max} T = \text{constant}$,

where the value of the constant is 0·293 cm. degrees. Leads to $E_{max} T^{-5} = $ a constant, and also to the equation $E_\lambda = \lambda^{-5} f(\lambda T)$.

Planck's formula : $\qquad E_\lambda = c_1 \lambda^{-5} \dfrac{1}{e^{c_2/\lambda T} - 1}$,

accurate for all values of λT.

Wien's formula : $\qquad E_\lambda = c_1 \lambda^{-5} e^{-c_2/\lambda T}$,

which is usually used in practical problems.

The constants c_1 and c_2 of Planck's and Wien's formulae are called the first and second radiation constants, and have the values $4\cdot94 \times 10^{-15}$ c.g.s. and 1·43 cm. degree respectively.

Planck's formula agrees with both the Displacement Law and Stefan's Law. For by differentiating Planck's formula and applying the usual test for a maximum, the condition $\lambda_{max} T = \text{constant}$ is found to hold ; and by integrating the expression over all values

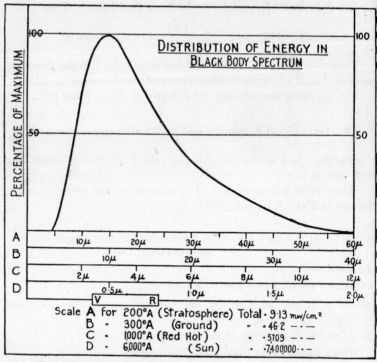

FIG. 182.—Graph summarising laws of black-body radiation. The same curve fits all temperatures if the ordinate scale for each is proportional to T^{-5} and the abscissa scale to T.

Reproduced from The Meteorological Glossary by permission of the Controller of H. M. Stationery Office.

of λ from zero to infinity the value of the total radiation is obtained, and this is shown to be proportional to the fourth power of T.

Fig. 182 provides an instructive summary of the laws of black-body radiation. Wien's Displacement Law, $\lambda_{max} T = \text{const.}$, shows that if we plot the distribution curves for black bodies at different temperatures, the maxima will all be at the same horizontal distance from the origin if we choose for each temperature a scale for plotting wave-lengths such that the horizontal distance representing λ is directly proportional to the absolute temperature. Now, Stefan's Law states that the total energy emitted per sq. cm. per sec. is proportional to the fourth power of the absolute temperature ; and the total energy, $\int E_\lambda \, d\lambda$ (or $\int y \, dx$ since E_λ is plotted up the Y-axis and λ along the X-axis) is represented by the area under the curve. The areas beneath the curves for the different temperatures are thus proportional to the fourth power of the absolute temperature, if the scales are not adjusted. But if, after altering the wave-length scale as above, the energy scale is altered so that the vertical distance representing one energy unit is *inversely* proportional to the *fifth* power of the absolute temperature, all the curves have the same area, and all coincide since $E_{\max} T^{-5} = $ a constant.

Four wave-length scales are shown, ranging from 200° A., the temperature of the stratosphere, to 6,000° A., an estimated value for the temperature of the sun (which is not a perfect black body). The actual absolute E_λ scales are not given but would be proportional to T^{-5} in each case. Comparing Scale A and Scale D, it can be seen that as the sun's absolute temperature is thirty times as great as that for the stratosphere, the distance representing 30μ on Scale A represents only 1μ on Scale D. The area under the curve, which represents 9·13 milliwatts per sq. cm. (1 milliwatt $= 10^4$ ergs/sec.) on Scale A, represents $9{\cdot}13 \times (30)^4$, or 7,400,000 milliwatts per sq. cm. on Scale D.

MEASUREMENT OF HIGH TEMPERATURES

There are two difficulties in applying the laws of radiation to the measurement of high temperatures.

(*a*) The laws hold only for perfectly black bodies, and no actual radiating surface is a perfectly black body, though many are approximately black.

(*b*) The laws have only been verified directly within the range of ordinary thermometers, and though we have every reason to believe that they hold at all temperatures there is no direct way of putting this belief to the test. The agreement between the values of very high temperatures measured by completely different radiation methods is satisfactory, which does suggest that this extrapolation is justified.

Three distinct methods seem to be available :

1. *The total radiation method*, using Stefan's Law $E_{\text{net}} = \sigma(T^4 - T_0{}^4)$.

The energy emitted per square centimetre per second is measured, and the temperature T calculated if σ and T_0 are known. This is the basis of the Total Radiation Pyrometer, which is calibrated to give direct readings of T.

2. *Displacement law method.* The radiation from the source is dispersed into a spectrum by means of a fluorite prism, and a linear bolometer moved along the spectrum to determine the wave-length $\lambda_{\max}$ of maximum emission. As $\lambda_{\max}T = 0.293$, T can be evaluated. This method was tested by Lummer and Pringsheim, and appeared to give consistent results ; though if the surface is not a black body, the displacement law does not hold at all, and it is not just a question of applying a small correction to the figure 0.293. The method has not been applied in practice to the design of pyrometers, but has been used to estimate the temperature of the sun (p. 407).

3. *The distribution law method,* using Wien's equation $E_\lambda = c_1 \lambda^{-5} e^{-c_2/\lambda T}$, or the more accurate Planck's equation if necessary. There are two ways of using this law.

(a) *Using the spectral distribution of the source itself.*

Two wave-lengths λ and l, both known, are selected.

The ratio E_λ/E_l is determined experimentally.

Then, using the Wien formula,

$$E_\lambda = c_1 \lambda^{-5} e^{-c_2/\lambda T}, \quad E_l = c_1 l^{-5} e^{-c_2/lT}.$$

Taking logarithms,

$$\ln\left(\frac{E_\lambda \lambda^5}{c_1}\right) = -\frac{c_2}{\lambda T}, \quad \ln\left(\frac{E_l l^5}{c_1}\right) = -\frac{c_2}{lT}.$$

Subtracting,

$$\ln\left(\frac{E_\lambda \lambda^5}{E_l l^5}\right) = \frac{c_2}{T}\left(\frac{1}{l} - \frac{1}{\lambda}\right).$$

$$\therefore \ T = c_2\left(\frac{1}{l} - \frac{1}{\lambda}\right) \div \ln\left(\frac{E_\lambda \lambda^5}{E_l l^5}\right).$$

Thus, if c_2, the second radiation constant, be known, T can be calculated ; while, if for a standard source at a known temperature T' the ratio E_λ'/E_l' be found for the *same two wave-lengths* λ and l,

$$T' = c_2\left(\frac{1}{l} - \frac{1}{\lambda}\right) \div \ln\left(\frac{E_\lambda' \lambda^5}{E_l' l^5}\right),$$

and

$$\frac{T}{T'} = \ln\left(\frac{E_\lambda' \lambda^5}{E_l' l^5}\right) \div \ln\left(\frac{E_\lambda \lambda^5}{E_l l^5}\right).$$

This method has been used in particular cases. Dobson, Griffith, and Harrison, in " Photographic Photometry ", describe the determination of the temperature of the high-pressure arc by this method. They found E_λ/E_l by measuring the density at the points corresponding to λ and l of the image of the spectrum on a photographic plate. Planck's formula was actually used, instead of the simpler Wien's formula, by these workers.

(b) *Comparing E_λ from the unknown for one fixed wave-length λ with E_λ for that same wave-length for a comparison source at known temperature.*

A fixed wave-length λ, usually red light of about 6500 Å.U., transmitted through a red filter which allows a narrow band about 200 Å.U. in width to pass through, is used. For this wave-length, at all temperatures likely to be met with in practice, Wien's formula can safely be applied.

The source whose temperature is to be found is viewed through the red glass, and a lamp whose filament is maintained at a known temperature is placed between the source and the glass. The simplest method of working, applicable when the temperature of the source is not above the highest temperature to which the lamp filament can be heated, is to adjust the temperature of the filament until this is invisible against the background of the source. Then, as both are equally bright in light of wave-length λ, E_λ is the same for both, and the temperature of the source is the same as that of the lamp. This is the principle of the *disappearing filament pyrometer*.

If, however, the temperature T to be measured is greater than T_1', that of the comparison lamp, E_λ for the source exceeds E_λ' for the lamp. Using Wien's formula,

$$E_\lambda' = c_1\lambda^{-5}e^{-c_2/\lambda T'}, \quad E_\lambda = c_1\lambda^{-5}e^{-c_2/\lambda T}.$$

$$\therefore \frac{E_\lambda'}{E_\lambda} = \frac{e^{-c_2/\lambda T'}}{e^{-c_2/\lambda T}} = e^{c_2/\lambda(1/T - 1/T')}.$$

$$\therefore \ln\frac{E_\lambda'}{E_\lambda} = k\left(\frac{1}{T} - \frac{1}{T'}\right), \quad \text{where } k = \frac{c_2}{\lambda}.$$

The ratio E_λ'/E_λ is either fixed at a known fraction by using a filter or rotating sector which transmits this fraction, when the temperature of the lamp is adjusted to give a match ; or else the ratio E_λ'/E_λ is determined directly by ordinary optical photometric means, using a *polarising photometer*.

Instruments using the total radiation law for the measurement of high temperatures are called " radiation pyrometers " as a rule, while pyrometers using the distribution law are usually called " optical pyrometers ".

Total radiation pyrometer. The Féry total radiation pyrometer is shown in Fig. 183. A concave mirror C focuses the beam of radiation which enters through the aperture AA, on to the thermocouple receiver N, in front of which is a limiting diaphragm. The cold junction of the couple is shielded from radiation, by a tongue and a box M surrounding the couple. The mirror may be a gold film deposited on glass, or a film of gold or nickel on copper. The E.M.F. of the thermocouple is recorded on a millivoltmeter attached to the terminals shown.

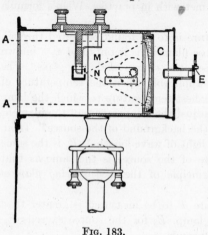

As the steady temperature excess of the hot junction depends on the rate at which it receives radiation from the source (if Newton's Law of Cooling can be assumed, it should be proportional to this excess), and if the E.M.F. of the couple is proportional to the temperature difference between its hot and cold junctions, the millivoltmeter readings should be proportional to $(T^4 - T_0^4)$, or to T^4 approxi-

Fig. 183.

mately, if T is very large compared with T_0. The millivoltmeter can thus be graduated to read temperatures directly.

It is important that the image of the source be focused accurately on the diaphragm, and this is done by moving the mirror C. The diaphragm is observed through a hole in C by the eyepiece E. Provided the image is large enough to cover the hole in the diaphragm, the distance from source to instrument has no effect on the readings, except that due to different absorption by different thicknesses of the intervening air. If the distance between pyrometer and source is doubled, then, by the law of inverse squares, the total radiation received by C is reduced to one fourth ; but as the diameter of the image is halved, its area is reduced also to one fourth, so the radiation falling on unit area of the image per second is unaltered.

The reading of the instrument is not as a rule quite proportional to the fourth power of the absolute temperature of the source, for several reasons. The E.M.F. of the thermocouple is not strictly proportional to the temperature difference between the junctions ; stray reflections from the walls of the box enclosing the thermocouple produce disturbances, the steady rate of loss of heat from the hot junction of the thermocouple is not strictly proportional to the temperature excess, and conduction along the couple wires causes a slight temperature rise in the cold junction. When the instrument is calibrated, it is found that the reading is proportional to *some power* of T, but this varies between 3·8 and 4·2, instead of being exactly 4.

It has been stated that the reading is independent of the distance of the source, provided the image covers the diaphragm. As geometrical optics, this is quite true. But the rise in temperature of the plate covering the diaphragm, and the consequent expansion of the hole, depends on the total energy falling on the plate ; the reading is a little higher if the source is close, because this aperture is a little larger. Atmospheric absorption, particularly due to water vapour and carbon dioxide, convection currents from source to instrument, and the effects of stray reflections within the receiver, all vary to some extent with the distance.

The total radiation pyrometer is usually calibrated between 800° C. and 1400° C. by sighting it on the inside of an electrically heated muffle furnace, the radiation from which approximates to that from a black body. The temperature of the exact portion of the interior on which the instrument is focused is measured by one or more platinum-rhodium thermocouples. In actual use, the *emissivity* e_λ / E_λ of the hot surface under examination must be known, so that the readings can be corrected for the fact that this is not a perfectly black body.

Temperatures above 1400° C. can be measured by the aid of a rotating sector between the source and the pyrometer. The transmission ratio (that is, the fraction of the incident energy transmitted) is readily found, for this is simply *angular width in degrees of clear part* ÷ 360°, since an opaque disc from which a clear sector of, say, 60° has been cut out will, if rotated fairly rapidly in front of the pyrometer, allow only 60/360 of the radiation falling on it in any given time to reach the pyrometer. If μ be the transmission factor of the sector, $T°$ K. the temperature of the source, and $T_{obs}°$ K., the indication of the pyrometer, the radiation from a source at temperature T_{obs} (which is proportional to T_{obs}^4) is reproduced by a fraction μ of the radiation from a source at temperature T (which is proportional to T^4).

Thus $$T_{obs}^4 = \mu T^4, \quad \text{and} \quad T = T_{obs} \div \sqrt[4]{\mu}.$$

Disappearing filament pyrometer. This is essentially a telescope, the objective of which focuses a real image of the source upon the filament of a standard lamp. This is viewed by means of an ordinary eyepiece through a piece of red glass, shown outside the eyepiece in Fig. 184, but usually mounted between the eyepiece and the filament. The temperature of the standard lamp is adjusted by means of a rheostat until the filament is indistinguishable from the background. Then E_λ for red light is the same for both source and filament, which are thus both at the same temperature. The lamp circuit contains an ammeter, which is calibrated to read temperatures directly.

Since, if absorption due to the air be neglected, the brightness of the image formed by the objective is independent of the distance of the object, the distance between pyrometer and source does not matter.

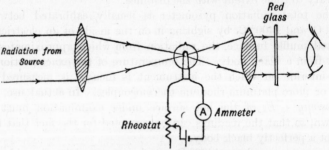

FIG. 184.—Disappearing filament pyrometer.

The disappearing filament pyrometer can be used as it is up to 1400° C., the maximum temperature at which it is convenient to run a standard lamp. For higher temperatures, filters or rotating sectors must be used to reduce the radiation from the source in a known proportion, as described on p. 399.

Let such a filter or sector transmit a fraction μ of the radiation from the source at temperature T, and let the filament disappear when its temperature is T'. Then, if E_λ and E_λ' are the emissive powers for source and filament at T and T' respectively, then as μE_λ just matches E_λ', $\dfrac{E_\lambda'}{E_\lambda} = \mu$.

But
$$\ln \frac{E_\lambda'}{E_\lambda} = k\left(\frac{1}{T} - \frac{1}{T'}\right).$$

$$\therefore \ln \mu = k\left(\frac{1}{T} - \frac{1}{T'}\right),$$

whence the value of T is found.

Wanner optical pyrometer. This is really a polarising *photometer*, and to understand it thoroughly reference should first be made to an account of plane polarised light. The chief feature of interest is that the comparison electric lamp is at a *fixed* but unknown temperature. Fig. 185 is a very simplified version of the apparatus, sufficient detail only being given to explain the principle.

Radiation from the source passes through a diaphragm and falls on a Rochon prism, a doubly refracting calcite prism which produces two beams of plane polarised light, polarised in planes at right angles to one another as represented by the arrows $\longleftrightarrow$ and $\updownarrow$, and emerging in slightly different directions. A biprism bends down one of these, the $\longleftrightarrow$ beam to pass through a diaphragm which obstructs the other. Radiation from the comparison source is similarly treated by the Rochon prism, but it is the $\updownarrow$ beam which is bent *up* to pass through the diaphragm.

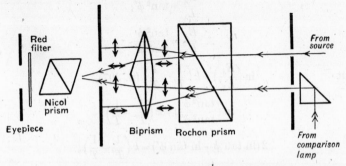

Fig. 185.—Scheme of Wanner optical pyrometer.

Two beams of light, polarised at right angles to one another, fall on the Nicol prism, and then pass through a red filter as used on the disappearing filament pyrometer. A suitable lens system (not shown) enables an observer looking through the prism to see two semicircular patches of light side by side.

Let E_λ be the intensity (intensity in the photometric sense is the same as emissive power) of the radiation of the red light from the source at unknown temperature $T°$ K., and L_λ the intensity of light of the same wave-length from the standard lamp. In one position of the Nicol prism, the light from the lamp is completely extinguished and that of the source fully transmitted ; call this position 1. When the Nicol prism has been rotated through an angle of 90° (into position 2), light from the lamp is fully transmitted, while that from the source is extinguished. Rotating the Nicol prism from position 1 to position 2 thus causes the brightness of the patch of light due to the lamp to grow brighter, and that due to the source to grow dimmer, so there will be one position of the Nicol prism at which both patches are equally bright. If ϕ be the angle turned through by the Nicol prism from position 1 when this occurs, the optical theory leads to the equation

$$\frac{E_\lambda}{L_\lambda} = \tan^2 \phi.$$

But here we do not know the temperature of the lamp filament ; all that is known is that it is steady. Repeating the experiment with another source at a known absolute temperature $T_1'°$ K., E_λ' being the intensity, and ϕ' the observed angle from position 1 :

$$\frac{E_\lambda'}{L_\lambda} = \tan^2 \phi',$$

$$\therefore \frac{E_\lambda}{E_\lambda'} = \frac{\tan^2 \phi}{\tan^2 \phi'}.$$

But $$\ln \left(\frac{E_\lambda}{E_\lambda'} \right) = k \left(\frac{1}{T'} - \frac{1}{T} \right) \text{ (p. 397)},$$

$$\therefore \ln \left(\frac{\tan^2 \phi}{\tan^2 \phi'} \right) = k \left(\frac{1}{T'} - \frac{1}{T} \right) ;$$

or $$2 \left(\ln \tan \phi - \ln \tan \phi' \right) = k \left(\frac{1}{T'} - \frac{1}{T} \right),$$

the relation between $\ln \tan \phi$ and $1/T$ being linear.

DIVERGENCE BETWEEN TRUE AND APPARENT TEMPERATURES

with Pyrometers sighted upon different materials in the open

RADIATION PYROMETER

Observed Temp. Degrees Centigrade.	True Temperature. Degrees Centigrade.				
	Molten Iron.	Molten Copper.	Copper Oxide.	Iron Oxide.	Nickel Oxide.
600	—	1130	720	630	710
650	—	1210	775	—	755
700	—	1290	830	735	800
750	—	—	890	—	845
800	1200	—	945	840	895
850	1270	—	1000	—	940
900	1340	—	1060	945	985
950	1410	—	1115	—	1030
1000	1475	—	1170	1050	1075
1050	1550	—	—	—	1120
1100	1610	—	—	1155	1165
1150	1680	—	—	—	1210
1200	1750	—	—	1260	1255

OPTICAL PYROMETER (using red light $\lambda = 0.65\mu$)

Observed Temp. Degrees Centigrade.	True Temperature. Degrees Centigrade.						
	Molten Copper.	Molten Iron.	Solid Iron Oxide.	Solid Nickel Oxide.	Nichrome or Chromel.	Molten Slag.	Bright Platinum.
700	—	—	700	701	702	—	750
800	—	—	801	802	804	—	861
900	—	—	902	904	906	—	973
950	1088	—	953	955	958	—	1030
1000	1150	—	1004	1007	1010	—	1087
1050	1213	—	1055	1058	1063	—	1144
1100	1277	1183	1106	1110	1116	—	1202
1150	1341	1239	1158	1162	1170	—	1260
1200	1405	1296	1210	1215	1224	—	1320
1250	1470	1353	—	1267	—	—	1375
1300	1536	1410	—	1320	—	—	1435
1400	—	1525	—	—	—	1455	1555
1500	—	1641	—	—	—	1565	1675
1600	—	1758	—	—	—	1670	—
1700	—	1876	—	—	—	1780	—
1750	—	1935	—	—	—	1830	—

Comparison of total radiation and optical pyrometers. The total radiation pyrometer is direct-reading and needs no setting by the observer. It can be used with continuous-recording instruments. Also, it can be used for lower temperatures than optical pyrometers.

Departure from black-body conditions of the surface under test, and the absorbing effect of carbon dioxide and water vapour, affect the total radiation pyrometer much more than the optical pyrometers, with their restricted range of wave-lengths to which these gases are relatively transparent. When the total radiation pyrometer is enclosed in a vacuum containing the furnace, its readings agree with those of an optical pyrometer to less than 0·5° at 1750° C., and to about 4° at 2800° C.

The polarising pyrometer is the better of the two optical pyrometers since (a) there is no need for neutral filters or rotating sectors to cut down the radiation from the source, even at the highest temperatures, and (b) the comparison electric lamp can be checked from time to time against a photometer standard. On the other hand, the disappearing filament pyrometer enables the telescope to be focused sharply on the exact point at which the temperature is required, and it is the simpler of the two optical pyrometers in use.

The tables on p. 403, from the Cambridge Instrument Co.'s pamphlet " The Accurate Measurement of Temperature ", show the considerable difference between the observed (equivalent black-body) temperature and the true temperature for surfaces of different emissivities.

TEMPERATURES OBTAINED BY RADIATION METHODS

Stefan's Law and Wien's Displacement Law are deducible using thermodynamics, by considering a reversible engine in which the working substance is radiation. As the behaviour of a reversible engine is independent of the nature of the working substance, it follows that the temperature T appearing in the radiation formulae is the temperature measured on the absolute thermodynamic scale.

Both total radiation and optical pyrometers thus indicate the absolute temperature on the thermodynamic scale of a black body to which they are exposed. But as few actual surfaces approximate to black bodies, the readings must either be corrected for departure of the surface from blackness, if this can be done, or accepted with the reservation that they do not represent absolute temperatures on the Kelvin scale.

With the total radiation pyrometer which has been calibrated on a black body, the true temperature T on the absolute scale is obtained from the observed temperature T_{obs} if the emissivity (the ratio emissive power of surface/emissive power of black body) is known. The equation obtained from Stefan's Law is $T_{obs}^4 = \epsilon T^4$, where ϵ is the emissivity. If the emissivity is not known, the reading T_{obs} is still a valuable piece of information ; it is called the brightness temperature of the surface examined.

With the optical pyrometer which has been calibrated on a black body, the true absolute temperature T can be calculated by Wien's formula from the reading T_{obs} if the emissivity of the surface under examination for the range of wave-lengths used is known. If the emissivity is not known, the value of T_{obs} is still very useful ; it is called the brightness temperature of the surface *for this wave-length range*.

The emissivity can only be determined experimentally by examining the radiation from the surface when it is maintained at a known temperature which is measured by some independent method, so radiation and optical pyrometers can only really be relied on to give temperatures *on the Kelvin scale* within the range of other types of thermometer.

The colour temperature of a non-black body X is the temperature at which a black body must be maintained in order that the distribution of energy in the spectrum of X may be matched as closely as possible. If X is radiating very nearly as a black body, the colour temperature will be fairly near the true temperature ; if not, the colour temperature can only be regarded as a concise way of describing the *spectrum of the radiation*, for it yields little other useful information about the body itself.

Temperature of the sun's surface. Determination of the rate at which the sun's radiation falls on unit area of the earth's surface enables the total energy emitted per square centimetre per second from the sun to be calculated, and thus by applying Stefan's Law the sun's temperature can be found.

The energy received per square centimetre of the earth's surface in unit time, the earth being at its mean distance from the sun and the radiation falling normally upon the absorbing surface, when corrected for the absorption of the atmosphere, is called the solar constant, S. The mean value of S is about 1·93 calories per sq. cm. per minute, or about $1·34 \times 10^6$ ergs per sq. cm. per second. The value of S at any time is obtained by allowing the sun's radiation to enter a hollow chamber through an aperture of known area ; the inside of the chamber is blackened to absorb the radiation, and the rate of reception of energy is found by surrounding the chamber with a continuous flow calorimeter. The rate of supply of heat by radiation is measured by reproducing the same temperature rise by supplying heat electrically at a known rate when the apparatus is screened from radiation. Such an instrument is called a pyrheliometer (Fig. 186). Elaborate corrections for the absorption of the atmosphere must be made.

Another type of pyrheliometer, due to Ångström, comprises two exactly similar metal strips, blackened on one side, one strip being exposed to the source of radiation, while the other is protected from the radiation by a double-walled screen. Two thermo-junctions of constantan-copper, arranged differentially, are attached, one to the back of each strip. An electric current is passed through the screened strip, and is adjusted until no current flows between the two thermo-junctions, showing that the temperatures of the two strips are equal. The electrical energy expended is then equal to the radiated energy absorbed by the exposed strip, and the absolute value of the radiation in C.G.S. units can be readily calculated. The strips can be exposed alternately to the radiations to be measured,

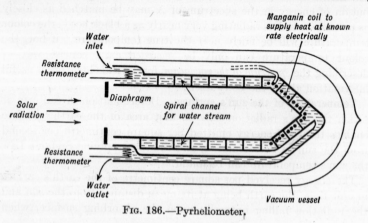

FIG. 186.—Pyrheliometer,

enabling any slight errors due to mechanical inequality in the strips to be eliminated.

The radius of the sun is $4 \cdot 33 \times 10^5$ miles, and the mean distance of the earth from the sun is $9 \cdot 28 \times 10^7$ miles. Thus, if E be the energy emitted per square centimetre per second at the sun's surface, by the time it has reached the earth's distance it has spread out to cover an area $\left(\dfrac{9 \cdot 28 \times 10^7}{4 \cdot 33 \times 10^5}\right)^2$ times as large, whence

$$S = E \left(\frac{4 \cdot 33 \times 10^5}{9 \cdot 28 \times 10^7}\right)^2, \quad \text{or} \quad E = S \left(\frac{9 \cdot 28 \times 10^7}{4 \cdot 33 \times 10^5}\right)^2 = 46,000S.$$

The value of S is $1 \cdot 34 \times 10^6$ ergs per sq. cm. per second, so

$$E = 46,000 \times 1 \cdot 34 \times 10^6 = 6 \cdot 16 \times 10^{10} \text{ ergs per sq. cm. per second.}$$

Using Stefan's Law, and taking the value of σ as $5 \cdot 75 \times 10^{-5}$ units, since $E = \sigma T^4$.

$$6 \cdot 16 \times 10^{10} = 5 \cdot 75 \times 10^{-5} \times T^4.$$

$$\therefore \quad T = \sqrt[4]{\frac{6 \cdot 16 \times 10^{10}}{5 \cdot 75 \times 10^{-5}}} = 5720° \text{ absolute.}$$

This is the temperature of the black body which would have the same value of E as that computed for the sun ; that is, the *brightness temperature* of the sun's surface.

The surface temperature of the sun has also been estimated by applying Wien's Displacement Law ; that is, finding the wave-length λ_{max} cm. at which E_λ is greatest, and using the equation $\lambda_{max}T = 0 \cdot 293$, obtaining the *colour temperature*.

The sun's temperature increases from the surface towards the centre, and the radiation actually emitted originates at many different depths and temperatures, the outer layers absorbing more or less selectively a great deal of the radiation from within. Thus the radiation finally emitted certainly cannot correspond to that of a black body at a definite temperature. Further, the absorption of the radiation from within is least at the centre of the sun's disc because the rays pass perpendicularly through the outer layers, and greatest at the edges, where the path through the outer layers is most oblique. The value of λ_{max} for the radiation from the centre of the disc is 4580 Å.U., and for the radiation from the edge 5050 Å.U. Thus T is $0 \cdot 293/4580 \times 10^{-8} = 6400°$ absolute for the radiation from the centre and $T = 0 \cdot 293/5050 \times 10^{-8} = 5800°$ absolute for the radiation from the edge. This calculation is of doubtful value, since it is not legitimate to apply the displacement law at all to a non-black body ; but the temperatures obtained are of the same order as that given by the total radiation methods. Recent results for the colour temperature based on visible spectrum measurements have given values as high as 7100° K., while for the ultra-violet spectrum the figure is as low as 4800° K. It will be seen that the colour temperature is more a means of describing an observed spectral distribution than a temperature reading in the ordinary sense.

It should be emphasised again that these figures are not "the temperature of the sun " ; they are the surface temperature of a black body which would have the same total radiation or spectral distribution as is measured. Different methods of approach have suggested very much higher local temperatures, even at the surface. The ionising properties of the radiation from bright eruptions on the sun, as evidenced by the effect on the upper atmosphere, are those of ultra-violet radiation from a body at 10,000° to 20,000° K. The spectrum of the solar corona contains lines at one time ascribed to an as yet unknown element " coronium " ; efforts are now being made to reconcile them with the lines which would be emitted by atoms of iron, nickel, or calcium in a very highly ionised state such as would require a very high temperature indeed. This, and the breadth of the lines themselves, suggest temperatures of the order 660,000° K. to 2,300,000° K. in the corona, according to the Swedish physicist Edlén (see " Nature ", December 26, 1942). The physical meaning of such a " temperature " is as yet unknown. Prof. M. N. Saha has recently suggested that nuclear fission, rather than any such exceedingly high coronal temperature, may be responsible for these highly ionised atoms.

It is accepted nowadays that the *internal* temperature of the sun must be about 20,000,000° K. The argument leading to this conclusion is as follows. Radiation has mass associated with it at the fixed rate of 1 gm. for every 9×10^{20} ergs of radiant energy. The sun radiates 3.8×10^{33} ergs per second, and thus loses 4.2×10^{12} gm. per second, or 250 million tons a minute. This is accounted for by nuclear reactions in which four hydrogen nuclei, or protons, of mass totalling 4.030 units on the usual atomic weight scale, combine to form a helium nucleus of mass 4.003 units, yielding 0.027 units of mass in the form of radiation which, originating as γ-rays or X-rays, is absorbed in the outer layers of the sun and re-emitted as temperature radiation. The chain of nuclear reactions, involving carbon nuclei which play the part of nuclear catalysts, has been worked out ; and the important point is that this chain of reactions is one which can only take place at a temperature of at least 20,000,000° K. The supply of protons in the sun is gradually dwindling by this process ; but at the lowest estimate the supply should allow the sun's present rate of emission for another two thousand million years. These figures have been taken from an article by Sir James Jeans in " Nature " of January 2, 1943.

Residual rays. The selective reflection of quartz, fluorite, and other materials for certain wave-lengths in the infra-red has been the subject of several investigations (see Preston's " Theory of Heat ", pp. 577, 578). For these wave-lengths the substances act like perfect mirrors, while absorbing radiations of shorter and longer wave-lengths, so that after several reflections from surfaces of a given material the resulting rays (residual rays) are a beam of practically monochromatic radiation. The wave-length of the residual rays of quartz is about $8\cdot8\mu$; this happens to be in the region of the spectrum where the atmosphere is exceedingly transparent, several hundred yards of air at ordinary pressure causing little diminution of the intensity.

This is the basis of a new form of radiation pyrometer devised in America by J. Strong, and described briefly in the " Journal of Scientific Instruments " of January 1942. Radiation from the source, which may be at some great distance, is reflected from five polished quartz surfaces to isolate the $8\cdot8\mu$ band, and finally falls on a compensated vacuum thermocouple. This is calibrated using black bodies at the ice point and the steam point, and has been used between $-100°$ C. and $+100°$ C., giving an accuracy of $0\cdot1°$ C. It has also been used to estimate the " infra-red " surface temperature of the sun, the result indicated being 7080° K.

QUESTIONS ON CHAPTER IX

1. Distinguish between conduction, convection, and radiation of heat, giving your conception of the way in which each takes place.

The bulb of a thermometer is coated with a very thin layer of lamp-black. How will its readings compare with those of an uncoated thermometer placed near it in the open (*a*) in bright sunshine, (*b*) on a clear and dry night, (c) on a damp and cloudy night? In each case give reasons for your answer. (J.M.B.)

2. Describe one experiment to show that a polished metal surface is a poor absorber of heat, and one experiment to show that such a surface reflects a high proportion of a beam of light falling upon it.

Briefly compare heat and light radiations from the standpoint of (a) velocity, (b) effect at a distance, (c) simple refraction, (d) transmission through material substances. (J.M.B.)

3. A block of metal is heated and (a) exposed to ordinary atmospheric conditions, or (b) placed in a high vacuum. State concisely the factors that govern the rate at which its temperature falls under conditions (a) and (b).

Energy is supplied at the rate of 165 watts to a closed cylindrical canister 5 cm. in radius and 15 cm. high, filled with water and exposed to the air of the room, which is at 15° C. It is found that the temperature of the water remains steady at 80° C. Find the rate of heat loss per unit area of the vessel per degree C. excess temperature. Estimate also the fall of temperature in a minute when the energy supply is shut off. Neglect the weight of the canister itself. (L.)

4. Describe and explain the steps to be followed in order (i) to insulate thermally a quantity of liquid, and (ii) to keep the temperature of a liquid constant at about 50° C. (L.)

5. A hot and a cold body are placed a few centimetres apart in a room. In what ways is the cold body heated by the hot one? How would you demonstrate the effect of each way? How would you make the loss of heat from a hot body to the surroundings very small? (C.S.)

6. Give an account of the different ways in which a body may lose heat.

Explain how the losses of heat from a vacuum flask are reduced. (O. & C.)

7. Define " coefficient of thermal conductivity ". A rod of copper of which the coefficient of thermal conductivity is 0·92 c.g.s. units is maintained at 500° C. at one end while the other end is in contact with a block of ice. If the rod is well lagged and is 100 cm. long and 2 sq. cm. in cross-section, find the mass of ice melted per minute.

(Latent heat of fusion = 80 cal./gm.) (O. & C.)

8. Describe the various ways in which heat can be transmitted from one body to another.

A copper block, of mass 200 grams, is suspended in a vacuum by a copper wire 10 cm. long and 1 mm. in diameter. If the copper is initially at 100° C. above its surroundings, find the rate at which it begins to cool, assuming that radiation can be neglected. (Specific heat of copper = 0·093 ; thermal conductivity of copper = 0·90.) (O. & C.)

9. Define the coefficient of thermal conductivity of a substance. If the numerical value of the coefficient for a substance is 0·003 when the units of mass, length, time, and temperature are one gram, one centimetre, one second, and one degree centigrade respectively, what will

be its numerical value when these units are changed to one pound, one foot, one second, and one degree Fahrenheit respectively?

One end of a uniform bar is kept in steam and the other in melting ice. Show that when a steady state is reached, the distribution of temperature along the bar is linear if the bar is lagged so that there is no loss of heat by radiation. (1 lb. = 450 gm. ; 1 ft. = 30·5 cm.) (O. & C.)

10. Describe a method of determining the thermal conductivity of a solid of high conductivity.

The metal of a boiler is 1·5 cm. thick. Find the difference of temperature between its faces if 32 kg. of water is evaporated from the boiler per sq. metre per hour. Why is this difference so much less than that between the flue gases and the water in the boiler? (Latent heat of steam = 540 calories per gm. ; thermal conductivity of metal of boiler = 0·15 c.g.s. units.) (C.)

11. Describe one way of measuring the heat conductivity of copper.

A metal object is embedded in a block of ice at 0° C. Show that it may gradually travel through the block under gravity, and discuss the factors which determine the rate of travel.

If the piece of metal is a vertical lead cylinder (density 11 gm. per c.c., heat conductivity 0·08 cal. per sq. cm. per sec. per unit temperature gradient), calculate the maximum rate at which it would descend, making the simplifying assumptions that the heat-flow is vertical and that there are no frictional forces.

(Pressure coefficient of melting-point of ice = 8×10^{-9} ° C. per dyne.)

(O.S.)

12. What is meant by the coefficient of thermal conductivity of a substance?

Calculate approximately the heat passing out per minute through the walls and windows of a room 7 by 5 by 3 metres if the walls are of brick 20 cm. thick and have windows of glass 0·5 cm. thick and of total area 5 square metres. The temperature of the room is 20° C. above that outside. The thermal conductivity of brick and of glass may be taken as 12×10^{-4} and 17×10^{-4} c.g.s. units respectively. (O.)

13. A bar of metal whose length is l and whose thermal conductivity is k has a heating coil of resistance R wound round one end, and is jacketed so as to prevent loss of heat from the sides or from the heated end. The far end is open to the air and is found to acquire a temperature T when a current i passes through the heating coil. Deduce the temperature of the heated end after equilibrium is attained and indicate the nature of the temperature distribution along the bar. (C.S.)

14. Describe a method of measuring the thermal conductivity of a poor conductor, such as glass or indiarubber.

A is a compound slab made up of two layers, one of thickness d_1 and thermal conductivity k_1, the other of thickness d_2 and thermal conductivity k_2. B is a slab of thickness $d_1 + d_2$ and thermal conductivity k. One face of each slab is maintained at θ_1° C., and the other at θ_2° C. until a steady state is reached. If the rate of conduction of heat per unit area through the two slabs is the same, find the relation between k_1 and k_2. (O. & C.)

15. Define the coefficient of heat conductivity of a material.

A bungalow is rectangular in cross-section, with sides 10 metres by 8, and has a flat roof 3 metres above the ground. The average thickness of its sides and roof is 15 cm., and they are constructed of a cement whose conductivity is 6×10^{-4} calories per sq. cm. per unit temperature gradient. The windows have a total area of 10 square metres, and are of glass 3 mm. thick, whose conductivity is $2 \cdot 5 \times 10^{-3}$. The bungalow is maintained at a temperature above that of its surroundings. What fraction of the total loss of heat by conduction is lost through the windows?   (O. & C.)

16. Define thermal conductivity and explain how you would measure the thermal conductivity of a good conductor.

A composite metal bar of uniform section is made up of lengths of 25 cm. of copper, 10 cm. of nickel and 15 cm. of aluminium, each part being in perfect thermal contact with the adjoining part. The copper end of the composite rod is maintained at 100° C. and the aluminium end at 0° C. The whole rod is lagged so that it may be assumed that no heat losses occur at the sides. When the conditions have become constant the junctions of copper-nickel and nickel-aluminium are at t_1° C. and t_2° C. respectively. Calculate the values of t_1 and t_2, assuming the values : thermal conductivity of

copper - 0·92 cal. per sec. per sq. cm. per unit temperature slope.
nickel - 0·14   ,,   ,,   ,,
aluminium 0·50   ,,   ,,   ,,   (L.)

17. Define thermal conductivity and explain how it can be measured in a particular case.

In estimating the rate of cooling of the earth Kelvin used the following data. Conductivity of earth's crust = 0·005 calories per sq. cm. per unit centigrade temperature gradient per second. Thermal capacity of surface rock per c.c. = 0·5 calories per degree centigrade. Temperature gradient at surface 1° C. per 30 metres. Radius of earth = 6×10^8 cm. Assuming the earth to be homogeneous, find the annual cooling.   (C.S.)

18. State the laws of heat conduction, and describe a method for the measurement of the specific conductivity of a good conductor.

A boiler supplies steam to a 100 H.P. turbine, whose efficiency is 15 per cent. The temperature of the water is 150° C. and that of the outer boiler-wall 300° C. What is the minimum surface of the boiler exposed to the furnace if the thickness of the wall is 4 mm.?

(Conductivity of the material of the boiler = 0·9 calories per sec. per square cm. per unit temperature gradient ; 1 H.P. = 746 watts ; mechanical equivalent of heat $4 \cdot 2 \times 10^7$ ergs per calorie.)   (O. & C.)

19. A thin walled copper pipe 6 cm. in diameter passes through a water bath at 0° C. Brine at − 10° C. is circulated through the pipe, and a layer of ice 5 cm. thick has formed round it. How long will it take for the next half millimetre to form? (Thermal conductivity of ice = 0·005 c.g.s. units, latent heat of fusion of ice = 80 calories per gram.)   (O.S.)

20. Describe an accurate form of ice calorimeter.

A pond is covered with ice 4 centimetres thick; the temperature of the air above the ice is $-12°$ C. At what rate, expressed in centimetres per hour, will the ice thicken?

(The thermal conductivity of ice is $0 \cdot 0052$ in C.G.S. units. The density of ice is $0 \cdot 92$ grams per c.c. The latent heat of fusion of ice is 80 calories per gram.) (O.S.)

21. Give an account of a method of comparing the thermal conductivities of two metals in the form of rods.

The thickness of ice on a lake is 5 cm. and the temperature of the air is $-10°$ C. At what rate is the thickness of the ice increasing, and approximately how long will it take for the thickness of the ice to be doubled?

(Data as for question 20.) (O. & C.)

22. Define thermal conductivity, and give an account of some way of finding its value experimentally for either a metal or cork.

If a uniform layer of ice, 10 cm. thick, has formed on a pond, find approximately how long it will take to increase in thickness by 1 mm. if the temperature of the surface is $-5°$ C., the thermal conductivity of ice $0 \cdot 005$ C.G.S. centigrade units, the latent heat of fusion of ice 80 cal. per gm., and 1 c.c. of water forms $1 \cdot 09$ c.c. of ice. (J.M.B.)

23. What is meant by the statement that the thermal conductivity of brickwork is $0 \cdot 0012$ C.G.S. centigrade units?

Calculate the heat passing per hour through the brick walls, 25 cm. thick, of a room 5 metres square and 3 metres high, if the inside and outside surfaces have temperatures of $15°$ C. and $0°$ C. respectively. (Include doors and windows in the area of the walls.) (J.M.B.)

24. Define thermal conductivity and describe critically a method of measuring it for a bad conductor.

A wire of resistivity 2×10^{-4} ohms per cm.^{3} and 1 mm. in diameter carries a current of 10 amps. If it is covered uniformly with a cylindrical layer of insulating material having a coefficient of thermal conductivity of 6×10^{-4} calories cm.$^{-1}$ degree^{-1} sec.$^{-1}$ and a diameter of 1 cm., what is the temperature difference between the inner and outer surfaces of the insulator? (1 cal. $= 4 \cdot 2$ watt-secs.) (C.S.)

25. Give an account of the properties of infra-red radiations and describe how these properties may be investigated. (C.S.)

26. A platinum wire is raised gradually in temperature. Give the character of the radiation from the wire as the temperature increases and show how you would study the character of the radiation experimentally. (C.S.)

27. The filament of an electric lamp A is of diameter d, and carries a current c_1, while that of a similar lamp B has diameter nd and carries a current c_2. Find the ratio of c_1 to c_2 if the temperatures of the filaments are the same. You may neglect end losses and assume that each filament is in vacuo. (C.S., *part question*.)

28. Discuss the relation between absorption and radiation. Do you agree with the statement " bodies absorb when cold the radiation they give out when hot "?

(C.S.)

29. Discuss Prevost's theory of exchanges, and explain how it may be used to find the relation between the radiating and absorbing powers of a surface.

(C.S.)

30. What is meant by the emissive power and the absorptive power of a body for radiation?

What is meant by a black body?

Discuss the observation that objects are invisible when they are viewed through a small hole in a constant temperature enclosure raised to incandescence.

(C.S.)

31. Give definitions of conduction, convection, and radiation.

A certain piece of glass is said to be nearly transparent to visible light, but to absorb a large percentage of heat radiation. Describe experimental arrangements you would use to investigate the accuracy of this statement, explaining how you would use your apparatus. (O.)

32. Explain what is meant by the emissivity of a surface. Describe experiments to show the following :

(a) Good reflectors are poor emitters.

(b) Radiant heat is long wavelength light.

(c) Silica is much more transparent to heat rays than glass.

(d) The radiation in a cavity depends only on the temperature of the walls (supposed uniform) and not on the material of which they are made.

(O.S.)

33. Describe what you understand by a train of waves, and show that it can transmit energy. The energy reaching the earth's surface from the sun is 2 cals. per min. per cm.^{2} What is the energy density of sunlight at the earth's surface in ergs per c.c.?

(O.S.)

34. How can the existence of radiation from a hot but not luminous body be demonstrated, and the laws of transmission, reflection, and refraction of such radiation investigated? Compare its behaviour in these respects with that of light. What reasons are there to conclude that the radiation is of the same type as light but of longer wavelength?

(O. & C.)

35. Describe and compare any two accurate methods of measuring high temperatures.

(C.S.)

36. How can the temperature of a furnace be determined from observations on the radiation emitted?

Calculate the apparent temperature of the sun from the following information :

Sun's radius : $4 \cdot 4 \times 10^5$ miles.

Distance from earth : $9 \cdot 2 \times 10^7$ miles.

Solar constant : $0 \cdot 14$ watt per sq. cm.

Stefan's constant : $5 \cdot 7 \times 10^{-5}$ ergs cm.$^{-2}$ sec.$^{-1}$ deg.$^{-4}$ (J.M.B.)

37. Describe a method of measuring the heat received from the sun at the earth's surface.

Assuming this to be 1·5 cal. per sq. cm. per min. and the conductivity of the earth's crust to be 0·0027, what must the temperature gradient in the ground be in order that the heat escaping may just be balanced by the heat received?   (C.S.)

38. Trace the transformation of electrical energy in (a) a vacuum tungsten lamp, (b) a gas-filled tungsten lamp. To what do you ascribe the higher efficiency of the latter as a source of light?

(O. & C., *part question*.)

39. Two long tungsten wires A and B, of the same length and of radii r_1 and r_2 respectively, are maintained at the same temperature, under the same conditions, by steady currents i_1 and i_2 respectively. If the difference of potential between the ends of A is V_1, find that between the ends of B.   (C.S., *part question*.)

40. State the factors which control the rate of cooling of a body, and describe experiments in illustration of your answer.

(C.W.B., *part question*.)

CHAPTER X

HEAT PHENOMENA IN THE ATMOSPHERE

Introduction. The atmosphere is a mixture of gases extending to a great height above the surface of the earth. Going upwards the density falls off nearly exponentially (or by " compound interest "), and there is no sharp edge. The highest of the conducting layers of the ionosphere (the region from which radio waves are reflected) is at a height of about 300 km., and auroras are sometimes observed at even greater heights, so the atmosphere can be considered as extending at least for several hundred kilometres up, although extremely tenuous at great heights.

Dry air at sea level has the following percentage composition :

	By volume	By weight
Nitrogen	78·03	75·48
Oxygen	20·99	23·18
Argon	0·94	1·29
Carbon dioxide	0·03	0·045

There are also traces of the inert gases neon, helium, krypton, xenon. Below about 15 km., the air is uniformly mixed ; above this level, the heavier molecules dwindle most rapidly, so the composition varies at different heights. But for most purposes dry air is best regarded as a single uniform gas of " molecular weight " about 29, and atmospheric air as a mixture of this gas with varying proportions of water vapour. The atmosphere is the working substance of a vast heat engine ; the prime source of the energy liberated in the gigantic operations of the weather is the sun, but the air is *almost entirely heated and cooled from below*—sources and sinks are the warm and cold parts of the earth's surface.

Supposing that the sun's radiation corresponds closely to that of a black body at about 6000° K., about one half of the energy is in the visible part of the spectrum and most of the rest in the short-wave infra-red region below 35,000 Å.U. (3.5μ). The extreme ultra-violet part of the spectrum is absorbed by atomic oxygen and ozone at very high altitudes, and the extreme infra-red part by water vapour in the lowest layers, but these represent only a very small fraction of the total energy, and the air is transparent to a very high proportion of the sun's radiation. Much of the radiation is reflected back to space from the earth's surface and from clouds, and some is similarly lost by diffuse scattering; but something like half the energy is absorbed by the earth's surface.

The temperature attained by different parts of the earth's surface under given radiation intensity depends on three factors :

1. *The proportion of the radiation that is absorbed.*

2. *The volume of substance affected.* In the case of the ground, this depends on the conductivity of the surface, and generally the effect is confined to within a few inches of the surface. With water, the radiation penetrates to a depth of several feet before being completely absorbed, and turbulence and mixing may spread the effect to even greater depths.

3. *The heat capacity per unit volume.* The temperature change of the sea is always very much less than that of the land under similar conditions, because more of the radiation is reflected, a greater volume of material receives heat, and the heat capacity per unit volume is very much greater. A rise in temperature of 30° F. on the ground may be accompanied by a change of less than 1° F. at the surface of the sea.

The heating effect of the sun is greatest when the sun is highest in the heavens. This is because less radiation is reflected at small angles of incidence, the path through the atmosphere is shorter and there is less loss by scattering, and the area to be covered by a given beam of radiation is less, so that the radiation received per unit area is greater. Fig. 187 illustrates this point.

Heat is conducted from the warmed surface of the earth to the layer of air close to it, and then spreads through the lower layers

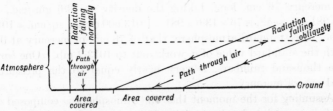

FIG. 187.—Heating of ground depends on altitude of sun.

of the atmosphere by convection and mixing. The earth's surface also loses heat to space by radiation, behaving as a black body at about 300° K., the whole of the radiation being in the form of long-wave infra-red rays, of wave-lengths between 5μ and 50μ, with a maximum at 10μ. Dry air is transparent to the whole of this radiation, but water vapour absorbs very strongly the regions $5\text{-}8\mu$, and $15\text{-}50\mu$ having many sharp characteristic absorption lines in these regions ; the effect of water vapour is thus to aid the atmospheric absorption of heat, and also to retard the rate of loss from the ground, as the energy absorbed by a layer of water vapour is re-radiated again in all directions, much of it back again towards the earth. The region $8\text{-}15\mu$ is not absorbed by water vapour, and this radiation escapes unhindered if the atmosphere is clear ; cooling of the earth's surface by radiation on a still cloudless night takes place by radiation between these limits.

Clouds obstruct the passage of radiation of all wave-lengths, both to and from the earth. The sun's radiation is almost entirely reflected back to space from the top of the cloud, while the whole spectrum of the earth's long-wave radiation is absorbed and re-radiated, much of it downwards towards the earth again. The cloud layer acts as a thermostat ; for if the temperature of the earth's surface rises, increased evaporation gives increased cloud, which cuts off more of the sun's radiation ; and similarly if the temperature falls, less of the sun's radiation is reflected owing to diminished cloud.

Pressure. The mercury barometer is the standard instrument for the observation of pressure at ground level, and aneroid barometers calibrated against mercury barometers are used in other circumstances. The unit of pressure in which the readings are commonly expressed nowadays is the millibar (mb.). One millibar equals one thousand dynes per square centimetre. The pressure of a column of mercury 76 cm. long, taking the density as 13·6 gm./c.c., and $g = 981$ cm./sec.², is $76 \times 13\cdot6 \times 981 = 1,013,600$ dynes/sq. cm. $= 1013\cdot6$ mb. The standard atmosphere, that of 76 cm. of mercury at 0° C. with the standard value of g, works out to 1013·2 mb. One *bar*, or one thousand millibars, is very nearly equal to the pressure of 75·1 cm. of mercury.

Assuming for the moment that the atmosphere is composed of a perfect gas of molecular weight M, maintained throughout at a

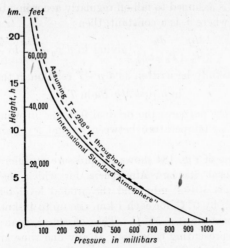

Fig. 188.—Variation of pressure with height.

uniform temperature T, the variation of pressure with altitude can be calculated.

Let the pressure at the ground be p_0 dynes/sq. cm., and that at height h cm. be p dynes/sq. cm. Let ρ gm./c.c. be the density at pressure p.

Then $dp = -g\rho \, dh$ gives the change in pressure dp for a rise dh.

Now, considering *one mole*, $pV = RT$ and $\rho = M/V$, so $\rho = pM/RT$.

$$\therefore \; dp = -p\frac{Mg}{RT}\, dh, \quad \therefore \; \frac{dp}{p} = -\frac{Mg}{RT}\, dh.$$

$$\therefore \; \ln p = -\frac{Mg}{RT}\, h + const.$$

As $p = p_0$ when $h = 0$, the constant is $\ln p_0$;

$$\therefore \; \ln p/p_0 = -\frac{Mgh}{RT}.$$

$$\therefore \; p/p_0 = e^{-Mgh/RT}.$$

Substituting the values $M = 29$, $g = 981$ cm./sec.^{2},

$$T = 288° \text{ K.}, \; R = 8·3 \times 10^7 \text{ ergs./mole/°C.},$$

the dotted curve of Fig. 188 is obtained.

The temperature is not, of course, constant at the ground level value. If it is assumed to fall off regularly according to the formula $T = T_0 - ah$, where a is a constant, then

$$dp/p = -\frac{Mg}{R}\frac{dh}{(T_0 - ah)}, \text{ giving } \ln p/p_0 = \frac{Mg}{Ra}\ln\frac{T_0 - ah}{T_0};$$

which can usefully be written as a $p - T$ relation in the form

$$\ln p/p_0 = Mg/Ra \ln T/T_0.$$

But for most purposes the original formula, in which T is taken as the average temperature between ground level and h, is close enough.

The full line of Fig. 184 shows the pressure at different heights in the International Standard Atmosphere, for which the pressure at ground level is 1013·2 mb., and the ground level temperature of 15° C. falls off by 6° C. for each 1 km. rise up to 11 km., after which it remains constant at −55° C. This, of course, is an ideal state of affairs not representing conditions at any one time and place, but can be taken as representing average conditions for many purposes.

The same calculation can be applied to any one individual gas in the air, if M now means the molecular weight of that gas, and p_0 and p its partial pressures at ground level and height h. It can be seen that, for a given value of p/p_0 the product Mh must have the same value for each constituent ; that is, the heavier the gas, the lower is the level at which its partial pressure is reduced to any given fraction, say 1/1000, of the surface value, so the heavier gases dwindle most rapidly. This result, applicable only to a column of gas at rest, does not hold at all in the lowest 15 km. of the atmosphere, where there is thorough mixing ; at greater heights it may very well represent the facts approximately.

Temperature. Temperature readings in the upper air are usually made nowadays by aircraft equipped with apparatus to record simultaneously the temperature, pressure, and relative humidity, or by free balloons carrying radio-meteorographs, which give out continuous radio signals indicating the values of the readings required. The pioneer work in investigating the upper air was done using free sounding balloons (*ballons-sonde*), which carried very light self-recording bimetallic thermographs and a small aneroid barograph. Conditions and results of course vary widely, but the following represents the general features common to all ascents.

(1) Once above the first few hundred feet and in the free air

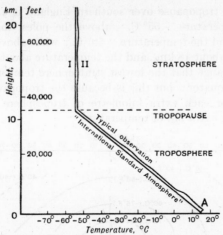

FIG. 189.—Variation of temperature with altitude.

where the effect of surface features can be neglected, there is a progressive fall in temperature as the height increases. The rate of fall of temperature with respect to altitude, is called the lapse rate. The lapse rate in an individual ascent may vary from level to level, the value always being less than $10°$ C./km., and may even be negative over some part of the ascent (*inversion of temperature*). Inversions occur either when a layer of warm air from another place arrives in the upper atmosphere, or when the layers nearest to the ground are for some reason very considerably cooled. A uniform lapse rate of $6°$ C. per km. is considered to obtain in the ideal standard atmosphere. It is found that, for any one station, the average value of the lapse rate at heights well clear of local ground disturbances is always very close to this value, whatever the latitude or average ground temperature of the station.

Fig. 189 illustrates the temperature distribution in the international standard atmosphere, and also a typical record of the temperature at different heights, showing variations in the lapse rate; and an inversion appears at A.

(2) The lapse rate does not persist to the greatest heights. At a certain level in the atmosphere, called the **tropopause**, the fall in temperature ceases, and above this level the temperature is constant. The whole of the atmosphere below this level is called the **troposphere**, and the region above it is called the **stratosphere**. The

height of the tropopause over southern England is about 11 km., and the temperature −55° C. ; above the poles, the tropopause is at 9 km., and the temperature −50° C. ; while above the equator the height is about 18 km., and the temperature about −80° C. It may seem strange that the lowest stratosphere temperature should be over the equator ; but this is because the tropopause is highest there, and for each extra kilometre of troposphere there is the corresponding extra fall of temperature.

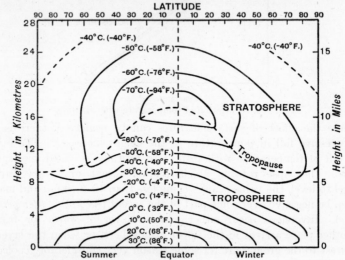

Fig. 190.—General variation of temperature with altitude at different latitudes. Left, summer ; right, winter.

By permission of the Controller of H. M. Stationery Office.

Fig. 190 illustrates the mean temperature distribution and the way in which it varies with latitude ; the left-hand side of the diagram shows the mean summer distribution, the right-hand side that for winter. It will be seen from this diagram that, within the stratosphere itself, the temperature *increases* very slowly with increasing height ; it is believed that this increase persists up to great heights, and that at about 50 km. the temperature is as high as at the earth's surface. There are three consistent pieces of evidence pointing to this : (1) a layer of ozone, which absorbs ultra-violet light, and hence is heated, has been detected by optical means ; (2) the incandescence of meteors, according to the theory of Lindemann and Dobson, requires a fairly high atmospheric temperature ; (3) abnormal audibility of distant explosions can be explained by the reflexion of the sound from a warm layer in the upper air.

Clouds and precipitation. Clouds are classified into four main groups or families according to their heights, and each family is further subdivided into classes or genera, making ten fundamental types.

CLASSIFICATION OF CLOUDS

	High clouds.	Medium clouds.	Low clouds.	Clouds with marked vertical development.
Mean upper level	12,000 m.	6,000 m.	2,000 m.	12,000 m.
Mean lower level	6,000 m.	2,000 m.	Close to ground	500 m.
Genus - -	Cirrus (*Ci*) Cirro-cumulus (*Cc.*) Cirro-stratus (*Cs.*)	Alto-cumulus (*Ac.*) Alto-stratus (*As.*)	Strato-cumulus (*Sc.*) Stratus (*St.*) Nimbo-stratus (*Ns.*)	Cumulus (*Cu.*) Cumulo-nimbus (*Cb.*)

Cirrus (or the prefix *cirro-*) indicates high cloud, *alto* medium cloud, *cumulus* (or *cumulo-*) accumulated isolated patches or heaped formation, *stratus* (or *strato-*) a layer of cloud, and *nimbus* (or *nimbo-*) a heavy type of rain-cloud.

When the temperature of the air as a whole is reduced below the dew-point, a cloud is formed as the vapour condenses out in the form of small droplets of water (or, at low temperatures, small ice crystals). Condensation invariably happens as soon as saturation is reached, as the necessary nuclei (p. 196), in the form of minute salt particles originating from the sea, are always present in sufficient numbers.

The droplets in a cloud fall slowly towards the ground. The effect of air resistance is proportional to the speed at which they fall, so they eventually fall with a steady velocity (called the terminal velocity) at which the effect of air resistance just balances the weight of the drop. The larger the drop, up to a limiting diameter of 5·5 mm., the greater is the value of the terminal velocity. Water drops of diameter greater than 5·5 mm. are broken up into smaller drops as they fall, so 5·5 mm. represents the greatest possible diameter for a raindrop, and 8·0 metres per second its greatest speed through the air. It should be noted that this is the speed *relative to the air*; in a vertical upward current of 8·0 metres per second raindrops of this diameter would remain poised at a constant height above ground, while an upward current exceeding this value would transport them upwards.

Diameter of drop, in mm. - -	0·01	0·1	1·0	2·0	3·0	4·0	5·0	5·5
Terminal velocity, in metres per sec. - - -	0·003	0·32	4·4	5·9	6·9	7·7	8·0	8·0

The chief difference between a cloud and a fall of rain lies in the rate of settling relative to the ground. A cloud comprising droplets of 0·01 mm. diameter will at first settle very slowly indeed. It may be supposed that the droplets collide and coalesce, falling faster as they grow, and collecting further small drops as they fall; by the time they have reached a diameter of a millimetre or two they may either (1) fall as rain with the considerable terminal velocity of four or five metres per second, or (2) if there is an upward current of sufficient velocity, stay up aloft as a cloud and continue to grow.

As the temperature falls, on the average, 6° C. for each kilometre rise, a ground temperature of 15° C. means that at all heights above 2500 metres the temperature is below the freezing point; that is, all except the lowest clouds are on the whole below the freezing point. This does not mean that most clouds necessarily consist mainly of ice crystals. Small droplets can be supercooled far below the normal freezing point and still remain liquid, while larger drops tend to freeze more readily.

Low clouds, up to a height of about 3000 metres, usually consist entirely of water droplets, whatever the temperature, provided the droplets are small; but if the droplets are cold enough to freeze and at the same time large enough to fall, freezing occurs and they are precipitated as snow. The beautiful and varied forms of snowflakes are formed by the joining together of the small crystals of ice formed from individual droplets. The medium clouds, up to about 4500 metres, contain chiefly supercooled water, though some ice crystals are present due to the freezing of the larger drops. The high cirrus clouds above 6,000 metres consist chiefly of ice crystals.

The usual form of frozen precipitation is snow or sleet. Hail and soft hail occur under conditions of violent disturbance, and are usually associated with thunderstorms. The first stage in the formation of a hailstone is the freezing of a fairly large drop ; for this to happen, the temperature must be well below 0° C., and there must be a strong vertical upward current, sufficient to prevent the drop from falling. Once the drop has frozen, it may grow either by collecting small supercooled cloud droplets, which freeze on it instantaneously and form the loose white roe-like structure of soft hail, or else by picking up droplets at temperatures only slightly below 0° C., which spread over the surface and freeze slowly, forming a solid shell of clear ice. The first process usually takes place in the colder regions at the top of the cloud, where the smaller droplets will in any event be swept by the upward currents, and the second in the less cold lower levels. A hailstone may be swept upwards by ascending currents and fall down to the lower part of the cloud several times before it becomes large enough to fall to the ground. A section across such a stone will show successive rings of white ice (collected at the top of the cloud) and clear ice (formed in the lower levels), from which its life-history can be deduced. Hailstones do not, of course, break up in falling, and hence can have diameters and velocities greatly in excess of the 5·5 mm. and 8 metres/sec. which are the limiting values for raindrops.

The cooling which leads to the formation of a cloud may occur in a variety of ways. Apart from one or two easily understood thermal processes, such as the cooling of a mass of warm saturated air by direct mixing with a current of cold air, or the cooling of the layers near the ground when this itself has cooled by radiation (giving rise to a low cloud known as mist or fog according to its denseness and opacity), the chief general cause of cloud formation is cooling by adiabatic expansion on account of the decrease in pressure as a mass of saturated air ascends. The various ways in which this may be caused may be classified as (1) *irregular upward currents*, or turbulence, (2) *local orographic effects*, that is, the tendency of hills and mountain ranges to force upwards a current of air directed against their sides, (3) *large-scale convection currents*, such as occur over land masses on a fine warm day, and (4) *a general ascent over a wide area.* The last two are particularly general in their incidence, and are discussed more fully later on.

Condensation on solid surfaces. On a clear still night, radiative cooling of the ground is considerable. When the ground is cooled below the dew-point of the air just above it, moisture is deposited as dew. If the ground temperature falls below the freezing point, ice is deposited, or dew already deposited is frozen ; in both these cases the result is a layer of hoar-frost. The temperature of poorly conducting surfaces, and bodies of large surface area and low thermal capacity, such as leaves and blades of grass (though some of the observed moisture is exuded from within and not deposited) falls rapidly and so they collect substantial deposits.

Rime and glazed frost. These are both caused by the precipitation of supercooled water droplets, which solidify after deposition. Instantaneous freezing of the whole drop does not occur, since latent heat is evolved with solidification, and this has to be extracted by the surroundings, a process which takes time. If the drops are very small and very cold, they may freeze rapidly, without coalescing with other drops, giving a white deposit similar in appearance to hoar-frost, which is called rime. If the drops are large and only a little below the freezing point, freezing may be so slow that a film of water is first formed, and the result is a layer of clear ice known as glazed frost.

Dangerous ice accretion can occur on aircraft flying through clouds containing supercooled water droplets, due to the deposition of rime and glazed frost. Hail, snow, or ice crystals already present in the cloud can do little harm, since they do not stick to the surfaces of the machine. Really dangerous icing only occurs if the aircraft is flying through rain or cloud composed of supercooled water droplets, with the temperature between $0°$ C. and $-11°$ C. ; this temperature range rarely covers a difference in altitude of more than 2,500 metres, and whenever possible icing is avoided by flying at an altitude outside this range.

ATMOSPHERIC MOVEMENT

Stability of the atmosphere. When a liquid, which is practically incompressible, is heated from below, it is easy to forecast what will happen. The heated portion at the bottom becomes less dense than the rest of the liquid, and forthwith rises to the top. With the atmosphere, however, things are not so simple. The heated portion becomes less dense, and starts to rise ; it rises to a region of lower pressure, and expands adiabatically, thereby falling in temperature. There are now two possibilities. It may be either warmer and therefore less dense than the surrounding atmosphere at this level, in which case it continues to rise ; or the adiabatic expansion may have lowered the temperature so much that it is cooler and denser than the surrounding atmosphere, in which case it sinks again. In the first case, the atmosphere is said to be *unstable*, and once convection starts it continues as a steady upward current ; in the second case the atmosphere is *stable*, or in stable equilibrium, and steady upward currents do not occur. The rate of decrease of temperature with height in the ascending mass of air can be calculated from the laws of adiabatic expansion ; if this is less than the lapse rate in the surrounding atmosphere, there is instability, while if this is greater than the lapse rate, the atmosphere is stable.

Suppose at first that the rising air is perfectly dry, and consider one gram molecule. The relation connecting temperature and pressure for adiabatic change is

$$T^\gamma / p^{\gamma-1} = \text{constant (p. 259), or } T^\gamma p^{1-\gamma} = \text{constant.}$$

Differentiating, $\gamma T^{\gamma-1} p^{1-\gamma} \, dT + (1-\gamma) p^{-\gamma} T^\gamma \, dp = 0$, whence, cancelling and re-arranging, $\dfrac{dT}{dp} = \dfrac{\gamma-1}{\gamma} \dfrac{T}{p}$.

The vertical rate of decrease of pressure with altitude is given by $dp/dh = -g\rho$ (p. 419),
and the temperature lapse rate

$$\frac{dT}{dh} = \frac{dT}{dp} \cdot \frac{dp}{dh} = -g\rho \frac{\gamma-1}{\gamma} \frac{T}{p}.$$

Now, $pV = RT$ or $p\dfrac{M}{\rho} = RT$; so $\dfrac{\rho T}{p} = \dfrac{M}{R}$,

$$\therefore \quad \frac{dT}{dh} = -\frac{Mg}{R} \frac{\gamma-1}{\gamma}.$$

Substituting the values $M = 29$, $R = 8\cdot3 \times 10^7$ erg/mole/°C.,

$$g = 981 \text{ cm./sec.}^2, \quad \gamma = 1\cdot40,$$

$$\frac{dT}{dh} = -\frac{29 \times 981 \times 0\cdot288}{8\cdot3 \times 10^7} = \text{nearly } -10^{-4} \text{ °C./cm.}$$

$$= -10° \text{ C./km. approximately.}$$

The value 10° C./km. is called the **dry adiabatic lapse rate**. Supposing " standard atmosphere " conditions with a lapse rate of 6° C./km., when a mass of dry air rises a distance x km. it cools some $10x°$ C. below its ground-level temperature, while the surrounding air has fallen only $6x°$ C. below the ground-level temperature. The ascending air is $4x°$ C. cooler than the surrounding air, is denser, and sinks again. Thus a mass of perfectly dry air will always be stable provided the actual lapse rate does not exceed 10° C./km., an event which rarely happens, except close to the ground. The calculation for perfectly dry air holds approximately for moist air, provided the relative humidity is low.

The fall in temperature of an ascending mass of air saturated with water vapour is very much less than that of dry air under similar conditions. This is because, as soon as the temperature falls slightly, water vapour condenses and latent heat is evolved. The rate of fall of temperature with height for air saturated with water vapour is called the **saturated adiabatic lapse rate**. The value depends on the temperature, and approaches the dry adiabatic lapse rate at very low temperatures because then the absolute amount of water vapour present per unit volume of air is very small. The value at 15° C. is about 5° C./km. ; at 0° C., 6·2° C./km. ; and at −20° C., 8·6° C./km. On a day when the actual lapse rate is 6° C./km., the temperature of a mass of saturated air at 15° C. rising x km. falls $5x°$ C., while the surrounding air falls $6x°$ C. The ascending mass is now warmer and less dense than the surrounding air, and continues to rise and deposit moisture until its temperature has fallen to the value at which the saturated adiabatic lapse rate exceeds the actual lapse rate. The state of affairs when the actual lapse rate exceeds the saturated adiabatic lapse rate is called *conditional instability* ; for it offers the possibility of instability if there is saturated air present. Hence a knowledge of the relative humidity is essential, in addition to the value of the actual lapse rate, before it can be said whether there is instability or not.

There are three chief ways in which instability can arise, given other favourable conditions. These are: (1) by surface heating from below, when a mass of air of high relative humidity is warmed by contact with the ground; (2) when a current of cold air flows over a current of warmer air; for example, if the wind in the lower air is a warm southerly wind, while that in the upper air is a cooler south-westerly; (3) at the cold front (p. 441) of a typical frontal depression, where cold air sweeps underneath a layer of warm moist air, forcing it to rise; this is dealt with later.

In most cases the occurrence of instability is marked by violent large-scale upward currents, giving large cumulus clouds, and resulting in heavy rain and thunderstorms.

The actual lapse rate may have any value up to that for the dry adiabatic, and will vary with height in any individual observation. On hot sunny days, the lapse rate for the first few thousand feet above the ground may approach the dry adiabatic value; inside a cloud, the lapse rate is that for saturated adiabatic conditions. Inversions of temperature are frequent, with a layer of warm air above cooler layers. These may occur as the result of strong local cooling at ground-level, either when the earth cools by radiation at night under still conditions, or when a current of air from warmer regions has its lower layers cooled as it sweeps over the ground. Inversions accompany extremely stable conditions.

The tephigram. A short-range forecast of local upper air conditions can be given if (1) the lapse rate at different levels, and (2) the relative humidity at each level, have been observed. Instability may occur if the actual lapse rate exceeds the saturated adiabatic lapse rate at the particular level, and will occur if the relative humidity at that level is high enough.

The usual way of representing the temperature-pressure observations is on a temperature-entropy diagram (p. 286) called a t-ϕ diagram or tephigram (ϕ being the symbol for entropy). On this, horizontal and vertical rectangular axes are taken for temperature and entropy respectively, but the entropy co-ordinates are not actually calculated and plotted. Instead, the appropriate calculations are done once for all when the paper is being prepared, and lines of equal pressure, sloping upwards across the diagram from left to right, enable each point to be plotted from the temperature and pressure readings.

Actually, the meteorologist fixes on another quantity instead of entropy, which has the same property of being constant throughout adiabatic change. A given mass of dry air, whatever adiabatic changes it may undergo, will always return to a given temperature if compressed adiabatically to a given pressure. The temperature which would be taken up by the air at any point in the atmosphere, if it were dry and were compressed adiabatically to a standard pressure of 1000 mb., is called the potential temperature at that point. For adiabatic change the equation $T^\gamma p^{1-\gamma} = constant$ holds, so, if p mb. and $T°$ K. be the actual pressure and temperature, the potential temperature $\theta°$ K. at 1000 mb. is given by $\theta^\gamma (1000)^{1-\gamma} = T^\gamma p^{1-\gamma}$, or as $\gamma = 1.40$, $\dfrac{\theta^{1.4}}{1000^{0.4}} = \dfrac{T^{1.4}}{p^{0.4}}$, whence $\dfrac{\theta}{(1000)^{.288}} = \dfrac{T}{p^{.288}}$.

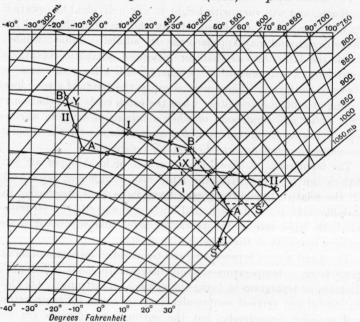

Fig. 191.—Tephigram. (*By permission of the Controller of H.M. Stationery Office.*)

Lines of equal temperature, vertical.

Lines of equal entropy or potential temperature, horizontal.

Lines of equal pressure, as calculated from formula, sloping up from left to right.

Lines showing saturated adiabatic lapse rate, sloping up from right to left.

This perhaps complicates matters from the point of view of the physicist, and it may be simpler to think in terms of entropy; but it is instructive to see how the lines of equal pressure are drawn in. If the potential temperature θ (usually plotted on a logarithmic scale) and temperature T are taken as co-ordinates, the locus of all points with a given value of p is obtained from the formula above.

The first important point about the tephigram, then, is that adiabatic change is represented by a horizontal line, since the entropy (and potential temperature) is always the same throughout adiabatic change. The horizontal direction is thus that of the dry adiabatic lapse rate, and the more nearly horizontal the plotted line lies, the closer is the actual lapse rate to the dry adiabatic value.

Lines showing the saturated adiabatic lapse rate for various initial conditions are shown as smooth curves sloping upwards across the diagram from right to left.

Dew-point lines, which indicate the conditions under which given amounts of water vapour will just saturate a given mass of dry air are also drawn in on the paper.

Fig. 191 represents a simplified tephigram (with the dew-point lines omitted for the sake of clearness). It is taken from " Meteorology for Aviators ", by R. C. Sutcliffe. The records of two ascents are plotted on it.

UPPER AIR OBSERVATIONS PLOTTED IN FIG. 191

Pressure (mb.) - -	1012	1000	950	900	850	800	750
Ascent I. Temp. (F.) -	51	52	55	53	50	47	42
Ascent II. Temp. (F.) -	76	75	69	63	56	48	39
Pressure (mb.) - -	700	650	600	550	500	450	400
Ascent I Temp. (F.) -	38	30	21	11	—	—	—
Ascent II Temp. (F.) -	30	22	13	3	- 7	- 11	- 15

For ascent I, there is an inversion of temperature between the surface S and A, from A to B the lapse rate is less than that for the saturated adiabatic, while beyond B it is greater. There can be no instability of saturated air at levels below B; above B there is conditional instability, and relative humidity values are required for further pronouncement of conditions there. For ascent II, the saturated adiabatic lapse rate is exceeded all the way from the surface to A, while from A to B the lapse rate is less than that for the saturated adiabatic value, and conditions should be stable. If the relative humidity in the lower levels is high, instability occurs, and if cloud is formed it will extend upwards at least as far as A, flattening out in the stable region AB.

The dew-point lines are omitted in Fig. 187, but it can be seen how they help to complete the information already obtained. Let us suppose that in ascent II the plotted line cuts the appropriate dew-point line for the observed relative humidity at the point X. Below the level of X, instability is only conditional; above this level actual instability occurs. Hence the cloud base can be expected to be at about the height of X. Further, it can be seen that instability actually persists above the point A, which could scarcely have been guessed in the absence of humidity data. For the criterion of stability is the saturated adiabatic line through the point X at which saturation begins; so long as the plotted curve lies below this, there is instability, and stable conditions begin above the point Y, at which the saturated adiabatic lapse rate overtakes the actual lapse rate. The upper limit of cloud formation should thus be at about the level represented by Y.

Pressure distribution at mean sea-level. The synoptic chart or "weather map" is compiled from simultaneous observations of the weather conditions at a large number of stations, which are telegraphed to the Meteorological Office. The charts published daily in peace-time covered the whole of the northern hemisphere. The most important single observation is the pressure, which is reduced to what it would have been if the station were at sea-level. Lines joining places at which the pressure has the same value are called isobars, and the isobars form patterns on the map which can best be likened to the contour lines on an ordinary map of a varied stretch of country such as the Lake District. Anyone quite unfamiliar with the actual stretch of country, and quite unskilled in map-reading, would be struck by the way in which the contour lines form systems which, though differing considerably in details, can be classified into groups according to general resemblance in type.

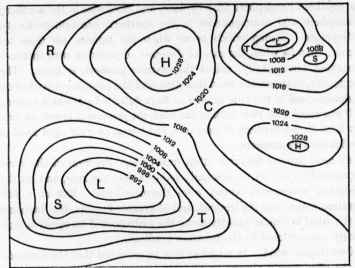

FIG. 192.—Isobars showing different pressure systems.
By permission of the Controller of H. M. Stationery Office.

Similarly, the widely varying patterns of the isobars reveal pressure systems which can be classified into a few general types, as follows (the letters refer to Fig. 192):

1. *Depression, cyclone, or " low "* (*L*). A centre of low pressure, with winds blowing nearly along the isobars in an *anticlockwise* sense in the northern hemisphere. The inner isobars form closed curves.

2. *Secondary depression* (*S*). An offshoot from a larger depression, in which the isobars are not necessarily closed.

3. *Trough of low pressure*, or V-shaped depression (*T*).

4. *Anticyclone or " high "* (*H*). A system with more or less closed isobars, the pressure highest in the centre, winds blowing *clockwise* in the northern hemisphere.

5. *Ridge or wedge of high pressure* (*R*).

6. *Col* (*C*).

The direction of the wind at ground-level is usually nearly along the isobars, but in general slightly inclined towards the direction in which the pressure is lower ; that is, slightly inwards in a cyclone, and slightly outwards from the centre of an anticyclone. The sense is anticlockwise in the northern hemisphere and clockwise in the southern hemisphere for a cyclone, and clockwise in the northern hemisphere and anticlockwise in the southern hemisphere for an anticyclone. Strong winds occur when the isobars are close together, that is, when the rate of decrease of pressure with distance measured horizontally, called the pressure gradient, is large. The connection between the wind direction and the pressure distribution is summarised in the rule known as **Buys Ballot's Law**, which states :

If you stand with your back to the wind, the pressure is lowest on your left hand in the Northern Hemisphere, and lowest on your right hand in the Southern Hemisphere.

As local ground features often modify the direction of the wind considerably, it may occasionally happen that the rule, and all the foregoing statements about wind direction, fail. But at a few hundred feet above the ground, and at greater heights, the direction of the wind is almost exactly along the isobars, and its speed is very nearly proportional to the pressure gradient.

Geostrophic wind. It might at first be expected that the direction of the wind would always be directly towards a centre of low pressure, and directly away from a centre of high pressure ; that is, that the flow of air would always be in the direction of the pressure gradient instead of at right angles to it. But this tendency is frustrated by the rotation of the earth, which acts so as to give the moving air an acceleration at right angles to its path. This acceleration is always directed to the right of the path in the northern hemisphere, and to the left in the southern hemisphere, and its value is $2V\omega \sin \phi$, where V is the velocity of the wind, ω the angular velocity of rotation of the earth, and ϕ the latitude. If there are no other effects to consider, steady motion of the wind is only possible when this acceleration due to the earth's rotation is exactly equal and opposite to the acceleration due to the pressure gradient. As the acceleration $2V\omega \sin \phi$ acts at right angles to the motion of the air, and directly opposes the pressure gradient, the air must move at right angles to the pressure gradient, and the wind must blow along the isobars. When only the effects of pressure gradient and the earth's rotation are important, this happens, and the wind is called the geostrophic wind.

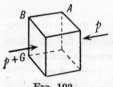

FIG. 193.

Consider a cube of air of 1 cm. side (Fig. 193),

with two faces A and B perpendicular to the pressure gradient, the value of which is G. If p be the pressure in absolute units at A, the pressure at B is $p + G$, the forces on A and B are p and $p + G$ dynes, and the resultant force on the cube is G dynes. If ρ gm. per c.c. be the density of the air, the mass of the cube is ρ gm., and the acceleration due to G is G/ρ cm./sec.^{2}

Thus steady motion occurs when

$$2V\omega \sin\phi = G/\rho \quad \text{or} \quad V = \frac{G}{2\omega\rho \sin\phi}.$$

Hence V is proportional to the pressure gradient for given values of ρ and ϕ; if G and ϕ are fixed, V decreases as ρ decreases with increasing altitude, while if G and ρ are fixed V increases as $\sin\phi$ decreases; that is, as the equator is approached. The equation is not valid for values of ϕ less than about 10°, for it suggests an *infinite* value for V when $\phi = 0$.

Providing the conditions are steady and the isobars nearly straight and parallel, the formula gives a good approximation to the value of the velocity of the wind at heights of 1000 ft. or so above the ground at latitudes greater than about 10°. The wind velocity can be read off from the weather map by measuring the separation of the isobars with a scale graduated in accordance with the formula.

Gradient wind. The geostrophic wind calculation holds strictly only for parallel straight isobars. To adapt this more closely to the case of a cyclone or anticyclone, suppose that the isobars are circular. If the air is moving steadily with uniform velocity V in a circle of radius r, an acceleration of V^2/r towards the centre must be provided. This must be furnished by the resultant of the accelerations G/ρ and $2V\omega \sin\phi$.

In a depression, the wind moves anticlockwise (in the northern hemisphere) and the pressure gradient effect G/ρ inwards opposes the geostrophic effect $2V\omega \sin\phi$ which is to the right of the path and therefore outwards; so

$$V^2/r = G/\rho - 2V\omega \sin\phi.$$

In an anticyclone, the wind moves clockwise (in the northern hemisphere), the pressure gradient acts outwards, and the geostrophic effect, to the right of the path, acts inwards, so

$$V^2/r = 2V\omega \sin\phi - G/\rho.$$

The value of V obtained from the appropriate equation is called the **gradient wind velocity.**

Both the geostrophic and gradient wind calculations hold only for winds well above the surface of the earth. Friction at the ground reduces V below the value necessary to balance G; hence winds at ground-level are always less strong than the calculations indicate, and are deflected by the pressure gradient towards the low-pressure side of the theoretical direction.

Thermal wind. Suppose for the moment that the pressure at the earth's surface is uniform over a large area, while the temperature is not. Consider two points A and B some distance apart. If the temperature at and above B is greater than the corresponding values for A, the air above B is less dense than that above A, so the pressure falls off less rapidly above B. At a height of some thousand metres or more the pressure above B exceeds that above A, so that there is a pressure gradient acting from B to A, then there will be a wind at right angles to this, following the geostrophic calculation, and called the **thermal wind.**

This is, of course, an ideal case; in practice, the thermal wind is superposed on the gradient wind, and the actual wind in the upper air is the vector resultant of the two. As the poles are always the coldest part of the earth, there is always a horizontal temperature gradient directed southwards in the northern hemisphere, and a consequent pressure gradient directed northwards in the upper air. Thus the general tendency of the thermal wind is from west to east, and it is generally observed that winds in the upper air show a westward tendency as compared with the winds at ground level.

Mean pressure distribution and general circulation of the atmosphere. If the *monthly average value* of the pressure is taken as the basis of an isobar map for the whole world, it is found that the mean pressure distribution for a given month varies little from year to year. In January, for example, there are large centres of high pressure in the northern hemisphere over western Canada and central Asia, and a centre of low pressure over Iceland, while in the southern hemisphere there are large centres of high pressure in the South Atlantic, the South Pacific, and the Indian Ocean. In July, the distribution in the southern hemisphere is roughly the same as for January, but in the northern hemisphere centres of high pressure appear over the North Atlantic and North Pacific, while the centres of low pressure appear over north-east Canada and in the neighbourhood of the Himalayas.

The general month-by-month trend of the winds, governed by the same rules as in actual individual cyclones or anticyclones, is roughly in the direction of these average isobars. The main wind distributions are generally classified as :

1. A belt of calms or of light variable winds, with converging air on the equator (doldrums).

2. Belts of trade winds between the doldrums and lat. 30° N. and 30° S. blowing from the north-east in the northern and from the south-east in the southern hemisphere.

3. Belts of light variable winds, with diverging air which descends from higher levels in about lat. 30° N. and 30° S. (horse latitudes).

4. Regions of prevailing south-westerly winds in middle latitudes of the northern hemisphere, and north-westerly winds in middle latitudes of the southern hemisphere.

5. Around the poles regions of outflowing winds with a component from the east.

This is the ideal planetary wind circulation, which is approximately that over large ocean areas ; over large land masses, the winds are modified to a great extent by local factors.

WEATHER FORECASTING

It is well known that a change in the barometric height and a change in the wind usually accompany a change in the weather, and observant people can, from these and other signs, give a fairly good forecast of the local weather for a few hours ahead. These local signs are, however, merely evidence of large-scale changes affecting areas perhaps a thousand miles in diameter ; the weather and weather changes over a huge area can be predicted from a sequence of synoptic charts showing the general wind and pressure changes over it. For example, if a depression centred over Iceland has been observed moving steadily south-east during yesterday and today, tomorrow's weather over a wide area can be forecast if (a) it can be stated where the depression is likely to be then, and (b) the type of weather to be expected in each region of a depression is known. This is the general principle underlying synoptic weather forecasting ; for further information, reference should be made to one of the standard meteorological publications.

The general weather distribution in a typical depression was given by Abercromby about the middle of the last century, and for fifty years or so little was discovered about the way in which depressions originate or how the weather changes associated with them come about, so that forecasting consisted in essence of making an intelligent guess, based on the past behaviour of similar depressions, as to where the one considered would next move. But from about 1920 onwards the polar front or frontal theory of the origin and structure of depressions has revolutionised forecasting and placed it on a much firmer scientific basis.

Frontal theory of depressions. The depression is the pressure system of greatest interest to the meteorologist, for it is characterised by activity, motion, and change. Depressions arise and disappear, and may during their life-time move many hundreds of miles, bringing a more or less regular sequence of varied weather conditions to the places over which they pass. Anticyclones, often nearly stationary and maintaining steady calm conditions for a long period, can perhaps be regarded merely as uninteresting areas which are free from depressions. But something far-reaching in effect is steadily happening in the anticyclone; the relatively stagnant air is acquiring the temperature of the ground below it, and becoming a *homogeneous air mass* of practically uniform temperature and humidity. When the anticyclone is eventually disturbed, this air mass moves as a whole.

The chief sources of the air masses arriving in temperate regions are the more or less permanent anticyclones at the poles and in the tropics; the properties depend on whether they originate over sea (maritime) or over land (continental), and air masses are thus classified as :

Polar : in general cold and unstable :

> *Maritime :* moist.
>
> *Continental :* very dry, cold in winter, possibly warm in summer.

Tropical : in general warm, moist, and stable :

> *Maritime :* always very moist.
>
> *Continental :* not always moist, may be very hot and dry.

When two air masses of different types meet, there is a more or less sharp zone of transition called a **frontal surface.** This is inclined to the surface of the earth, and the line in which the frontal surface meets the ground is called a **front**. A cold front is one at which cold air is moving so as to overtake warmer air, and a **warm** front one in which warm air is overtaking cold air.

The frontal theory of depressions is due to the Norwegian meteorologist Bjerknes and his collaborators, who, during the War of 1914-18 were obliged to find some means of forecasting based on observations made in Norway alone. A close network of observing stations was set up, and the information gave very accurate and detailed pictures of conditions in a depression. The word " front " was chosen in its war-time sense, as indicating a region of conflict between two different air masses.

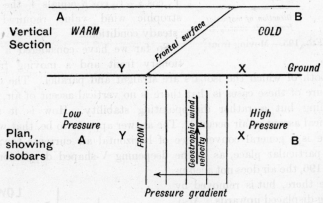

FIG. 194.—Section and plan of frontal surface.

From " Meteorology for Aviators ", by permission of the Controller of H. M. Stationery Office.

Fig. 194 indicates a vertical section through a frontal surface separating a warm air mass A from a cold air mass B, and a plan showing the isobars. As the colder air is denser, the pressure at X should be greater than the pressure at Y, and there should be a steady pressure gradient directed from X to Y. It might be expected that the cold air would therefore sweep under the hot air and raise it. But such a system will be stable if there is a wind of the geostrophic value V appropriate to the pressure gradient, blowing parallel to the isobars, with the warm mass on the left and the cold mass on the right, or if the *relative velocity* of the two masses has this value and this sense. In this case, the frontal surface remains stationary, the slope being something like 1 in 100 to 1 in 150.

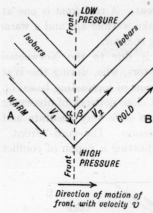

Direction of motion of
front, with velocity v

FIG. 195.—Moving front.

If the front is in motion, the arrangement of the isobars may be as shown in Fig. 195. Both air masses are moving, with different velocities and in different directions. Let V_1 be the velocity of the cold mass, at an angle α to the front, and V_2 the velocity of the warm mass at an angle β to the front. Then $V_1 \sin \alpha = V_2 \sin \beta = v$, the velocity with which the front itself moves, while the relative velocity $V_1 \cos \alpha + V_2 \cos \beta$ equals V the geostrophic wind value required for steady conditions.

So far we have considered a stationary front and a moving front, in both of which the isobars are straight and parallel. The chief feature of these cases is that there is no vertical ascent of air, and nothing but a rather disappointing stability. How is it that vertical ascent of air occurs? The answer appears to be, that when there is a general convergence of horizontal air currents towards any particular place, as in the deepening V-shaped depression of Fig. 196, the air does not accumulate there, but is removed by being displaced upwards. Also, owing to ground friction, winds always blow slightly towards the centre of any depression, and hence there is always an ascending current of air from the centre of low pressure. Interesting weather conditions do not develop until the stable front has been disturbed and converted into a depression.

The successive stages in the formation of a depression on a stationary front are illustrated in Fig. 197. The first stage (a)

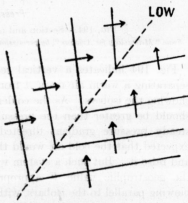

FIG. 196.—Motion of air in V-shaped depression.
From " Meteorology for Aviators", by permission of the Controller of H. M. Stationery Office.

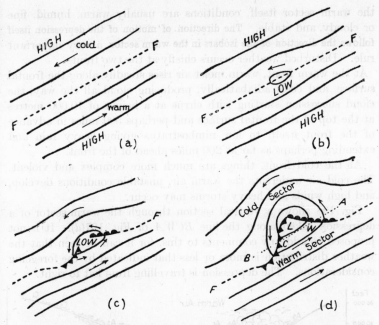

FIG. 197.—Stages in formation of a depression at a stationary front.

From "Meteorology for Aviators", by permission of the Controller of H. M. Stationery Office.

shows the stationary front with the warm air mass to the south and the cold air mass to the north, the usual case in the European area. The front *FF* is stationary, but the air masses themselves are travelling parallel to *FF* in opposite directions as the arrows indicate. Instability, with a small low-pressure region, develops at some point on the front, as in (*b*). The reason why this should start has not been explained, but the frontal theory is a description of the way in which depressions are observed to develop, and not an attempt to give theoretical explanations at every step. A kink in the front results, with warm air intruding and forming a **warm front** (indicated by a round-studded line) on the right, and the cold air sweeping round and forming a **cold front** (indicated by a spiked line) on the left. The depression deepens and grows, the whole moving along in the direction of motion of the warmer air. In the fully developed depression (*d*), the region between the cold front and the warm front is called the **warm sector,** and the remainder the **cold sector.** Within the warm sector itself, conditions are usually warm, humid, fine or cloudy, and stable. The direction of motion of the depression itself follows the direction of the isobars in the warm sector, a very important rule. Disturbed weather occurs chiefly at the two fronts.

At the warm front, warm moist air rises steadily along the frontal surface and cools adiabatically, producing cloud all the way, the cloud succession starting with cirrus at a height of 10,000 metres at the top of the frontal surface and perhaps 500 miles in advance of the front itself, to low nimbostratus giving heavy rain and extending perhaps as far as 200 miles ahead of the front.

At the cold front, things are much more complex and violent. The cold air undercuts the warm air, unstable conditions develop, and high winds and heavy storms may occur.

Fig. 198 shows a vertical section through the warm sector of a depression taken along the line $BCWA$ of Fig. 197(d). It is not proposed to add any comments to this, for it can be seen that the weather distribution is more or less that indicated by the foregoing considerations. The depression is travelling from left to right.

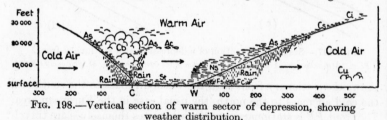

FIG. 198.—Vertical section of warm sector of depression, showing weather distribution.

From " Meteorology for Aviators ", by permission of the Controller of H. M. Stationery Office.

Fig. 199 indicates the general weather and cloud distribution in a typical warm-sector depression.

In the later stages in the life of a depression, the cold front sweeps round and overtakes the warm front ; that is, the whole of the warm sector air, which rises at both fronts, is lifted clear of the ground. The depression is then said to be " occluded ". After this stage is reached the depression may remain stationary for some time, eventually filling up and disappearing. Most depressions are occluded by the time they have reached England. The maps on p. 444 show the final stages in the occlusion of a depression, the cold front moving eastward from the Atlantic and overtaking the warm front over the British Isles.

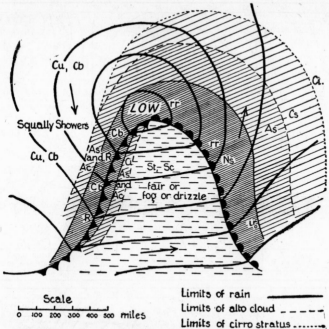

FIG. 199.—Plan of warm sector of depression, showing weather distribution.

From " Meteorology for Aviators", by permission of the Controller of H. M. Stationery Office.

The frontal theory describes the average depression of temperate regions, but depressions may arise in several other ways. Regions of low pressure may be developed over large land masses by surface heating of the ground (thermal depressions) or in regions where local vertical instability arises (instability depressions). Mountain ranges may either obstruct the flow of the wind so that it tends to blow round, forming large-scale eddies on the lee side which amount to small depressions, or the retarding of a cold front by a mountain barrier may give the equivalent of a warm sector on the lee side ; depressions formed in either of these ways are called orographic depressions.

Conclusion. In this chapter an attempt has been made to show how the meteorologist applies physical principles to the study of weather phenomena. The great progress that has been made in

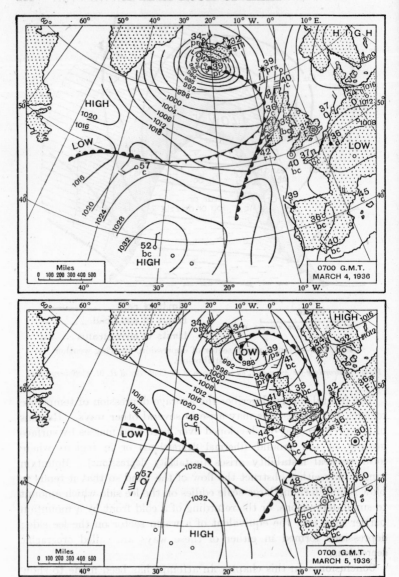

FINAL STAGES IN THE OCCLUSION OF A DEPRESSION.
Reproduced by permission of the Controller of H. M. Stationery Office.

this field, where observations are often difficult to make and are rarely so complete as could be wished, and where the observer has no control at all over the conditions, is a fascinating story which will well repay further study. The following are recommended for further reading :

1. " Meteorology for Aviators ", by Dr. R. C. Sutcliffe (H. M. Stationery Office).

2. " Weather Study ", by Prof. D. Brunt (Nelson).

Both of these have been used freely in preparing this chapter.

3. " A Short Course of Elementary Meteorology ", by W. H. Pick.   ⎫ Published by
4. " The Weather Map ".   ⎬ H. M. Stationery
5. " The Meteorological Glossary".   ⎭ Office.

APPENDIX I

METHOD OF DIMENSIONS

THE student is probably familiar with, or will surely eventually meet, the method of dimensions as applied to other branches of Physics. It has proved a fruitful means of attacking convection problems in Heat (see p. 365), but there seems to be no agreement and much perplexing discussion as to the dimensions of thermal quantities. This appendix is largely based on P. W. Bridgman's *Dimensional Analysis* (Oxford University Press).

The chosen fundamental standards to which physical measurements are referred are those of mass, length, and time ; that is, starting in the c.G.s. system with the unit of mass (the gram), of length (the centimetre), and of time (the second), the units of all other purely *mechanical* quantities can be derived from these three.

For example, the unit of volume is the cubic centimetre (cm.³), of area the square centimetre (cm.²), of density one gm. per cm.³ (or gm. cm.⁻³), of acceleration one centimetre per second gained per second (cm. per sec.², or cm. sec.⁻²). The powers of the fundamental units which appear in the unit of the derived quantity are called the dimensions of the quantity in mass, length, and time, and capitals M, L, T, with or without brackets, are used to denote these dimensions. Thus the dimensions of volume are L^3, of density ML^{-3}, of acceleration LT^{-2}. Proceeding in this way, as *force = mass × acceleration*, the dimensions of force are MLT^{-2}; pressure, which is *force per unit area*, has dimensions MLT^{-2}/L^2, or $ML^{-1}T^{-2}$; and work which is *force × distance*, dimensions ML^2T^{-2}, which are also the dimensions of energy.

Numerical coefficients (pure numbers or numerics) are of zero dimensions ; but a " constant ", such as for example R or g, may have dimensions, and as a general rule most " constants of proportionality " introduced into equations turn out to possess dimensions.

The dimensional symbols usually denote possible operations. The statement that the dimensions of area are L^2 means that, whatever the magnitude of an area, or the magnitude of the length standard chosen, the *operation* of comparison with the standard of length has to be performed twice, directly or indirectly, in order to measure it. A ratio between two quantities of the same kind is of zero dimensions, since this is independent of the units used to effect the individual measurements, and can be determined without the use of any standards at all.

446

In heat, two new fundamental units are chosen—the unit of temperature difference (the centigrade or Fahrenheit degree) and the unit of quantity of heat (the calorie, or B.Th.U. or other thermal unit) ; and the operation of measuring a temperature can be denoted by the dimensional sign θ. and that of measuring a quantity of heat *in terms of the thermal unit of heat* by the sign H. For the measurement of heat *in energy units*, no fresh unit is needed ; the operation required is the measurement of a quantity of energy, already denoted dimensionally by ML^2T^{-2}.

Now, thermal measurements, like all other physical measurements, are based on mechanical *observations*. It is true that the operations of weighing and timing really reduce to watching a pointer—that is, observing a *length* only—but many people feel that some combination of the three dimensions, M, L, T might be found to represent θ.

The equations defining a temperature on any scale, such as

$$\frac{t}{100} = \frac{p - p_0}{p_{100} - p_0} \quad \text{for the constant volume scale,}$$

or

$$\frac{\theta_1}{\theta_2} = \frac{Q_1}{Q_2} \quad \text{for the Kelvin absolute scale,}$$

are indeterminate as to the dimensions of temperature in terms of M, L, and T. They state that the *ratio* between two temperatures equals the *ratio* between two pressures or between two quantities of energy. There is nothing here to state that the dimensions of temperature are those of pressure or of energy, or that it is a dimensionless ratio itself. The equations state that, to measure a temperature interval, it must be compared in a certain way with a standard temperature interval, and this operation is best indicated by the unique dimensional symbol θ.

Although it is fairly widely stated that the dimensions of temperature are those of energy, ML^2T^{-2}, it is hard to see any good reason for this, or to reconcile it with the ordinary conception of temperature as hotness, something to be measured in intensity and not in quantity. The recent suggestions by Benham (L^{-1}) and Brown (L^2T^{-2}) merely illustrate the obvious fact that an indeterminate equation has innumerable solutions, and these are arbitrary choices purporting to represent (or reveal) the *nature* of temperature. But can this be done?

Consider for a moment the game of chess. The move requiring one operation by a knight requires two successive operations by the queen. Expressing this in a notation analogous to that of dimensions, $Kt = Q^2$. Thus there is an essential identity of *nature* between a knight and a queen squared ; or, on the chessboard, royalty is the square root of knighthood! Such a line of argument often appears intelligible in the particular case when the symbols refer to the dimensions of physical quantities, but any meaning attributable to it is at least limited. The notation of dimensions is a servant to be employed when helpful ; it is not a medium capable of revealing the occult.

To Bridgman, the important point is, not the actual dimensions allotted to a quantity, but the classification of physical quantities into two kinds. First, non-dimensional quantities, the magnitudes of which are independent of the size of the units selected. Secondly, dimensional quantities, the magnitudes of which depend on the size of the units selected, and to which dimensions can be ascribed *in any consistent and convenient way*. This clears the ground well ; for whatever may be said in favour of any chosen M, L, T dimensions for temperature, as they are unnecessary and inconvenient in applying dimensions in thermal problems we shall disregard them.

The dimensions of thermal quantities can be expressed in two convenient systems. First, the purely thermal system, in which quantity of heat is measured in thermal units ; secondly, the dynamical system, in which quantity of heat is measured in energy units. The dimensions of the more important quantities and " constants " are listed below.

(It will be seen that, if the dimensions ML^2T^{-2} be allotted to θ, the dimensions of R and k are zero. But the numerical values of these quantities very obviously depend on the system of units chosen, so that it seems hard to defend such a choice.)

Quantity.	Thermal dimensions.	Dynamical dimensions.
Temperature - - - -	θ	θ
Quantity of heat - - -	H	ML^2T^{-2}
Heat capacity per unit mass (absolute specific heat) -	$HM^{-1}\theta^{-1}$	$L^2T^{-2}\theta^{-1}$
Heat capacity per unit volume	$HL^{-3}\theta^{-1}$	$ML^{-1}T^{-2}\theta^{-1}$
Relative specific heat - -	0	0
Temperature gradient - -	$L^{-1}\theta$	$L^{-1}\theta$
Thermal conductivity - -	$HL^{-1}T^{-1}\theta^{-1}$	$MLT^{-3}\theta^{-1}$
Entropy - - - -	$H\theta^{-1}$	$ML^2T^{-2}\theta^{-1}$
" Constant."		
J - - - - - -	$ML^2T^{-2}H^{-1}$	0
R - - - - - -	$ML^2T^{-2}\theta^{-1}$	$ML^2T^{-2}\theta^{-1}$
Boltzmann's Constant $k = R/\mathcal{N}$	$ML^2T^{-2}\theta^{-1}$	$ML^2T^{-2}\theta^{-1}$
Stefan's Constant - - -	$HL^{-2}T^{-1}\theta^{-4}$	$MT^{-3}\theta^{-4}$
First radiation constant, c_1 -	HL^3T^{-1}	ML^5T^{-3}
Second radiation constant, c_2 -	$L\theta$	$L\theta$

SOME USES OF DIMENSIONS IN HEAT PROBLEMS

Conversion from one set of units to another. One general use of dimensions is in facilitating the conversion of numerical results from one system of consistent units to another. It is doubtful if much labour is saved in the case of thermal quantities, chiefly because the commoner British units are often not " consistent ". To convert a value expressed in c.g.s. centigrade units to lb.-ft.-sec. Fahrenheit units, proceed as follows : 1. Write down the dimensions of the quantity. 2. Write down the value of each c.g.s. unit in British units. 3. Substitute these values for the symbols in the dimensional formula. 4. Work out the result, which gives the number by which the c.g.s. value must be multiplied to give the British value.

EXAMPLE. The thermal conductivity of copper is 0·9 c.g.s. units ; what is its value in consistent British units (B.Th.U. per sec. per sq. ft. per °F. per ft.)?

The thermal dimensions of conductivity are $HL^{-1}T^{-1}\theta^{-1}$.

$$1 \text{ calorie} = 1/253 \text{ B.Th.U.}$$
$$1 \text{ cm.} = 1/30·4 \text{ ft.}$$
$$1 \text{ C. deg.} = 9/5 \text{ F. deg.}$$

So the conversion factor is

$$(1/253)^1 \times (1/30·4)^{-1} \times (9/5)^{-1} = \frac{30·4 \times 5}{253 \times 9} = 0·0672,$$

and the conductivity of copper is thus $(0·9 \times 0·0675) = 0·061$ units. In B.Th.U. per *hour* per sq. ft. per °F. per ft., as 1 sec. is 1/3600 hour, and time occurs as T^{-1}, the conversion factor is $0·0672 \times 3600 = 242$; and to obtain the value in the commonly used units, B.Th.U. per hour per sq. ft. per °F. per *inch* (with both the foot and the inch used as length units), it suffices to remember that 1 °F. per inch is 12 °F. per foot, whence the conversion factor is $242 \times 12 = $ about 2920.

EXAMPLE. If the value of J is $4·2 \times 10^7$ ergs per calorie, find its value in ft.-lb. per B.Th.U.

The thermal dimensions of J are $ML^2T^{-2}H^{-1}$.

$$1 \text{ gm.} = 1/454 \text{ lb.}$$
$$1 \text{ cm.} = 1/30·4 \text{ ft.}$$
$$1 \text{ cal.} = 1/253 \text{ B.Th.U.}$$

The conversion factor from the absolute c.g.s. units to the corresponding absolute British units (*foot-poundals* per B.Th.U.) is thus

$$(1/454)^1 \times (1/30·4)^2 \times (1/253)^{-1} = \frac{253}{454 \times 925} = 0·000603.$$

So J is $4·2 \times 10^7 \times 0·000603 = 4·2 \times 6030 = 25400$ ft.-poundals/B.Th.U., and as there are 32·2 ft.-poundals to one ft.-lb. in these latitudes, J is $25400/32·2 =$ about 778 ft.-lb. per B.Th.U.

(Note, by the way, that the *dimensions* of g, the acceleration of gravity, are not involved in this last step ; we are concerned here only with its numerical value, as the number of ft.-poundals in one ft.-lb.)

Dimensions applied to convection problems.

(a) **Rayleigh's equation, for forced convection.** Consider a solid body of definite shape, of linear extent l, immersed in a stream of fluid of heat capacity per unit volume s and conductivity k. The fluid streams past the solid with steady velocity v, and the steady temperature difference between the body and the stream is θ. It is required to find how r, the rate of transfer of heat from the body to the stream, depends on the factors listed.

Suppose the expression for r can be written in the simple form $r = A l^\alpha \theta^\beta v^\gamma s^\delta k^\epsilon$, where A is a numerical constant independent of the system of units chosen. Obviously, A can only be independent of change of units if such change affects both sides of the equation equally, whence the dimensions of both sides of the equation must be the same.

Writing in the dimensions of the individual terms :

for r, HT^{-1} ; for l, L ; for θ, θ ; for v, LT^{-1} ;

for s, $HL^{-3}\theta^{-1}$; for k, $HL^{-1}T^{-1}\theta^{-1}$;

the equation is written dimensionally as

$$HT^{-1} = L^\alpha \theta^\beta (LT^{-1})^\gamma (HL^{-3}\theta^{-1})^\delta (HL^{-1}T^{-1}\theta^{-1})^\epsilon,$$

or $\qquad HT^{-1} = H^{\delta+\epsilon} L^{\alpha+\gamma-3\delta-\epsilon} T^{-\gamma-\epsilon} \theta^{\beta-\delta-\epsilon}.$

Equating the indices of H, L, T, θ on both sides,

$$\delta+\epsilon=1 ; \quad \alpha+\gamma-3\delta-\epsilon=0 : \quad -\gamma-\epsilon=-1 ; \quad \beta-\delta-\epsilon=0.$$

We here have four equations, with five indices to determine. These cannot be found independently and uniquely, so we express four of them in terms of the fifth, thus :

$$\alpha=1+\gamma ; \quad \beta=1 ; \quad \delta=\gamma ; \quad \epsilon=1-\gamma.$$

Putting in the values of the indices in the original equation,

$$r = A l^{1+\gamma} \theta v^\gamma s^\gamma k^{1-\gamma}, \quad \text{or} \quad r = A l \theta k \left(\frac{lvs}{k}\right)^\gamma.$$

Now, as γ may have any value so far as we know, the general solution will be the sum of a series of such expressions, which is written

$$r = l \theta k \cdot f\left(\frac{lvs}{k}\right),$$

where f is some function of $\left(\frac{lvs}{k}\right)$.

Thus, other things being constant, the rate of transfer of heat under forced convection conditions is proportional to θ, the temperature excess.

The formula can be rearranged as

$$\frac{r}{l\theta k}=f\left(\frac{lvs}{k}\right),$$

where both the left-hand side $r/l\theta k$ and the expression in the bracket lvs/k are combinations of quantities arranged to have zero dimensions, and are called dimensionless products.

(b) **The problem of free or natural convection.** In addition to the quantities l, θ, s, and k, we may expect that when the flow of fluid past the solid results from natural convection currents, additional factors to be considered will be the viscosity η of the fluid (dimensions $ML^{-1}T^{-1}$), its density ρ (dimensions ML^{-3}), and its coefficient of expansion a (dimensions θ^{-1}), while the acceleration of gravity, g (dimensions LT^{-2}), appears instead of the velocity v.

The expression for r can be written as before in the form

$$r=Al^{\alpha}\theta^{\beta}s^{\gamma}k^{\delta}\eta^{w}\rho^{x}a^{y}g^{z},$$

and the indices determined, though not uniquely, in the same way. If it is decided to work in terms of the dynamical dimensions, M, L, T, and θ, there will be four independent equations available to determine eight unknown indices. The indices are, however, not really independent. For example, the Archimedes upthrust maintaining fluid flow depends on both a and g together, and the fluid speed resulting from a given upthrust may be expected to depend on η and ρ jointly.

The equation can thus be simplified to

$$r=Al^{\alpha}\theta^{\beta}s^{\gamma}k^{\delta}(\eta/\rho)^{x}(ga)^{y},$$

which has six unknowns instead of eight, and can be solved to give a relation with two undetermined functions of dimensionless products, thus

$$\frac{r}{l\theta k}=F\left(\frac{\theta gas^{2}l^{3}}{k^{2}}\right)\cdot f\left(\frac{s\eta}{k\rho}\right),$$

which is the formula given in Roberts' *Heat and Thermodynamics* (p. 242).

This is only one of a large number of alternative formulæ derivable in this way, so the method of dimensions is not an automatic device for short-circuiting the ordinary processes of physical theory and analysis and obtaining an equivalent result. First, a real appreciation of the physics involved is required in order (a) to select the relevant factors on which r depends, (b) to group together those such as η and ρ, or g and a, which are not physically independent in the problem, and (c) to select appropriate dimensionless combinations to make independent dimensionless products. Secondly, the formula obtained is not " the " result, is not necessarily a correct result, but is merely a formula which is physically possible.

The formula given above has been found experimentally to apply for a wide range of fluid substances, both liquid and gaseous, over wide temperature ranges. It will be noted that it is not an explicit " law of cooling " ; indeed, without experimental work to find the form of F, this formula is not very helpful on that particular point.

APPENDIX II

ACCURACY

AN error or uncertainty of 1 mm. in measuring a length of about 2 cm. is a proportional error of 1 part in 20, or 0·05, or a percentage error of 5 per cent., which is considerable. The same uncertainty in measuring a length of 20 metres is 1 part in 20,000, or 0·005 per cent., which for most practical purposes is negligible. The proportional or percentage error, and not the absolute size of the error, is the important thing in assessing accuracy.

The accuracy of an experiment can be assessed in two ways. Before the work is undertaken, the expected maximum error can be forecast, and we can call this the expected limit of accuracy. After the result has been obtained, each observation being repeated several times (as it should be), the agreement between the individual observations is a measure of the accuracy actually attained. The term " accuracy " as applied in this book to the usual school experiments refers to the expected limit ; as applied to the published work of scientists, it refers to the nearness of approach to theoretical expectation which is attained.

Expected limit of accuracy. Suppose that we are determining the value of a quantity x from observations of the three quantities p, q, and r, and that the true values of all these quantities are related by the equation $x = p^a q^b r^{-c}$, which is to be used to calculate x.

Let the expected small errors in the observed quantities be δp, δq, δr, so that the observed value of p may lie anywhere between $p + \delta p$ and $p - \delta p$, and can be written $p \pm \delta p$, or $p \left(1 \pm \dfrac{\delta p}{p} \right)$; similarly for q and r. The value of x obtained by using the observed values in the formula may lie anywhere between $x + \delta x$ and $x - \delta x$, and can be written $x\left(1\pm\dfrac{\delta x}{x}\right)$, the proportional error being $\dfrac{\delta x}{x}$.

Thus

$$x\left(1\pm\frac{\delta x}{x}\right)=\left[p\left(1\pm\frac{\delta p}{p}\right)\right]^a\left[q\left(1\pm\frac{\delta q}{q}\right)\right]^b\left[r\left(1\pm\frac{\delta r}{r}\right)\right]^{-c}.$$

The maximum value of the computed result occurs when the individual errors all have their maximum expected values, and all conspire together in the same sense—that is, when the actual errors are $+\delta p$, $+\delta q$, and $-\delta r$.

Hence

$$x\left(1+\frac{\delta x}{x}\right)=\left[p\left(1+\frac{\delta p}{p}\right)\right]^a\left[q\left(1+\frac{\delta q}{q}\right)\right]^b\left[r\left(1-\frac{\delta r}{r}\right)\right]^{-c}.$$

or $\qquad x\left(1+\dfrac{\delta x}{x}\right)=p^aq^br^{-c}\cdot\left(1+\dfrac{\delta p}{p}\right)^a\left(1+\dfrac{\delta q}{q}\right)^b\left(1-\dfrac{\delta r}{r}\right)^{-c}.$

But $\qquad x=p^aq^br^{-c};$

so $\qquad 1+\dfrac{\delta x}{x}=\left(1+\dfrac{\delta p}{p}\right)^a\left(1+\dfrac{\delta q}{q}\right)^b\left(1-\dfrac{\delta r}{r}\right)^{-c}.$

Expanding each bracket on the right-hand side by the binomial theorem, and rejecting squares and higher powers of the small quantities $\dfrac{\delta p}{p}$, etc.,

$$1+\frac{\delta x}{x}=\left(1+a\,\frac{\delta p}{p}\right)\left(1+b\,\frac{\delta q}{q}\right)\left(1+c\,\frac{\delta r}{r}\right),$$

and multiplying out and rejecting the products of $\dfrac{\delta p}{p}$, $\dfrac{\delta q}{q}$, $\dfrac{\delta r}{r}$ taken two and three at a time,

$$1+\frac{\delta x}{x}=1+a\,\frac{\delta p}{p}+b\,\frac{\delta q}{q}+c\,\frac{\delta r}{r},$$

so $\qquad \dfrac{\delta x}{x}=a\,\dfrac{\delta p}{p}+b\,\dfrac{\delta q}{q}+c\,\dfrac{\delta r}{r}.$

Now $\dfrac{\delta x}{x}$ is the proportional error in the result, and $\dfrac{\delta p}{p}$, $\dfrac{\delta q}{q}$, and $\dfrac{\delta r}{r}$ are the proportional errors in the observed quantities ; thus the rule for finding the expected limit of error is as follows :

(1) Multiply the proportional error of each factor by the power (regardless of sign) to which it is raised in the formula, and then (2) take the sum of all the terms thus obtained ; this gives the expected proportional error in the result.

EXAMPLE. The apparent coefficient of expansion of a liquid is measured as on p. 105, using a balance sensitive to 0ˑ01 gm., and a thermometer which can be read to 0·1° C.

The following readings were taken :

Mass of empty bottle, 20·00 gm.   Initial temp.,   14·0° C.
Mass of bottle + liquid   Final temp.,   65·4° C.
  before heating,   72·50 gm.
Mass of bottle + liquid
  after heating,   70·00 gm.
    Each with expected limit   Each with expected limit of
      of 0·01 gm.   0·1° C.

The quantities to be used in the formula

$$a = \frac{\text{mass expelled}}{\text{mass left in} \times \text{temp. rise}},$$

are all obtained by differences between the observations ; and as, for example, the first weighing may be 0·01 gm. too high, and the third 0·01 gm. too low, the error in the difference may be 0·02 gm.

Thus,

Mass expelled = 2·50 gm.   Rise in temp. = 51·4° C.
Mass left in = 50·00 gm.
With expected limit of 0·02 gm.   With expected limit of 0·2° C

Then $a = \dfrac{2·50}{50·00 \times 51·4} = 0·0009731$, using four-figure tables.

The proportional error in   2·50 gm. is $\dfrac{0·02}{|2·5}$,   =   0·008.

  ,,   ,,   ,,   in 50·00 gm. is $\dfrac{0·02}{50}$,   =   0·0004.

  ,,   ,,   ,,   in 51·4°   is $\dfrac{0·2}{51·4}$,   =   0·00391.

As each of these quantities appears to the first power in the formula, the proportional error in a is $0·008 + 0·0004 + 0·00391$, which is $0·0123$, or 1 part in 81, or 1·23 per cent.

The arithmetical result, 0·0009731, is thus reliable to only about 1·2 per cent., and the last two figures are meaningless ; and the result should be recorded to *two* significant figures as " 0·00097, with an expected maximum uncertainty of 1·2 per cent." Do not fall into the " four-figure table trap ", which yawns open at the end of every experiment ; record the result to the number of significant figures consistent with the expected accuracy, and no more. If you should be working with an accuracy warranting four significant figures, remember that four-figure tables are useless, since the fourth figure of the result obtained by their use is unreliable.

The accuracy attained. The errors actually occurring in an experiment may be either random errors or systematic errors.

(a) *Random errors*, arising from slight changes in the experimental conditions and in the alertness of the observer, are as likely to be on one side as the other. Purely fortuitous errors are distributed according to the same probability law as governs the distribution of molecular velocities in a gas. We need not go into this, except to state that it shows that large random errors are less likely to occur than small ones. Thus, if a large number of observations of the same quantity are made, it is probable that the majority of them carry only small errors, whence the mean of a large number of observations is likely to be closer to the true result than any one individual reading. This is the reasoning behind repetition of readings and averaging ; it is not just " hoping the high readings will balance the low readings "—for if, on account of some systematic error all the readings are " low ", averaging will not help matters— it is a scientific means, based on the laws of chance, of reducing the effect of random errors, and of random errors only.

Let x_1, x_2, x_3, ... be the values of the individual observations, and m the value of their average, or arithmetic mean. The difference $(x_1 - m)$, $(x_2 - m)$, ... of the individual observations from the mean are called their *deviations*. Squaring the deviations gives the terms $(x_1 - m)^2$, $(x_2 - m)^2$ .... . By finding the average value of the squares of the deviations, and taking the square root of this average, a quantity called the root mean square deviation, or standard deviation, is obtained. The standard deviation is the figure usually employed as a measure of the " spread " of the observations due to random errors, and represents the accuracy actually attained.

In the table below, the first column gives the results of ten determinations of the coefficient of expansion of a liquid by the method of pp. 105 and 454. The second column gives the mean, the third the individual deviations, the fourth the squared deviations, the fifth the average value of the squared deviations, and the last column the square root of the average of the squared deviations, or the standard deviation.

Value of a.	Mean.	Deviation.	(Deviation)^2	Average (Deviation)^2	Standard Deviation.
97×10^{-5}		0	0	18.7×10^{-10}	4.3×10^{-5}
94		-3×10^{-5}	9×10^{-10}		
103		$+6$	36		
96		-1	1		
104	97×10^{-5}	$+7$	49		
92		-5	25		
100		$+3$	9		
94		-3	9		
97		0	0		
90		-7	49		

The standard deviation is thus 4·3 parts in 97, or about 4·5 per cent. This is nearly four times as great as the expected limit of accuracy ; but it is hardly possible to anticipate, except as a rough guess, the random errors before they occur.

(b) *Systematic errors* are dealt with in one of three ways. Either they are forestalled by suitably arranging the routine of the experiment so that they cannot contribute to the readings (for example, checking the zero error of a micrometer) ; or they are allowed to occur and are then corrected for (for example, the correction for the heat lost from a calorimeter, as on p. 50) ; or else they are eliminated by repeating the experiment under different conditions (for example, the elimination of the cooling correction in the Callendar and Barnes experiment, p. 71). Note that repetition under suitably changed conditions, very carefully thought out, is involved in the last of these methods ; it is not just a simple repetition to be followed by averaging, as in the case of random errors.

How can an observer feel confident in his results after all? It is true that a small standard deviation should, if sufficient readings have been taken, set his mind at rest as to *random error*. Systematic sources of error have to be sought for by varying the experimental conditions in as many ways as possible ; if any variation of conditions leads to an appreciable change in the result, it would be suspected that a systematic error is the cause. Thus, if every practicable variation of conditions has been tried, the observer should be satisfied that *systematic errors* have been dealt with also.

Probable error. The term " probable error " is often used, and this is sometimes intended to stand for the estimated limit of accuracy, and sometimes for the standard deviation, but strictly speaking it has a definite technical meaning different from either. The " most probable value " of the result can be calculated statistically from the observations, providing there are enough of them and that the errors are random. The " probable error " then denotes limits on either side of the most probable value, such that there is an even chance of the true result lying between those limits.

CONSTANTS

The following values have been assumed in working out examples unless other figures have been explicitly given :

$$\pi = 3 \cdot 1416 \qquad \log \pi = 0 \cdot 4971$$
$$e = 2 \cdot 718 \qquad \log e = 0 \cdot 4343$$

The symbol " ln " is used to denote logarithms to the base e.

$\ln 10 = 2 \cdot 303.$

$\ln x = 2 \cdot 303 \log x.$

$g = 981$ cm./sec./sec.

$J (J') = 4 \cdot 2$ joules per calorie.

LOGARITHMS

	0	1	2	3	4	5	6	7	8	9	1 2 3	4 5 6	7 8 9
10	0000	0043	0086	0128	0170	0212	0253	0294	0334	0374	5 9 13 / 4 8 12	17 21 26 / 16 20 24	30 34 38 / 28 32 36
11	0414	0453	0492	0531	0569	0607	0645	0682	0719	0755	4 8 12 / 4 7 11	16 20 23 / 15 18 22	27 31 35 / 26 29 33
12	0792	0828	0864	0899	0934	0969	1004	1038	1072	1106	3 7 11 / 3 7 10	14 18 21 / 14 17 20	25 28 32 / 24 27 31
13	1139	1173	1206	1239	1271	1303	1335	1367	1399	1430	3 6 10 / 3 7 10	13 16 19 / 13 16 19	23 26 29 / 22 25 29
14	1461	1492	1523	1553	1584	1614	1644	1673	1703	1732	3 6 9 / 3 6 9	12 15 19 / 12 14 17	22 25 28 / 20 23 26
15	1761	1790	1818	1847	1875	1903	1931	1959	1987	2014	3 6 9 / 3 6 8	11 14 17 / 11 14 17	20 23 26 / 19 22 25
16	2041	2068	2095	2122	2148	2175	2201	2227	2253	2279	3 6 8 / 3 5 8	11 14 16 / 10 13 16	19 22 24 / 18 21 23
17	2304	2330	2355	2380	2405	2430	2455	2480	2504	2529	3 5 8 / 3 5 8	10 13 15 / 10 12 15	18 20 23 / 17 20 22
18	2553	2577	2601	2625	2648	2672	2695	2718	2742	2765	2 5 7 / 2 4 7	9 12 14 / 9 11 14	17 19 21 / 16 18 21
19	2788	2810	2833	2856	2878	2900	2923	2945	2967	2989	2 4 7 / 2 4 6	9 11 13 / 8 11 13	16 18 20 / 15 17 19
20	3010	3032	3054	3075	3096	3118	3139	3160	3181	3201	2 4 6	8 11 13	15 17 19
21	3222	3243	3263	3284	3304	3324	3345	3365	3385	3404	2 4 6	8 10 12	14 16 18
22	3424	3444	3464	3483	3502	3522	3541	3560	3579	3598	2 4 6	8 10 12	14 15 17
23	3617	3636	3655	3674	3692	3711	3729	3747	3766	3784	2 4 6	7 9 11	13 15 17
24	3802	3820	3838	3856	3874	3892	3909	3927	3945	3962	2 4 5	7 9 11	12 14 16
25	3979	3997	4014	4031	4048	4065	4082	4099	4116	4133	2 3 5	7 9 10	12 14 15
26	4150	4166	4183	4200	4216	4232	4249	4265	4281	4298	2 3 5	7 8 10	11 13 15
27	4314	4330	4346	4362	4378	4393	4409	4425	4440	4456	2 3 5	6 8 9	11 13 14
28	4472	4487	4502	4518	4533	4548	4564	4579	4594	4609	2 3 5	6 8 9	11 12 14
29	4624	4639	4654	4669	4683	4698	4713	4728	4742	4757	1 3 4	6 7 9	10 12 13
30	4771	4786	4800	4814	4829	4843	4857	4871	4886	4900	1 3 4	6 7 9	10 11 13
31	4914	4928	4942	4955	4969	4983	4997	5011	5024	5038	1 3 4	6 7 8	10 11 12
32	5051	5065	5079	5092	5105	5119	5132	5145	5159	5172	1 3 4	5 7 8	9 11 12
33	5185	5198	5211	5224	5237	5250	5263	5276	5289	5302	1 3 4	5 6 8	9 10 12
34	5315	5328	5340	5353	5366	5378	5391	5403	5416	5428	1 3 4	5 6 8	9 10 11
35	5441	5453	5465	5478	5490	5502	5514	5527	5539	5551	1 2 4	5 6 7	9 10 11
36	5563	5575	5587	5599	5611	5623	5635	5647	5658	5670	1 2 4	5 6 7	8 10 11
37	5682	5694	5705	5717	5729	5740	5752	5763	5775	5786	1 2 3	5 6 7	8 9 10
38	5798	5809	5821	5832	5843	5855	5866	5877	5888	5899	1 2 3	5 6 7	8 9 10
39	5911	5922	5933	5944	5955	5966	5977	5988	5999	6010	1 2 3	4 5 7	8 9 10
40	6021	6031	6042	6053	6064	6075	6085	6096	6107	6117	1 2 3	4 5 6	8 9 10
41	6128	6138	6149	6160	6170	6180	6191	6201	6212	6222	1 2 3	4 5 6	7 8 9
42	6232	6243	6253	6263	6274	6284	6294	6304	6314	6325	1 2 3	4 5 6	7 8 9
43	6335	6345	6355	6365	6375	6385	6395	6405	6415	6425	1 2 3	4 5 6	7 8 9
44	6435	6444	6454	6464	6474	6484	6493	6503	6513	6522	1 2 3	4 5 6	7 8 9
45	6532	6542	6551	6561	6571	6580	6590	6599	6609	6618	1 2 3	4 5 6	7 8 9
46	6628	6637	6646	6656	6665	6675	6684	6693	6702	6712	1 2 3	4 5 6	7 7 8
47	6721	6730	6739	6749	6758	6767	6776	6785	6794	6803	1 2 3	4 5 5	6 7 8
48	6812	6821	6830	6839	6848	6857	6866	6875	6884	6893	1 2 3	4 4 5	6 7 8
49	6902	6911	6920	6928	6937	6946	6955	6964	6972	6981	1 2 3	4 4 5	6 7 8

FOUR-FIGURE LOGARITHMS

	0	1	2	3	4	5	6	7	8	9	1 2 3	4 5 6	7 8 9
50	6990	6998	7007	7016	7024	7033	7042	7050	7059	7067	1 2 3	3 4 5	6 7 8
51	7076	7084	7093	7101	7110	7118	7126	7135	7143	7152	1 2 3	3 4 5	6 7 8
52	7160	7168	7177	7185	7193	7202	7210	7218	7226	7235	1 2 2	3 4 5	6 7 7
53	7243	7251	7259	7267	7275	7284	7292	7300	7308	7316	1 2 2	3 4 5	6 6 7
54	7324	7332	7340	7348	7356	7364	7372	7380	7388	7396	1 2 2	3 4 5	6 6 7
55	7404	7412	7419	7427	7435	7443	7451	7459	7466	7474	1 2 2	3 4 5	5 6 7
56	7482	7490	7497	7505	7513	7520	7528	7536	7543	7551	1 2 2	3 4 5	5 6 7
57	7559	7566	7574	7582	7589	7597	7604	7612	7619	7627	1 2 2	3 4 5	5 6 7
58	7634	7642	7649	7657	7664	7672	7679	7686	7694	7701	1 1 2	3 4 4	5 6 7
59	7709	7716	7723	7731	7738	7745	7752	7760	7767	7774	1 1 2	3 4 4	5 6 7
60	7782	7789	7796	7803	7810	7818	7825	7832	7839	7846	1 1 2	3 4 4	5 6 6
61	7853	7860	7868	7875	7882	7889	7896	7903	7910	7917	1 1 2	3 4 4	5 6 6
62	7924	7931	7938	7945	7952	7959	7966	7973	7980	7987	1 1 2	3 3 4	5 6 6
63	7993	8000	8007	8014	8021	8028	8035	8041	8048	8055	1 1 2	3 3 4	5 5 6
64	8062	8069	8075	8082	8089	8096	8102	8109	8116	8122	1 1 2	3 3 4	5 5 6
65	8129	8136	8142	8149	8156	8162	8169	8176	8182	8189	1 1 2	3 3 4	5 5 6
66	8195	8202	8209	8215	8222	8228	8235	8241	8248	8254	1 1 2	3 3 4	5 5 6
67	8261	8267	8274	8280	8287	8293	8299	8306	8312	8319	1 1 2	3 3 4	5 5 6
68	8325	8331	8338	8344	8351	8357	8363	8370	8376	8382	1 1 2	3 3 4	4 5 6
69	8388	8395	8401	8407	8414	8420	8426	8432	8439	8445	1 1 2	2 3 4	4 5 6
70	8451	8457	8463	8470	8476	8482	8488	8494	8500	8506	1 1 2	2 3 4	4 5 6
71	8513	8519	8525	8531	8537	8543	8549	8555	8561	8567	1 1 2	2 3 4	4 5 5
72	8573	8579	8585	8591	8597	8603	8609	8615	8621	8627	1 1 2	2 3 4	4 5 5
73	8633	8639	8645	8651	8657	8663	8669	8675	8681	8686	1 1 2	2 3 4	4 5 5
74	8692	8698	8704	8710	8716	8722	8727	8733	8739	8745	1 1 2	2 3 4	4 5 5
75	8751	8756	8762	8768	8774	8779	8785	8791	8797	8802	1 1 2	2 3 3	4 5 5
76	8808	8814	8820	8825	8831	8837	8842	8848	8854	8859	1 1 2	2 3 3	4 5 5
77	8865	8871	8876	8882	8887	8893	8899	8904	8910	8915	1 1 2	2 3 3	4 4 5
78	8921	8927	8932	8938	8943	8949	8954	8960	8965	8971	1 1 2	2 3 3	4 4 5
79	8976	8982	8987	8993	8998	9004	9009	9015	9020	9025	1 1 2	2 3 3	4 4 5
80	9031	9036	9042	9047	9053	9058	9063	9069	9074	9079	1 1 2	2 3 3	4 4 5
81	9085	9090	9096	9101	9106	9112	9117	9122	9128	9133	1 1 2	2 3 3	4 4 5
82	9138	9143	9149	9154	9159	9165	9170	9175	9180	9186	1 1 2	2 3 3	4 4 5
83	9191	9196	9201	9206	9212	9217	9222	9227	9232	9238	1 1 2	2 3 3	4 4 5
84	9243	9248	9253	9258	9263	9269	9274	9279	9284	9289	1 1 2	2 3 3	4 4 5
85	9294	9299	9304	9309	9315	9320	9325	9330	9335	9340	1 1 2	2 3 3	4 4 5
86	9345	9350	9355	9360	9365	9370	9375	9380	9385	9390	1 1 2	2 3 3	4 4 5
87	9395	9400	9405	9410	9415	9420	9425	9430	9435	9440	0 1 1	2 2 3	3 4 4
88	9445	9450	9455	9460	9465	9469	9474	9479	9484	9489	0 1 1	2 2 3	3 4 4
89	9494	9499	9504	9509	9513	9518	9523	9528	9533	9538	0 1 1	2 2 3	3 4 4
90	9542	9547	9552	9557	9562	9566	9571	9576	9581	9586	0 1 1	2 2 3	3 4 4
91	9590	9595	9600	9605	9609	9614	9619	9624	9628	9633	0 1 1	2 2 3	3 4 4
92	9638	9643	9647	9652	9657	9661	9666	9671	9675	9680	0 1 1	2 2 3	3 4 4
93	9685	9689	9694	9699	9703	9708	9713	9717	9722	9727	0 1 1	2 2 3	3 4 4
94	9731	9736	9741	9745	9750	9754	9759	9763	9768	9773	0 1 1	2 2 3	3 4 4
95	9777	9782	9786	9791	9795	9800	9805	9809	9814	9818	0 1 1	2 2 3	3 4 4
96	9823	9827	9832	9836	9841	9845	9850	9854	9859	9863	0 1 1	2 2 3	3 4 4
97	9868	9872	9877	9881	9886	9890	9894	9899	9903	9908	0 1 1	2 2 3	3 4 4
98	9912	9917	9921	9926	9930	9934	9939	9943	9948	9952	0 1 1	2 2 3	3 4 4
99	9956	9961	9965	9969	9974	9978	9983	9987	9991	9996	0 1 1	2 2 3	3 3 4

	0	1	2	3	4	5	6	7	8	9	1 2 3	4 5 6	7 8 9
·00	1000	1002	1005	1007	1009	1012	1014	1016	1019	1021	0 0 1	1 1 1	2 2 2
·01	1023	1026	1028	1030	1033	1035	1038	1040	1042	1045	0 0 1	1 1 1	2 2 2
·02	1047	1050	1052	1054	1057	1059	1062	1064	1067	1069	0 0 1	1 1 1	2 2 2
·03	1072	1074	1076	1079	1081	1084	1086	1089	1091	1094	0 0 1	1 1 1	2 2 2
·04	1096	1099	1102	1104	1107	1109	1112	1114	1117	1119	0 1 1	1 1 2	2 2 2
·05	1122	1125	1127	1130	1132	1135	1138	1140	1143	1146	0 1 1	1 1 2	2 2 2
·06	1148	1151	1153	1156	1159	1161	1164	1167	1169	1172	0 1 1	1 1 2	2 2 2
·07	1175	1178	1180	1183	1186	1189	1191	1194	1197	1199	0 1 1	1 1 2	2 2 2
·08	1202	1205	1208	1211	1213	1216	1219	1222	1225	1227	0 1 1	1 1 2	2 2 3
·09	1230	1233	1236	1239	1242	1245	1247	1250	1253	1256	0 1 1	1 1 2	2 2 3
·10	1259	1262	1265	1268	1271	1274	1276	1279	1282	1285	0 1 1	1 1 2	2 2 3
·11	1288	1291	1294	1297	1300	1303	1306	1309	1312	1315	0 1 1	1 2 2	2 2 3
·12	1318	1321	1324	1327	1330	1334	1337	1340	1343	1346	0 1 1	1 2 2	2 2 3
·13	1349	1352	1355	1358	1361	1365	1368	1371	1374	1377	0 1 1	1 2 2	2 3 3
·14	1380	1384	1387	1390	1393	1396	1400	1403	1406	1409	0 1 1	1 2 2	2 3 3
·15	1413	1416	1419	1422	1426	1429	1432	1435	1439	1442	0 1 1	1 2 2	2 3 3
·16	1445	1449	1452	1455	1459	1462	1466	1469	1472	1476	0 1 1	1 2 2	2 3 3
·17	1479	1483	1486	1489	1493	1496	1500	1503	1507	1510	0 1 1	1 2 2	2 3 3
·18	1514	1517	1521	1524	1528	1531	1535	1538	1542	1545	0 1 1	1 2 2	2 3 3
·19	1549	1552	1556	1560	1563	1567	1570	1574	1578	1581	0 1 1	1 2 2	3 3 3
·20	1585	1589	1592	1596	1600	1603	1607	1611	1614	1618	0 1 1	1 2 2	3 3 3
·21	1622	1626	1629	1633	1637	1641	1644	1648	1652	1656	0 1 1	2 2 2	3 3 3
·22	1660	1663	1667	1671	1675	1679	1683	1687	1690	1694	0 1 1	2 2 2	3 3 3
·23	1698	1702	1706	1710	1714	1718	1722	1726	1730	1734	0 1 1	2 2 2	3 3 4
·24	1738	1742	1746	1750	1754	1758	1762	1766	1770	1774	0 1 1	2 2 2	3 3 4
·25	1778	1782	1786	1791	1795	1799	1803	1807	1811	1816	0 1 1	2 2 2	3 3 4
·26	1820	1824	1828	1832	1837	1841	1845	1849	1854	1858	0 1 1	2 2 3	3 3 4
·27	1862	1866	1871	1875	1879	1884	1888	1892	1897	1901	0 1 1	2 2 3	3 3 4
·28	1905	1910	1914	1919	1923	1928	1932	1936	1941	1945	0 1 1	2 2 3	3 4 4
·29	1950	1954	1959	1963	1968	1972	1977	1982	1986	1991	0 1 1	2 2 3	3 4 4
·30	1995	2000	2004	2009	2014	2018	2023	2028	2032	2037	0 1 1	2 2 3	3 4 4
·31	2042	2046	2051	2056	2061	2065	2070	2075	2080	2084	0 1 1	2 2 3	3 4 4
·32	2089	2094	2099	2104	2109	2113	2118	2123	2128	2133	0 1 1	2 2 3	3 4 4
·33	2138	2143	2148	2153	2158	2163	2168	2173	2178	2183	0 1 1	2 2 3	3 4 4
·34	2188	2193	2198	2203	2208	2213	2218	2223	2228	2234	1 1 2	2 3 3	4 4 5
·35	2239	2244	2249	2254	2259	2265	2270	2275	2280	2286	1 1 2	2 3 3	4 4 5
·36	2291	2296	2301	2307	2312	2317	2323	2328	2333	2339	1 1 2	2 3 3	4 4 5
·37	2344	2350	2355	2360	2366	2371	2377	2382	2388	2393	1 1 2	2 3 3	4 4 5
·38	2399	2404	2410	2415	2421	2427	2432	2438	2443	2449	1 1 2	2 3 3	4 4 5
·39	2455	2460	2466	2472	2477	2483	2489	2495	2500	2506	1 1 2	2 3 3	4 5 5
·40	2512	2518	2523	2529	2535	2541	2547	2553	2559	2564	1 1 2	2 3 4	4 5 5
·41	2570	2576	2582	2588	2594	2600	2606	2612	2618	2624	1 1 2	2 3 4	4 5 5
·42	2630	2636	2642	2649	2655	2661	2667	2673	2679	2685	1 1 2	2 3 4	4 5 6
·43	2692	2698	2704	2710	2716	2723	2729	2735	2742	2748	1 1 2	3 3 4	4 5 6
·44	2754	2761	2767	2773	2780	2786	2793	2799	2805	2812	1 1 2	3 3 4	4 5 6
·45	2818	2825	2831	2838	2844	2851	2858	2864	2871	2877	1 1 2	3 3 4	5 5 6
·46	2884	2891	2897	2904	2911	2917	2924	2931	2938	2944	1 1 2	3 3 4	5 5 6
·47	2951	2958	2965	2972	2979	2985	2992	2999	3006	3013	1 1 2	3 3 4	5 5 6
·48	3020	3027	3034	3041	3048	3055	3062	3069	3076	3083	1 1 2	3 4 4	5 6 6
·49	3090	3097	3105	3112	3119	3126	3133	3141	3148	3155	1 1 2	3 4 4	5 6 6

ANTILOGARITHMS

	0	1	2	3	4	5	6	7	8	9	1 2 3	4 5 6	7 8 9
·50	3162	3170	3177	3184	3192	3199	3206	3214	3221	3228	1 1 2	3 4 4	5 6 7
·51	3236	3243	3251	3258	3266	3273	3281	3289	3296	3304	1 2 2	3 4 5	5 6 7
·52	3311	3319	3327	3334	3342	3350	3357	3365	3373	3381	1 2 2	3 4 5	5 6 7
·53	3388	3396	3404	3412	3420	3428	3436	3443	3451	3459	1 2 2	3 4 5	6 6 7
·54	3467	3475	3483	3491	3499	3508	3516	3524	3532	3540	1 2 2	3 4 5	6 6 7
·55	3548	3556	3565	3573	3581	3589	3597	3606	3614	3622	1 2 2	3 4 5	6 7 7
·56	3631	3639	3648	3656	3664	3673	3681	3690	3698	3707	1 2 3	3 4 5	6 7 8
·57	3715	3724	3733	3741	3750	3758	3767	3776	3784	3793	1 2 3	3 4 5	6 7 8
·58	3802	3811	3819	3828	3837	3846	3855	3864	3873	3882	1 2 3	4 4 5	6 7 8
·59	3890	3899	3908	3917	3926	3936	3945	3954	3963	3972	1 2 3	4 5 5	6 7 8
·60	3981	3990	3999	4009	4018	4027	4036	4046	4055	4064	1 2 3	4 5 6	6 7 8
·61	4074	4083	4093	4102	4111	4121	4130	4140	4150	4159	1 2 3	4 5 6	7 8 9
·62	4169	4178	4188	4198	4207	4217	4227	4236	4246	4256	1 2 3	4 5 6	7 8 9
·63	4266	4276	4285	4295	4305	4315	4325	4335	4345	4355	1 2 3	4 5 6	7 8 9
·64	4365	4375	4385	4395	4406	4416	4426	4436	4446	4457	1 2 3	4 5 6	7 8 9
·65	4467	4477	4487	4498	4508	4519	4529	4539	4550	4560	1 2 3	4 5 6	7 8 9
·66	4571	4581	4592	4603	4613	4624	4634	4645	4656	4667	1 2 3	4 5 6	7 9 10
·67	4677	4688	4699	4710	4721	4732	4742	4753	4764	4775	1 2 3	4 5 7	8 9 10
·68	4786	4797	4808	4819	4831	4842	4853	4864	4875	4887	1 2 3	4 6 7	8 9 10
·69	4898	4909	4920	4932	4943	4955	4966	4977	4989	5000	1 2 3	5 6 7	8 9 10
·70	5012	5023	5035	5047	5058	5070	5082	5093	5105	5117	1 2 4	5 6 7	8 9 11
·71	5129	5140	5152	5164	5176	5188	5200	5212	5224	5236	1 2 4	5 6 7	8 10 11
·72	5248	5260	5272	5284	5297	5309	5321	5333	5346	5358	1 2 4	5 6 7	9 10 11
·73	5370	5383	5395	5408	5420	5433	5445	5458	5470	5483	1 3 4	5 6 8	9 10 11
·74	5495	5508	5521	5534	5546	5559	5572	5585	5598	5610	1 3 4	5 6 8	9 10 12
·75	5623	5636	5649	5662	5675	5689	5702	5715	5728	5741	1 3 4	5 7 8	9 10 12
·76	5754	5768	5781	5794	5808	5821	5834	5848	5861	5875	1 3 4	5 7 8	9 11 12
·77	5888	5902	5916	5929	5943	5957	5970	5984	5998	6012	1 3 4	5 7 8	10 11 12
·78	6026	6039	6053	6067	6081	6095	6109	6124	6138	6152	1 3 4	6 7 8	10 11 13
·79	6166	6180	6194	6209	6223	6237	6252	6266	6281	6295	1 3 4	6 7 9	10 11 13
·80	6310	6324	6339	6353	6368	6383	6397	6412	6427	6442	1 3 4	6 7 9	10 12 13
·81	6457	6471	6486	6501	6516	6531	6546	6561	6577	6592	2 3 5	6 8 9	11 12 14
·82	6607	6622	6637	6653	6668	6683	6699	6714	6730	6745	2 3 5	6 8 9	11 12 14
·83	6761	6776	6792	6808	6823	6839	6855	6871	6887	6902	2 3 5	6 8 9	11 13 14
·84	6918	6934	6950	6966	6982	6998	7015	7031	7047	7063	2 3 5	6 8 10	11 13 15
·85	7079	7096	7112	7129	7145	7161	7178	7194	7211	7228	2 3 5	7 8 10	12 13 15
·86	7244	7261	7278	7295	7311	7328	7345	7362	7379	7396	2 3 5	7 8 10	12 13 15
·87	7413	7430	7447	7464	7482	7499	7516	7534	7551	7568	2 3 5	7 9 10	12 14 16
·88	7586	7603	7621	7638	7656	7674	7691	7709	7727	7745	2 4 5	7 9 11	12 14 16
·89	7762	7780	7798	7816	7834	7852	7870	7889	7907	7925	2 4 5	7 9 11	13 14 16
·90	7943	7962	7980	7998	8017	8035	8054	8072	8091	8110	2 4 6	7 9 11	13 15 17
·91	8128	8147	8166	8185	8204	8222	8241	8260	8279	8299	2 4 6	8 9 11	13 15 17
·92	8318	8337	8356	8375	8395	8414	8433	8453	8472	8492	2 4 6	8 10 12	14 15 17
·93	8511	8531	8551	8570	8590	8610	8630	8650	8670	8690	2 4 6	8 10 12	14 16 18
·94	8710	8730	8750	8770	8790	8810	8831	8851	8872	8892	2 4 6	8 10 12	14 16 18
·95	8913	8933	8954	8974	8995	9016	9036	9057	9078	9099	2 4 6	8 10 12	15 17 19
·96	9120	9141	9162	9183	9204	9226	9247	9268	9290	9311	2 4 6	8 11 13	15 17 19
·97	9333	9354	9376	9397	9419	9441	9462	9484	9506	9528	2 4 7	9 11 13	15 17 20
·98	9550	9572	9594	9616	9638	9661	9683	9705	9727	9750	2 4 7	9 11 13	16 18 20
·99	9772	9795	9817	9840	9863	9886	9908	9931	9954	9977	2 5 7	9 11 14	16 18 20

INDEX

Absolute scale of temperature, 25, 140, 325
Absolute zero, 140
Absorption of radiation, 371, 375, 380
Absorptive power, 380
Accuracy, 452
Adiabatic change, 258
  curves, 261, 286
  demagnetisation, 323
  desorption, 321
  lapse-rate, 428
Alloys, 219
Ampere, 64
Andrews' experiments, 159
Ångstrøm unit, 369
Anticyclone, 433
Apparent coefficient of expansion, 101, 102, 105–108
Assmann psychrometer, 204
Atmospheric composition, 416
Atmospheric stability, 427

Balancing column method, 109–112
Barometer correction, 115
Berthelot's latent heat method, 57
  equation of state, 169
Bimetallic thermograph, 99
  thermostat, 98
Black body, 377
  source, 387
  spectrum, 388
  radiation laws, 393–395
Boiling, 180
Boiling by bumping, 197
Boiling point, 180
  and pressure, 6, 186
  elevation, 194
Bolometer, 382
Boltzmann's Constant, 152, 292, 391
Boyle's Law, 122, 123, 155, 157
Boyle temperature, 156, 170
Brightness temperature, 405, 407
British Thermal Unit, 32
Bunsen's ice calorimeter, 59
Buys Ballot's Law, 434

Caloric, 230
Calorie, 30
Calorimeter, 31

Callendar's radio-balance, 383
Callendar and Barnes' experiment, 71, 245
Callendar and Griffiths' bridge, 17
Callendar and Swann, 73
Carnot cycle, 277, 282
Cascade process, 308
Cavity radiation, 377
Centigrade degree, 2
Chappuis, 14
Charles' Law, 129
Chemical hygrometer, 199
Claude process, 312
Clausius' equation, 168
Clausius-Clapeyron equation, 185, 211, 294
Clement and Desormes, 262 sqq.
Clinical therometer, 9
Clouds, 423
Coefficient of expansion, cubical, 90
  linear, 81
  real and apparent, 101
  of gas at constant pressure, 129
Cold accumulator, 318
Cold front, 441
Collection of damp gas, 191
Colour temperature, 405
Comparator, 88
Compensated balance wheel, 95
  pendulum, 94
Conductivity, 328
Conductivity of bad conductor, 337
  gases, 346
  good conductor, 334
  liquids, 345
  tube method, 341
Conservation of energy, 228, 249
Constant pressure experiment, 129
Constant volume air thermometer, 12, 135, 141
  gas scale, 11
  gas thermometer, 14
Continuity of state, 158
Continuous flow calorimeter, 71
Convection, 363, 450
Cooling, 40–46, 65
  Newton's Law, 41–45, 47, 51, 53, 56, 57
  method for specific heat of liquid, 57

Cooling correction, 49
Cooling curves, 211
Correction of gas thermometer, 141
Corresponding states, 168
Critical constants, 164–167
Critical temperature, 158, 161
Crookes' radiometer, 372
Curie scale, 22, 324
Cycle pump, 124
Cyclone, 433

Dalton's Law of partial pressures, 147, 155, 180, 192
Davy's experiment, 231
Density,
  and temperature, 103
  of gas, 147
  of saturated vapour, 190
  of vapour, 188
Depression, 433
Depression of freezing point, 217
Despretz' experiment, 114
Dew, 199, 426
Dew point, 199
  hygrometers, 200
Diesel engine, 303
Dieterici's equation, 169
Differential air thermometer, 372
Differential steam calorimeter, 62
Dilatometer, 104
Dimensions, 367, 446
Disappearing filament pyrometer, 397, 400, 404
Displacement law, 390, 393, 396
Distillation, fractional, 221, 224
  steam, 192
Distribution formulae, 390–393
Dry flask experiment, 133
Dulong and Petit's Law, 73
  balancing column method, 109
  cooling experiments, 364
Dumas' vapour density method, 189

Efficiency, 279, 293
Elasticity, 91
Electrical calorimetry, 67
Electrical equivalent of heat, 64, 66, 72, 229, 239
Electrical hygrometer, 206
Electrolux refrigerator, 208
Emissive power, 378
Emissivity, 330
Energy, 29
Energy, conservation of, 228, 249
Energy density, 378
Entropy, 284, 286, 287, 291

Entropy-temperature diagram, 286, 429, 431
Equipartition of energy, 271, 391
Errors, 454–456
Ether thermoscope, 371
Eutectic, 218
Evaporation, 197
Exhaust pump, 125, 126
Expansion, 81 sqq.
Expansion of water, 112
External work, 246, 248, 260

Fahrenheit degree, 2
Film theory of convection loss, 366
First latent heat equation, 293
First law of thermodynamics, 229
Five-fourths power law, 41, 365, 451
Fizeau's expansion apparatus, 89
Flow of heat down cylindrical bar, 327, 332
  through cylindrical wall, 339
  through spherical shell, 340
  through composite walls, 343
Flue gas analysis, 356
Foot-pound, 30
Forced convection, 363, 450
Four-stroke cycle, 302
Fourth power law, 390
Fractional distillation, 221–224
Fractionating column, 229
Free convection, 363, 451
Freezing point, 211
  depression, 217
Freezing mixture, 218
Freezing of pond, 117, 344
Friction balance, 235, 237
Frontal theory of depressions, 438
Frontal surface, 439
Fundamental interval, 2
Fused silica, 100

" Gamma ", 262–273
Gas laws, 122 sqq.
Gas constant, 144–152
Geostrophic wind, 434
Glassware, 99
Glazed frost, 426
Gold point, 23
Good conductors, 334
Gradient wind, 435
Graham's Law of Diffusion, 154
Gregory and Archer's experiment, 347
Guard ring, 335, 336

Hail, 425
Hair hygrometer, 205

Hampson process, 310
Heat capacity, 33
Heating effect of electric current, 64
Heating of earth, 417
Helium, 319–321
Henning's latent heat method, 68
Heylandt process, 313
High temperature, measurement of, 19, 24, 395
Hoar frost, 426
Hope's experiment, 113
Humidity, 198
Hydrogen, 318, 319
Hygrometers, 199 *sqq.*
Hypsometer, 7

Ice point, 2, 6, 23
Ideal gas, 139–144, 149, 247 *sqq.*
Ideal gas scale, 4
Indicator diagram, 301
Infra-red radiation, 370
Ingen-Hausz' experiment, 333
Internal combustion engine, 301
Internal work, 249, 251
International atmosphere, 420
    joule, 227
    temperature scale, 13, 23
    volt, 64
Inversion temperature, 253, 256, 257
Isobars, 432
Isothermal change, 247
Isothermal curves, 159
Isotopes, 31

Jaeger and Steinwehr, 237
Joly's differential steam calorimeter, 62
Joule, 229
Joule's experiments on the equivalence of heat and work, 231–235
Joule and Playfair's experiment, 114
Joule-Kelvin effect, 252, 254, 307

Kannuluik and Martin, 350
Katharometer, 254
Kelvin scale, 4, 25, 140, 281
Kilowatt, 30
Kinetic theory, 74, 147, 155, 258
Kirchhoff's Law, 380
Kundt's tube, 354

Laby and Hercus, on conductivity of gases, 346
    on determination of " J ", 240
Lapse rate, 421, 428

Latent heat, 37
    equations, 295
    of evaporation, 38, 55, 57, 67, 68
    of fusion, 39, 53
Lees' method for bad conductors, 337
Leslie's cube, 373
Lever expansion apparatus, 85
Linde double column, 315
Linde process, 311
Liquefaction of gases, 307 *sqq.*
Liquid helium, 321
Liquid oxygen calorimeter, 61
Liquid oxygen plant, 317
Low temperature, 324

Maximum-and-minimum thermometer, 10
Maxwell distribution, 289
McLeod gauge, 128
Mechanical equivalent of heat, 64, 71, 229, 239, 245
Mean square velocity, 151
Melting point, 210
Mercury, absolute expansion of, 111
Mercury thermometers, 5, 21
Micrometer expansion apparatus, 87
Micron, 369

Nernst and Lindemann's calorimeter, 67, 70, 73
Newton's Law of cooling, 41–45, 49, 51, 56, 57, 364
Normal temperature and pressure (N.T.P.), 146
Nusselt equation, 367

Optical pyrometry, 21, 400
Orographic depression, 444
Osborne, Stimson, and Ginnings, 69, 242
Otto cycle, 302
Oxygen calorimeter, 61
Oxygen plant, 317
Oxygen point, 23

Peltier effect, 383
Pendulum compensation, 93
Perfect gas—*see* Ideal gas
Phase rule, 215, 216
Pirani gauge, 359
Planck's formula, 391, 393
Platinum resistance thermometry, 15, 24
Potentiometer, 18
Pound-degree C. unit, 32
Power, 30
Pressure, standard, 2

Pressure and altitude, 419
Pressure coefficient, 134, 138
Prevost's theory of exchanges, 375
Probable error, 456
Pyknometer, 105
Pyrheliometer, 406
Pyrometry, 21, 396 *sqq.*

Quantity of heat, 31
Quantum theory, 75, 391

Radiating power, 373
Radiation, 368
Radiation laws, 389–394
Radiation temperatures, 404
Radiation pyrometry, 21, 396 *sqq.*
Radio-balance, 383
Radiometers, 386
Radio-micrometer, 385
Random error, 454
Rankine cycle, 298
Ratio of specific heats of gas, 262–273
Rayleigh's convection equation, 450
Rayleigh's radiation formula, 390
Real coefficient of expansion, 101, 102, 107, 108
Real gas, 137
Real equation of state, 168, 257
Refrigerators, 208, 304
Regelation, 212
Regnault, 51, 111, 201
" Regulo ", 95
Relative humidity, 198
Residual rays, 409
Reversibility, 279, 288
Reynolds' Number, 367
Rime, 426
Ritchie's experiment, 374
Rowland's determination of " J ", 236
Ruchardt, 297
Rumford, 230

Saturated vapour, 162, 178, 179, 181–185
Scale of temperature, 3, 142
Searle's method for good conductor, 334
Secondary depression, 433
Second latent heat equation, 295
Second law of thermodynamics, 279, 292
Second virial coefficient, 157, 170
Simple-tube vapour-pressure experiment, 186

Sinker method for expansion of liquid, 107
Slow-oscillation method for " γ ", 267
Snow, 425
Solar constant, 384
Solders, 220
Solidification of hydrogen, 319
    of helium, 322
Specific gravity bottle experiment, 105
Specific heat, 33–36, 75
    of gas at constant pressure, 37, 51, 73
    of gas at constant volume, 37, 63
    ratio for gases, 262–273
Standard gas thermometer, 13
Steam distillation, 192
Steam engine, 299, 300
Steam point, 2, 7, 23
Stefan's Law, 389, 393
Stratosphere, 421
Sublimation, 213
Sulphur point, 23
" Sunvic " switch, 97
Superconduction, 325
Superficial expansion, 90
Supersaturated vapour, 196
Surface energy, 296
Surface tension, 296
Systematic error, 456

Temperature, 1
Tephigram, 429–431
Terminal velocity of raindrop, 424
Therm, 32
Thermal capacity, 33
Thermal conductivity, 327
Thermal insulation, 359
Thermal wind, 433
Thermocouple, 19, 24
Thermodynamics,
    First law, 229
    Second law, 279, 292
Thermoelectric pyrometers, 19, 24
Thermopile, 372, 384
Thermos flask, 360
Thermostats, 17, 95, 208
Thomson's hypothesis, 163, 170
Toepler pump, 127
Total radiation pyrometer, 396, 398, 404
Triple point, 213
Troposphere, tropopause, 421

Uniform temperature enclosure, 376, 379
Unsaturated vapour, 162

Vacuum calorimeter, 69
Vacuum flask, 360
Van der Waals' equation, 164, 249, 254
Vane radiometer, 386
Vapour density, 188–190
Vapour pressure, 179 *sqq.*, 193, 195
Velocity of sound, 153, 268
Victor Meyer's method, 189
Virial coefficients, 143, 157, 169
Virial expansion, 143
Volt, 64
Volume coefficient, 129, 132, 138

Wanner pyrometer, 401

Warm front, 441
Warm sector, 442
Water equivalent, 33
Watt, 64
Weather forecasting, 433 *sqq.*
Wet-and-dry bulb hygrometer, 202
Wet-flask experiment, 187
Wiedemann-Franz Law, 344
Wien's Displacement Law, 390, 393, 396
Wien's formula, 391, 393

X-rays, 91

Young's modulus, 91

ANSWERS TO EXAMPLES

Chapter I (p. 27)

4. 17·3° C. on the constant volume scale.   **7.** 47·7° C.

Chapter II (p. 78)

2. Thermal capacity, 8·0 cal. per C. degree ; specific heat 0·27.

3. 991° F.   **4.** 11·26 gm.   **7.** 2290 joules per gm.   **8.** 583° C.

11. 3·175 gm.   **13.** 0·62.   **14.** 30·5° C.   **17.** 0·088.   **18.** 0·12.

19. (a) (rate 1) : (rate 2) $= r_1^2 : r_2^2$.

    (b) (rate 1) : (rate 2) $= r_2 : r_1$. It is here assumed that the spheres are perfect thermal conductors.

21. 2·95 centigrade degrees per minute.   **22.** 10 gm. of water.

24. 59·6 cal. per gm.   **25.** 2·81 cal. per gm.   **26.** 4·95 centigrade degrees.

27. Graph gives rate of fall of temperature at 53° C. $= 0·4°$ C./sec. $\therefore$ rate of loss of heat at 53° C. $= 7·6$ cal./sec. Equating this to the rate of supply, $\dfrac{I^2 R}{4·2}$, R works out to 2·6 ohms.

Chapter III (p. 118)

1. 0·12 ft. too long.   **3.** 4·1 sec.   **4.** $3·016 \times 10^7$ dynes.

5. $1·42 \times 10^6$ dynes.   **7.** 20·4° C.   **8.** 2·57 c.c.   **16.** 0·00028 cm.

17. $l_0(1 + \alpha t)$; $l_0[1 + (\alpha - 3\lambda)t]$; $l_0 \dfrac{1 + (\alpha - 3\lambda)t}{1 + \lambda t}$.   **18.** 1/8.

19. 963·9 gm.   **20.** 76·54 cm.   **21.** 751·4 mm.   **22.** 2·5 mm.

Chapter IV (p. 172)

1. 4·0 c.c.   **2.** 22·5 cm. mercury, or 312·6 cm. of water.

3. 56 ft. 4 in.   **5.** 26 *complete* strokes.   **6.** 76·75 cm.

7. 0·122 gm.   **8.** 890 c.c.   **10.** 764 mm.   **11.** 5937 cu. m.

12. 87·76 cm.   **13.** $-270·6°$ C.   **15.** 107° C.

16. 0·028 gm. wt. per sq. cm.   **17.** 77·4 cm.

18. 34·5 lb. wt. per. sq in.   **19.** 274·4 degrees absolute.

24. 45 per cent.   **25.** $3·41 \times 10^{10}$ (cm. per sec.)^2.

26. $1·845 \times 10^5$ cm. per sec.   **27.** All ; 5/7.

29. $1·84 \times 10^5$ cm. per sec.   **30.** $4·613 \times 10^4$ cm. per sec.

31. 1898 metres per sec.   **32.** $3·55 \times 10^{11}$; $3·11 \times 10^{11}$.

Chapter V (p. 225)

1. 739·5 mm. ; 660 mm.   **3.** 9·97 metres.   **7.** 226·4 c.c.

9. 14·85 cm.   **14.** 1·1787 gm.   **15.** 100·38 cm.   **18.** 54·6° C.

19. Here the pressure defect $\dfrac{2T}{r} \cdot \dfrac{\sigma}{\rho - \sigma} \left(\text{or approximately, } \dfrac{2T}{r} \cdot \dfrac{\sigma}{\rho}\right)$ must equal
$0 \cdot 01s$, where s is the s.v.p. in dynes/sq. cm. at the temperature considered. By the method of p. 192, assuming necessary data, σ at pressure s is approximately $8 \times 10^{-10}s$ gm./c.c.

$$\therefore \frac{2 \times 80}{r} \times \frac{8 \times 10^{-10}}{1} \times s = 0 \cdot 01s$$

giving $r = 1 \cdot 28 \times 10^{-5}$ cm.

Chapter VI (p. 273)

2. $2/\pi$ lb. wt.   **3.** 778·7 ft. lb.

4. (a) 23·81 cal. ; (b) 25 centigrade degrees.

5. 0·66 centigrade degrees per second.

7. 83,810 cm. per sec.   **9.** $\theta = \dfrac{hg}{4 \cdot 2 \times 10^7}$.

10. Coke : $9 \cdot 141 \times 10^{-8}$ pence per calorie.
Electricity : $1 \cdot 79 \times 10^{-5}$ pence per calorie, so

cost of coke : cost of electricity = about 5×10^{-3}.

11. 4·17 joules per calorie.   **14.** $C_v = 0 \cdot 1559$ (cal. per gm. per C. degree).

15. R/J.   **16.** $4 \cdot 17 \times 10^7$ ergs per calorie.

17. $C_p = 0 \cdot 237$ (cal. per gm. per centigrade degree).

18. 0·491 (cal. per gm. per centigrade degree).

19. $4 \cdot 25 \times 10^7$ ergs per calorie.   **20.** $4 \cdot 16 \times 10^7$ ergs per calorie.

21. $4 \cdot 196 \times 10^7$ ergs per calorie.

25. Total energy supplied $= 540 \times 4 \cdot 2 \times 10^7 = 2 \cdot 27 \times 10^{10}$ ergs ; external work $= 76 \times 13 \cdot 6 \times 981 \times 1649 = 0 \cdot 17 \times 10^{10}$ ergs ; so internal work $= 2 \cdot 1 \times 10^{10}$ ergs.

Chapters VI and VII (p. 305)

2. Assuming isothermal conditions,

$$\text{work} = p_2 V_2 \ln 10 = 2 \cdot 302 \, p_2 V_2 \text{ ergs.}$$

As $p_2 = 10^7$ dynes per sq. cm., and $V_2 = \pi \times 200^2 \times 900$ c.c., and one kwh. is $3 \cdot 6 \times 10^{10}$ ergs, this gives $23 \cdot 02\pi$ kwh., or about 72 kwh.

4. 0·35° C.

6. First expansion gives $V = 2000$ c.c. at $p = 5 \times 10^5$ dynes per sq. cm., and does external work $p_1 V_1 \ln 2 = 10^9 \times 0 \cdot 693$ ergs.
Second expansion gives final pressure $1 \cdot 9 \times 10^5$ dynes per sq. cm., and temperature 228° absolute. External work done in second case is

$$\frac{1}{0 \cdot 4} (5 \times 10^5 \times 2000 - 1 \cdot 9 \times 10^5 \times 4000) = 6 \times 10^8 \text{ ergs.}$$

8. 0·99 cal. per gm. per centigrade degree.   **9.** $2 \cdot 35 \times 10^9$ ergs.

15. *Case 1.* Rate of heat supply to engine is 16·46 kw.
Case 2. To obtain 3 h.p., rate of heat supply to engine is 2·48 kw., so total rate of heat supply is $10 + 2 \cdot 48 = 12 \cdot 48$ kw.
So, *assuming no heat losses in transmission*, there is an improvement. It might be interesting to discuss whether any better results could be obtained with the condenser at a higher temperature still, using the heat rejected to the condenser as part of the 10 kw.

Chapter IX (p. 409)

3. 0·00096 cal./sq. cm./C. deg./sec.   2·0 centigrade degrees per minute.

7. 6·9 gm.   **8.** 0·0038 centigrade degrees per sec.

9. 0·0002.   **10.** 4·8 centigrade degrees.

12. $2\cdot52 \times 10^5$ cal. per min.   **13.** $\dfrac{li^2R}{KAJ} + T$.

14. $\dfrac{d_1}{k_1} + \dfrac{d_2}{k_2} = \dfrac{d_1 + d_2}{k}$.   **15.** 0·92.

16. 78·8° C. ; 23·5° C.   **17.** $5\cdot25 \times 10^{-7}$ centigrade degrees per annum.

18. 351 sq. cm.   **19.** 9 min. 38 sec.   **20.** 0·763 cm. per hour.

21. 14·74 hours.   **22.** About 49 minutes.   **23.** $1\cdot56 \times 10^6$ cal.

24. About 370 centigrade degrees.   **27.** $c_1/c_2 = n^{-3/2}$.

33. $4\cdot04 \times 10^{-5}$ ergs per c.c.   **36.** 5722° absolute.

37. 9·26 centigrade degrees per cm.   **39.** $V_2 = V_1 \dfrac{i_2}{i_1} \sqrt{\dfrac{r_1}{r_2}}$; or, $V_2 = V_1 \left(\dfrac{i_2}{i_1}\right)^{2/3}$.

PRINTED IN GREAT BRITAIN BY ROBERT MACLEHOSE AND CO. LTD
THE UNIVERSITY PRESS, GLASGOW

Books on Physics

A TEXT-BOOK OF PHYSICS FOR THE USE OF STUDENTS OF SCIENCE AND ENGINEERING. By J. DUNCAN, Wh.Ex., M.I.Mech.E. and S. G. STARLING, B.Sc., A.R.C.Sc. 20s. Also in Parts : Dynamics, 7s. ; Heat, Light and Sound, 8s. 6d. ; Magnetism and Electricity, 7s.

INTERMEDIATE PRACTICAL PHYSICS. By T. M. YARWOOD, B.Sc. 7s. 6d.

A TEXT-BOOK OF PRACTICAL PHYSICS. By H. S. ALLEN, M.A., D.Sc., and H. MOORE, A.R.C.Sc., B.Sc. Third Edition.

MECHANICAL PROPERTIES OF MATTER. By S. G. STARLING. B.Sc. 8s. 6d.

A TEXT-BOOK OF HEAT. By PROF. H. S. ALLEN, M.A., D.Sc. F.R.S. and R. S. MAXWELL, M.A., B.Sc. Part I (Intermediate Degree standard). 12s. Part II (Degree standard). 10s. 6d.

A TEXT-BOOK OF LIGHT. By G. R. NOAKES, M.A. 8s.

A TEXT-BOOK OF HEAT. By G. R. NOAKES, M.A.

A TEXT-BOOK OF ELECTRICITY AND MAGNETISM. By G. R. NOAKES, M.A. 8s. 6d.

MAGNETISM AND ELECTRICITY FOR STUDENTS. By H. E HADLEY, B.Sc. 8s. 6d.

MACMILLAN AND CO. LTD. LONDON

Books on Chemistry

INTERMEDIATE CHEMISTRY. By Prof. T. M. Lowry, C.B.E., D.Sc., F.R.S. and A. C. Cavell, B.A., B.Sc. Fourth Edition. 15s.

A COLLEGE COURSE OF INORGANIC CHEMISTRY. By Prof. J. R. Partington, M.B.E., D.Sc. 12s. 6d.

A TEXT-BOOK OF INORGANIC CHEMISTRY FOR UNIVERSITY STUDENTS. By Prof. J. R. Partington, M.B.E., D.Sc. Fifth Edition. 18s.

GENERAL AND INORGANIC CHEMISTRY. By Prof. J. R. Partington, M.B.E., D.Sc. 36s.

INTERMEDIATE CHEMICAL CALCULATIONS. By Prof. J. R. Partington, M.B.E., D.Sc. and Kathleen Stratton, M.Sc. 6s. 6d.

A TEXT-BOOK OF PHYSICAL CHEMISTRY. By Sylvanus J. Smith, M.A. 7s. 6d.

A CLASS-BOOK OF PHYSICAL CHEMISTRY. By Prof. T. M. Lowry, C.B.E., D.Sc., F.R.S. and Prof. S. Sugden, D.Sc., F.R.S. 7s.

THE PHASE RULE AND PHASE REACTIONS: Theoretical and Practical. By S. T. Bowden. D.Sc. 10s.

PRINCIPLES OF ORGANIC CHEMISTRY. By Sylvanus J. Smith, M.A. 15s.

QUALITATIVE ORGANIC CHEMISTRY. By Neil Campbell. 8s. 6d.

A SHORT HISTORY OF CHEMISTRY. By Prof. J. R. Partington, M.B.E., D.Sc. 7s. 6d.

MACMILLAN & CO. LTD. LONDON